PREDICTING THE PRICE OF CARBON

For Sir David MacKay, FRS (1967–2016) – physicist, author of *Sustainable Energy: Without the Hot Air*, government adviser and realist – who skilfully guided us to confront our energy realities (and be wary of politicians working on energy policies).

PREDICTING THE PRICE OF CARBON

How to Crack the Climate Change Code for Good

Richard H. Clarke

predictability.ltd.uk

First published in 2016

Predict Ability Limited, 11–13 First Floor, The Meads Business Centre, 19 Kingsmead, Farnborough, GU14 7SR, www.predictability.ltd.uk

ISBN 978-0-9954591-0-6

British Library Cataloguing-in-Publication Data.
A catalogue record for this book is available from the British Library.

CONTENTS

ACKNOWLEDGEMENTS

No book is a solitary effort and with *Predicting the Price of Carbon* I have had much assistance from friends, colleagues and family. The book has been four years in the making. During that time the regular, encouraging and sometimes challenging feedback I received from Dr Anthony Webster has been much appreciated. Anthony is a physicist who, like me, worked at the Culham Centre for Fusion Energy near Oxford. He was instrumental in making me think about climate change, not least because of all the excellent speakers he organised to come to CCFE.

Predict Ability Ltd (PAL), the company that embodies the ideas set out in the book, would not have come to fruition without the incisive and timely intervention of Dr Bruce Menzies, prize-winning geotechnical engineer and entrepreneur. Bruce had the vision to see that the underlying algorithms that I had developed to predict the trends in disasters and carbon pricing had practical and commercial applications. Through his mentoring and the computing genius of Edward Coe, who built PAL's online and software systems, we now have a suite of tools ready to meet the challenges of global carbon pricing.

I would also like to thank Susannah Coe, script editor, who helped turn the early manuscripts into production-ready copy for the book.

I gratefully acknowledge the valuable help and insights of Professor Emeritus John Benson (Lancaster University), Alister Doyle (Environmental Correspondent, Reuters), Dr Jan Eichner (Munich RE), Simon Frank (Schlumberger Norge AS), David Hone (Shell), Professor Peter Höppe (Munich RE), Neil Jackson (Energy Markets Trader), Brendan Lyons and Gloria Greenwood (Red Barn Publishing, book production), Professor Mark Maslin (University College London), Dr Robert Muir-Wood (RMS, London), Professor William J. Nuttall (Open University), Fred Pearce (Science Writer), and Dr Melanie Windridge (Tokamak Energy).

Finally, a special mention must go to Professor Myles Allen, whose inaugural lecture in 2011 provided the initial inspiration.

ILLUSTRATIONS

TABLES

ABOUT THE AUTHOR

Richard H. Clarke graduated in Chemical Engineering from the University of Birmingham in 1979 and joined UK Atomic Energy Authority at Harwell Laboratory, where he spent fifteen years leading projects related to the industrial air separation and offshore oil and gas industries. Richard is an expert on heat exchangers, cryogenics and helium resources.

In 1995 he joined the BOC Group in a worldwide role as Principal Heat Exchange Technologist in its UK and US industrial gases operations. In 2002 he returned to England to join the Culham Centre for Fusion Energy, Oxfordshire, managing a complex cryogenic plant for the European fusion energy project JET. At CCFE Richard initiated the Helium Resources Project with the University of Cambridge Judge Business School, BOC and CCFE. Richard was industrial tutor for the PhD student Zhiming Cai.

These roles were the catalyst for Richard's interest in climate change, with the result that he immersed himself full time in the scientific literature on the topic from 2012. This in turn led to the founding in 2015 of Predict Ability Limited (PAL) with prize-winning geotechnical engineer Dr Bruce Menzies and information technology consultant Edward Coe. PAL predicts global disaster trends, the true influence of climate change, and carbon prices.

Richard has authored many academic articles and has made keynote presentations at conferences on heat exchangers, helium resources and supply. He co-edited and co-authored *The Future of Helium as a Natural Resource*, published by Routledge. He is Director (Research) at PAL and a Fellow of the Institution of Chemical Engineers, London.

PREFACE

There is no doubting the passion of the scientists and engineers engaged in the quest for fusion energy. In research there is the kudos of discoveries and scientific papers but, underlying that, there is often to be found a deep social concern for the environment and a hope that, one day, fusion energy will provide the near-limitless clean energy our modern world demands.

It was in that context, as a chemical engineer, that I would talk with my physicist colleagues at the Culham Centre for Fusion Energy. I found that one of their deepest concerns was climate change. Almost every week there would be a colloquium in the Hans-Otto Wüster lecture theatre, where eminent speakers explained the urgency of the problem, and the energy technologies and policy solutions needed – including carbon pricing.

Towards the end of 2011 my involvement in a six-year project and a book, *The Future of Helium as a Natural Resource*,[1] was coming to an end. I was looking for a new challenge and unexpectedly found it at the inaugural lecture of Professor Myles Allen, Professor of Geosystem Science in the School of Geography and the Environment, University of Oxford, and Head of the Climate Dynamics Group in the University's Department of Physics.

In his 24 November 2011 lecture 'The people's planet: Reconnecting climate science, climate policy and reality',[2] Myles Allen highlighted the young science of event attribution. It appeared to be possible to determine the extent to which extreme weather events could be attributed to man-made or 'anthropogenic' emissions of greenhouse gases. The worst culprit is carbon dioxide (CO_2). Not only do we emit nearly 40 billion tonnes of the gas each year, but CO_2 molecules linger in the atmosphere for hundreds or even thousands of years and change our climate in complex and mostly damaging ways.

Out of this came the idea that lies behind *Predicting the Price of Carbon*. The concept is simply this: if the insurance industry and governments know how much climate-related loss and damage **L** there is per event, and if Professor Allen and colleagues could determine the proportions *x* attributable to our CO_2 emissions **C**, then surely it would be possible to put a price on carbon emissions? It follows, in essence, that the long-term price of carbon is

$$\mathbf{y} = \int (\mathbf{L} \times \boldsymbol{x})/\int \mathbf{C}$$

This book explores the many ways in which carbon price can be calculated.

As my ideas (and a sudden interest in the world of insurance!) took shape, Myles Allen forewarned me that the insurance industry thinks it has climate change priced-in. It also became apparent that event attribution was, indeed, an emerging science and that it might take some time before a global, accurate and near real-time attribution reporting system evolved.

Then there came a twist. Whilst collating the hundreds of articles, stories and data sources I had found in the fast-changing landscape of climate change, carbon pricing and insurance there was an astonishing blog in March 2014 by Roger Pielke Jr, Professor of Environmental Studies in the Center for Science and Technology Policy Research at the University of Colorado. His article 'Disasters cost more than ever – but not because of climate change'[3] appeared in the newly revamped *FiveThirtyEight*,[4] an online magazine covering poll analyses, politics, economics and sport. The editor-in-chief, Nate Silver, is the statistician and author of *The Signal and the Noise*[5] who correctly called all 50 states in the 2012 US presidential election. Silver had hired Pielke Jr as a contributing writer.

The climate science establishment took exception to Pielke Jr's insistence that the cost of disasters and catastrophes is due to economic factors and not climate change (or, at most, any sign of climate change will not be detectable for decades). Such was the furore following his article, Roger Pielke Jr and *FiveThirtyEight* decided to part ways. This was all new to me. I delved into a comprehensive dataset on disasters compiled by reinsurer Munich RE. All the analyses tended to support Pielke Jr's principal argument, that the cost of disasters was largely related to economic factors. However, concealed within the data there were some astonishing trends that led, in stages, to a deeper understanding of the complex interactions between disasters, economic activity, vulnerability and climate change.

By early 2015, my colleagues Dr Bruce Menzies, entrepreneur and geotechnical engineer, and information technology consultant Edward Coe and I decided we had enough of the picture to form a new company called Predict Ability Ltd. It was with great excitement and an increasing sense of awe that we gradually formulated our intricate combination of ideas and insights into a highly sophisticated suite of software tools that can predict what, where and, to some extent, when disasters are most likely to strike and the trend in disaster costs. In other words, we had produced a genuine world first: a tool that could scientifically and reliably predict the total cost of weather-related loss and damage worldwide. The tool, now a computing engine called *PALgamma*, also revealed that climate change is today increasing the number of disasters by about 20% and the proportion is rising yearly by about 0.5%. To capture this, we developed a scientifically sound method to obtain the 'global attribution factor' *x*. This, in turn, led us directly to a carbon price.

In deciding to publish *Predicting the Price of Carbon*, the Predict Ability Ltd team has two missions. Firstly, to show the rationale for carbon pricing, we need to understand climate change, why it is happening, its consequences and why carbon pricing is a key solution. By setting the scene in terms of evidence and policy, the aim is to identify effective strategies for mitigation (emission reduction) and adaptation (consequence reduction) and clarify the best carbon-pricing methods. Thus evolved *PALcarbon*, Predict Ability Ltd's carbon-pricing tool driven by the *PALgamma* engine, the bedrock of loss and damage prediction.

'Carbon intensity weighting' is a key feature of Predict Ability Ltd's carbon-pricing tool, *PALcarbon*. In essence, the carbon price of the most polluting fuels must be both rational and high enough to act as an incentive to switch to less polluting energy sources. Eventually, when (one day) the world has almost decarbonised, there must still be in place an energy levy or tax that helps pay for the ongoing damage that our era of CO_2 emissions has created. The 'carbon intensity weighting' method can be applied, in principle, to any carbon-pricing methodology, whether science-based or market-driven.

Secondly, the reader should understand that Predict Ability Ltd is making a number of business propositions as a natural progression from our astonishing

Figure 0.1. *Nobel Prize winning physical chemist Svante Arrhenius (1859–1927)[6] was 'arguably the father of climate-change science'.[7] (©Wikipedia, Creative Commons.)*

discoveries and developmental work. This includes features of the computing engine, *PALgamma*, which embodies the company's intellectual property.

In one sense, at least, this book does do what a reader would expect: it defines, quantifies and predicts the price (cost) of carbon dioxide emissions. This is done in several ways, the simplest of which is

$$\mathbf{y} = \exp^{0.02 \times (\text{year} - 1896)}$$

where **y** is the long-term or cumulative, carbon price and **t** is the year. 1896 is the year when the inflation-adjusted carbon price was \$1/tonne CO_2 (one US dollar per tonne carbon dioxide). It was also the year that the scientist Svante Arrhenius (Figure 0.1) clearly identified our global-warming vulnerability.[8] This simple exponential formula takes into account both the historical and expected (business-as-usual) emissions and the recorded and predicted loss and damage that can be attributed to climate change. At the next level there is

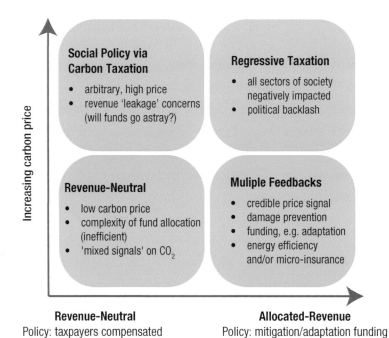

Figure 0.2. *The options for allocating the revenue generated by carbon-pricing schemes. (© Predict Ability Ltd.)*

a step-by-step carbon-pricing model (Chapter 8) that takes into account the essential elements of climate-change theory and established loss and damage relationships.

Finally, there is the fully featured *PALcarbon* software that enables users to determine long-term and spot prices in different energy sectors by taking into account the real-time proportion and carbon intensity of each fuel or energy type in an energy market. This has been produced as an app for the smart phone.

One of the biggest challenges, having determined the price of carbon, is how to implement a carbon-pricing strategy. There are two variants: 'cap and trade' schemes, where permits-to-emit are traded; and carbon taxation, where fossil fuels are taxed according to their emissions.

In both cases there is carbon revenue, i.e. the funds generated by a carbon-pricing scheme. How should the revenue be allocated? This is an important question. The four-leaf-clover diagram in Figure 0.2 highlights the benefits and drawbacks of four options: a high or low carbon price and either a revenue-neutral or revenue-allocated strategy.

With a revenue-neutral, high carbon price (as proposed in the US Congress), carbon pricing becomes a form of social policy and trillions of dollars have to be moved safely around the economy. If most of the revenue were used for other purposes (some of which may be climate-change-related), then a carbon tax would be highly regressive; it would hit low-income households hard.

If the carbon price is low, as Predict Ability Ltd shows it should be, there are again two options. A revenue-neutral scheme might work, but what would it achieve? Households would be a few hundred dollars per year better or worse off, but the administrative expenses would consume much of the revenue. The fourth option (low price and allocated revenue) is explored in various ways in *Predicting the Price of Carbon*. It appears to be the simplest, fairest and most effective carbon-pricing scheme. To work well, the market participants must think globally, because the impact of carbon emissions is worldwide.

We believe the reader will discover that *Predicting the Price of Carbon* tackles the consequences of climate change by:

- ▸ explaining how climate change influences disasters and catastrophe losses,
- ▸ formulating rational carbon-pricing schemes,
- ▸ urging the implementation of carbon pricing on a global scale,
- ▸ arguing the case for 'carbon intensity weighting' – why energy levies are needed, how to implement them, why we should start now, and
- ▸ proposing revenue allocation – with some strategies for the equitable and effective use of carbon-pricing scheme revenues.

If our work can be said to have nudged humankind towards an era of clean energy and a cleaner, fairer environment for generations to come, then I can ask no more.

Richard H. Clarke
Oxford, England
June 2016

Notes to Preface

1   Nuttall, W.J., Clarke R.H., Glowacki B.A. (eds.), *The Future of Helium as a Natural Resource*, Routledge (2012), https://www.routledge.com/products/9780415576970

2   Allen, M.R., 'The people's planet: Reconnecting climate science, climate policy and reality' (inaugural lecture, 24 November 2011), University of Oxford (2011), http://podcasts.ox.ac.uk/peoples-planet-reconnecting-climate-science-climate-policy-and-reality-0

3   Pielke Jr, R., 'Disasters cost more than ever – but not because of climate change', *FiveThirtyEight* (19 March 2014), http://fivethirtyeight.com/features/disasters-cost-more-than-ever-but-not-because-of-climate-change/

4   http://fivethirtyeight.com

5   Scheiber, N., 'Known unknowns' (review of *The Signal and the Noise: The Art and Science of Prediction* by Nate Silver, Penguin Press (2013)), *New York Times* (2 November 2012), http://www.nytimes.com/2012/11/04/books/review/the-signal-and-the-noise-by-nate-silver.html

6   Svante Arrhenius (19 February 1859 to 2 October 1927), Wikipedia (22 February 2016), https://en.wikipedia.org/wiki/Svante_Arrhenius

7   Sample, I., 'The father of climate change', *The Guardian* (30 June 2005), http://www.theguardian.com/environment/2005/jun/30/climatechange.climatechangeenvironment2

8   Arrhenius, S., 'On the influence of carbonic acid in the air upon the temperature of the ground', *Philosophical Magazine* and *Journal of Science*, Series 5, Vol. 41, pp. 237–276 (April 1896), http://www.rsc.org/images/Arrhenius1896_tcm18-173546.pdf

CHAPTER ONE

FEEDBACK IS EVERYTHING

Nature talks and we must listen

Hardly anywhere to be found in climate-change policy is the concept of feedback, of properly connecting emissions with loss and damage. Yet in science, in business and in nature, feedback is all-pervasive.

The People's Planet

It was just another email, a newsletter from the Environmental Change Institute at the University of Oxford, announcing a talk called 'The People's Planet' by Professor Myles Allen. He wanted to bring climate modelling down to earth. This was not a colloquium but a grand affair at the Examination Schools, with 500 people, a guest panel and an inauguration by the University's Chancellor. Amid all that excitement on 24 November 2011 the germ of an idea hatched.[1] This is the story of what followed.

Four years on, two diametrically opposed views of climate change are squaring up to each other. The existence of climate change is accepted in both. In one, a city seeks to adapt, regardless of who is to blame for sea-level rise. In the other, a global alliance is sought – the biggest in history – to switch the world away from carbon emissions.

The city of Miami, Florida, knows all about extreme weather. Storms and hurricanes are common. But the city officials are in a dilemma. They need to build a protective sea wall that will cost $300 million,[2] but there is no money. Exotic apartment buildings will be erected on the sea front, in harm's way, and the oligarchs who occupy them will fund the sea walls, in effect paying for their own and everyone else's protection. This is *adaptation*, the natural response of humans and living things to a threat.

In December 2015, heads of state and dignitaries from 195 countries gathered in historic surroundings in Paris to sign into being an agreement that will legally bind those nations to strict carbon-emission reduction targets. This is mitigation, the taking away of the cause of the problem that is man-made climate change. It is a very tall order indeed to navigate between economic and environmental collapse. The near-implosion of the UN 2009 Copenhagen Conference created a sense of despair; it was a barrier to progress. People today still struggle to rationalise their response to climate change.[3]

As the atmospheric concentration of carbon dioxide (CO_2) passed 400 ppm in 2013, Martin Wolf, the *Financial Times* commentator, seemed to want to throw in the towel on climate change.[4] Is it too complex, perverse and pervasive? It is indeed a wicked problem. Today, many thousands of bright minds are still at work trying to implement the resolutions of the UN's Climate Conferences, from the 1992 Kyoto Protocol onwards.

A good question, asked by Roger Pielke Jr in his book *The Climate Fix*, is this. Do the peoples of the world really want a pristine planet?[5] If so, we are heading at breakneck speed in the wrong direction. Now, it seems that that thought has finally sunk in. There is fear and scepticism; the public are angry with the climate scientists, who are trying to understand the hugely complex natural systems that surround the Earth. Every move they make is micro-examined and their motives are often called into question.[6]

Let us be clear. There is much that climate scientists and (most) climate sceptics agree on.[7] Man-made climate change is real. Anthropogenic (human-caused) CO_2 levels are rising. CO_2 is the most important greenhouse gas (GHG). Rising CO_2 levels cause global warming (or climate change, the now preferred term). On the questions of climate sensitivity (the planet's temperature response to each tonne of CO_2 emitted) and human influence on extreme weather events, there is much less agreement. A principal focus of this book is the interdependence of human activities and extreme weather.

Framing the Question

One of the most difficult things is to know how to talk about climate change without creating a polarised, sterile debate. Mike Hulme explores this question with great dexterity in his book *Why We Disagree About Climate Change* (CUP, 2009). It is a multi-dimensional question that crosses science, policy, beliefs, behaviour and business. The media have had a big influence on the direction and nature of the climate-change debate. Much of the press represents the interests of the *status quo*. There is evidence that uncertainty is creeping into previously well-established territory; one analysis showed that the use of 'hedging' words is increasing.[8]

What should be done? Start slowly, says the independent scientist James Lovelock, then react. Then it will be too late, replies the *Guardian* columnist George Monbiot.[9] Perhaps, to borrow the actor Clint Eastwood's well-worn phrase, 'how lucky do we feel?'

We live in a world of abundant fossil fuels – abundant in the sense that there's more than enough to cover the next few business cycles – but in one hundred years, well, we might be running low (we never actually run out of anything). Did governments create the climate change disaster to wean us off fossil fuels? Probably not, but there's every reason to think climate angst will help achieve that goal. The real problem now is that most energy companies – the coal, gas and oil producers – are still allowed to emit, or cause the emission of, CO_2 for free.[10] And, unlike other GHG pollutants, nature does not easily adsorb CO_2, sadly for us humans and most other species. The carbon debt we owe nature and our grandchildren, and theirs too, just keeps accumulating. Our grandparents could be forgiven for not knowing what they did, but we cannot.

A new fissure in the debate has rattled the energy industry. Bill McKibben, the environmentalist and activist, has called upon investors to withdraw investment – to divest – from companies associated with carbon-based energy. It started out with a few university pension funds and seems to be spreading.[11] Fred Pearce, the science writer, speculated in 2015 that the tide may have turned against fossil fuels.[12] Whatever the reason, the astonishing announcement from Shell that it is abandoning Arctic exploration delighted environmentalists.[13] Over $7 billion had been invested in the Arctic. In the same week the Governor of the Bank of England, Mark Carney, on 29 September 2015, warned investors – and particularly the insurance industry – that most fossil fuel assets might be un-burnable. There is a carbon asset bubble in the making.[14] The Carbon Tracker Initiative has said this in sober, financial terms for a while now.[15]

Another dimension is the question of global population. President Obama's chief scientific adviser John Holdren[16] wrote about over-population 40 years ago and at his inauguration he was heavily scrutinised by a Congressional panel to be sure he did not have 'proactive' views on population management.

We just have to face it. In our global technological society, energy – and lots of it – is an essential necessity of life, and in the future even more energy[17] – not less – will be required. The 2015 Paris agreement 'might cause a slight shift away from coal, that is all' says BP.[18] Not only is energy needed to serve a growing population and a growing middle class, it enables us to find, extract, purify and recycle the many other non-energy resources we need. Chemical engineer Alicia Valero Delgado, in her examination of global resources, starkly reminds us of how many elements we now take for granted that are becoming 'endangered', i.e. scarce.[19] Rare earth elements (REE), such as samarium, a powerful magnetic material, seem today to be essential for many aspects of renewable energy.

To compound it all, we live in an uncertain world and climate change is one of the biggest uncertainties yet. Never has the Earth, in recent geological times, been subjected to such a high and rapid CO_2 concentration spike. Yet we do not know for sure whether we will experience a 2°C, 4°C or 6°C average temperature rise or virtually none,[20] says Dieter Helm, Professor of Energy Policy at the University of Oxford. We live in a 'climate-model-driven mess', he asserts.

How much does climate change affect GDP? This book will explore that question too, but, apparently, climate change is not the worst offender. Domestic violence, worldwide, it is claimed, impacts GDP by over 10% – more than all the wars and unrest put together.[21]

Pakistan, a nuclear-armed country straddled by unrest, is one of the regions most at risk from climate change as extreme monsoon flooding continues to devastate farms and villages.[22] This is of great concern to its ally, the United States, and is often raised in government and defence meetings in the US. China, however, is growing its relationship with Pakistan, opening up a vast trade route and building infrastructure.[23]

Robert J. Shiller, Nobel Laureate and economist at Yale University, says we should 'expect surprises' (such events have been called 'Black Swans'). For example, interrelated with climate change, the world should expect sudden-onset water mega-problems in the coming decades as we continue to extract water from ancient wells and divert rivers for irrigation and hydropower. Large-scale hydro-electric schemes[24] now look ever more questionable in our changing, increasingly 'blocked'[25] climate.

Helm suggests we need a reality check. Energy efficiency and renewables will be swamped by global economic growth. The world is starting to re-carbonise, says Elizabeth Kolbert in *Field Notes from a Catastrophe*.[26] Mitigation alone is not enough. We are in danger of deluding ourselves. Today, with crude oil prices only just recovering to $50 per barrel and with governments still struggling to balance budgets following the 2008 market crash, it is hardly surprising that FiTs (Feed-in Tariffs) are being curtailed. In the UK, for example, solar, renewable heat and carbon capture & storage schemes are all now at risk.[27, 28, 29] Such are the vagaries of government intervention in mitigation and adaptation measures.

Carbon Pricing

The time for carbon pricing has arrived. Two key developments occurred in 2015. Firstly, six European energy companies agreed to seek a 'meaningful' carbon price in conjunction with the UN.[30] This was widely welcomed. Secondly, China has declared that it will run a carbon-trading scheme that could dwarf the EU Emission Trading System, starting in 2017.[31] And why? A meaningful carbon-pricing system is probably the single most effective strategy in combating climate change. It immediately raises significant revenue (which needs to be allocated wisely) and it sends a strong and hopefully reliable signal to industry that makes one thing abundantly clear: the need to switch to alternative, clean energy sources. David Hone, Chief Climate Adviser at Shell (one of the six European signatories), sets out the logic in his second book, *Why Carbon Pricing Matters*.[32] He shows that a carbon price reduces fossil-fuel production, for sound economic reasons, thereby reducing climate impact. Carbon pricing matters and the right form of carbon price matters even more.

In the 21st century we need to bring every idea to the table,[33] to tackle one of the biggest long-term problems of our time. This is where Predict Ability's big idea comes in. What we propose addresses actual damage, not prescribed development *per se*. We propose a carbon price based on the actual cost of man-made climate change, not an imposed 2°C target for which 'cap and trade'[34] schemes have been implemented. This is not to refute the merits of aiming for emission reductions, but to recognise that significant climate-related damage is already happening and that it will continue long after the last giga-tonne of CO_2 has been emitted. What we propose is global in scope and reach, and it rests with the United Nations, the World Bank and the world's governments, businesses and people to decide what the right balance needs to be. This is a groundbreaking development.

Notes to Chapter One

1   Webster, A.J., Clarke, R.H., 'An insurance-led response to climate change', arXiv:1509.01157v2 (7 October 2015), http://arxiv.org/abs/1509.01157

2   Paquette, D., 'Miami Beach trying to out-build climate change', *Portland Press Herald* (23 December 2014), http://www.pressherald.com/2014/12/23/no-sinking-feeling-among-buyers-builders-of-miami-beach-palaces-on-quicksand/

3   Gifford, R., 'Thirty-three reasons why we can't think clearly about climate change', *New Scientist* (8 July 2015), https://www.newscientist.com/article/mg22730290-300-33-reasons-why-we-cant-think-clearly-about-climate-change/

4   Wolf, M., 'Why the world faces climate chaos', *Financial Times* (14 May 2013), http://www.ft.com/cms/s/0/c926f6e8-bbf9-11e2-a4b4-00144feab7de.html

5   Pielke Jr, R., *The Climate Fix: What Scientists and Politicians Won't Tell You About Global Warming*, p. 14, Basic Books, New York (2010).

6   Helm, D., *The Carbon Crunch: How We're Getting Climate Change Wrong – and How To Fix It*, p. 16, Yale University Press (2012).

7   Davidson, S., 'Climate change: Where skeptics and theorists agree and disagree', *Communities Digital News* (30 May 2014), http://www.commdiginews.com/health-science/climate-change-where-theorists-and-skeptics-agree-and-disagree-18567/

8   Richardson, V., 'Media "hedging" on climate change?', *The Washington Times* (2 June 2014), http://www.washingtontimes.com/news/2014/jun/2/media-hedging-climate-change/

9   McElvoy, A., 'James Lovelock', BBC Radio 4 'Start the Week' (21 April 2014), http://www.bbc.co.uk/programmes/b0415h9t

10   Nyks, K., Scott, J.P., 'Do the Math – the movie', 350.org (22 September 2013), http://act.350.org/signup/math-movie/

11   Gelles, D., 'Fossil fuel divestment movement harnesses the power of shame', *The New York Times* (13 June 2015), http://www.nytimes.com/2015/06/14/business/energy-environment/fossil-fuel-divestment-movement-harnesses-the-power-of-shame.html

12   Pearce, F., 'Could global tide be starting to turn against fossil fuels?', *Yale University Environment 360* (13 January 2015), http://e360.yale.

edu/feature/could_global_tide_be_starting_to_turn_against_fossil_
fuels/2837/

13   Katakey, R., Zhu, W., 'Shell halts Alaska offshore exploration after failing
      to find enough oil', Bloomberg.com (28 September 2015), http://www.
      bloomberg.com/news/articles/2015-09-28/shell-to-stop-exploring-
      offshore-alaska-on-regulations-costs

14   Carney, M., 'Breaking the tragedy of the horizon – climate change and
      financial stability', Bank of England (speech given at Lloyd's of London) (29
      September 2015), http://www.bankofengland.co.uk/publications/Pages/
      speeches/2015/844.aspx

15   http://www.carbontracker.org/

16   John Holdren (born 1 March 1944), Wikipedia (5 March 2016), https://
      en.wikipedia.org/wiki/John_Holdren

17   Elliott, L., 'BP: Huge rise in energy demand at odds with climate change
      flight', *The Guardian* (17 February 2015), http://www.theguardian.com/
      business/2015/feb/17/bp-says-huge-rise-in-energy-demand-at-odds-
      with-climate-change-fight

18   Evans, S., 'Analysis: How BP's energy outlook has changed after the Paris
      agreement', *CarbonBrief* (12 February 2016), http://www.carbonbrief.org/
      analysis-how-the-bp-energy-outlook-has-changed-after-paris/

19   Capilla, A.V., Delgado, A.V., *Thanatia: The Destiny of the Earth's Mineral
      Resources: A Thermodynamic Cradle-to-Cradle Assessment,* World Scientific
      Publishing,   Singapore   (2014),   http://www.worldscientific.com/
      worldscibooks/10.1142/7323

20   Helm, D., *The Carbon Crunch,* p. 3.

21   Doyle, A., 'Violence at home costs $8 trillion a year, worse than war:
      Study', Reuters.com (9 September 2014), http://www.reuters.com/
      article/2014/09/09/us-abuse-costs-idUSKBN0H41AL20140909

22   Asianet, 'Pakistan among top ten countries worst hit by climate change',
      globalpost.com (11 April 2013), http://www.globalpost.com/dispatch/
      news/asianet/130411/pakistan-among-top-ten-countries-worst-hit-
      climate-change

23   Agence France-Presse, 'China to unveil $46bn investment in Pakistan
      during visit by Xi Jingping', *The Guardian* (20 April 2015), http://www.
      theguardian.com/world/2015/apr/20/china-to-unveil-46bn-investment-
      in-pakistan-during-visit-by-xi-jingping

24　Poindexter, G.B., 'Brazil's hydroelectric facilities almost dry due to drought', Hydroworld.com (29 October 2014), http://www.hydroworld.com/articles/2014/10/brazil-s-hydroelectric-facilities-almost-dry-due-to-drought.html

25　Carrington, D., 'Extreme weather becoming more common, study says', *The Guardian* (11 August 2014), http://www.theguardian.com/environment/2014/aug/11/extreme-weather-common-blocking-patterns

26　Kolbert, E., *Field Notes from a Catastrophe: Man, Nature, and Climate Change*, p. 147, Bloomsbury (2007).

27　Macalister, T., 'Slashing household solar subsidies will kill off industry, government told', *The Guardian* (27 August 2015), http://www.theguardian.com/environment/2015/aug/27/slashing-household-solar-subsides-kill-off-industry-government-feed-in-tariff

28　Murray, J., 'Report: Renewable Heat Incentive next in firing line as government assault on green policies continues', Businessgreen.com (3 September 2015), http://www.businessgreen.com/bg/news/2424406/report-renewable-heat-incentive-next-in-firing-line-as-government-assault-on-green-policies-continues

29　Hodgson, P., Brown, A., 'Drax announces plan to end further investment in White Rose Carbon Capture & Storage project', Drax.com (25 September 2015), http://www.drax.com/news/news-articles/2015/09/drax-announces-plan-to-end-further-investment-in-white-rose-carbon-capture-storage-project/

30　Editorial Board, 'The case for a carbon tax', *The New York Times* (6 June 2015), http://www.nytimes.com/2015/06/07/opinion/the-case-for-a-carbon-tax.html

31　West, J., 'China says it will start the world's biggest carbon market by 2017', *Mother Jones* (24 September 2015), http://www.motherjones.com/environment/2015/09/china-cap-and-trade-carbon-xi-obama-agreement

32　Hone, D., 'Why carbon pricing matters', Blogs.shell.com/climatechange (18 September 2015), http://blogs.shell.com/climatechange/2015/09/why-carbon-pricing-matters/

33　Carbon War Room (accessed 17 April 2016), https://carbonwarroom.com

34　Environmental Defense Fund, 'How cap and trade works', Edf.org (April 2016), https://www.edf.org/climate/how-cap-and-trade-works

CHAPTER TWO

EVIDENCE OF CLIMATE CHANGE

We need to deal with reality

What is the evidence of climate change? To what extent is it man-made? And what are our responses to this knowledge?

Our Globalised World

Coal is abundant and widespread.[1] We dig it up, burn it and raise steam, just like the Victorians did. Economic growth, beloved by politicians worldwide, drives the demand for coal. We burn 300 years' worth of fossil fuels every 300 seconds![2]

A central target – perhaps a key target – for environmentalists is the elimination of fossil-fuel subsidies.[3] They have been around for decades and are an inefficient way of delivering social policy to poor people in developing economies (four-fifths of the money goes to the middle classes). Many attempts to stop them end in civil unrest. Subsidies are of a similar magnitude to the $335 billion sent home by migrant workers in developed countries, and that is more than three times the world's total aid budget.[4]

A 2GW (giga-watt) coal plant[5] built in China – as elsewhere – will, over its lifetime, emit half a giga-tonne of CO_2 (500,000,000 tonnes of CO_2). Until recently, there were no rules about those emissions at all, although change is in the air: some believe that Chinese coal usage may peak in 2016.[6] But as China peaks, other nations may follow in her steps. Turkey has invested heavily in coal, exploiting cheap opencast reserves.[7] Moreover, coal-fired power stations worldwide consume as much water as 1 billion people.[8]

Some people say coal is too valuable to burn. In South Africa, in the era of apartheid, chemical engineers cleverly turned coal into fuels, chemicals, foodstuffs, fertilisers, pharmaceuticals and plastics.[9] Today, for all that stuff, oil is the preferred feedstock worldwide.

Every joule of renewable energy frees up another joule in the form of coal that, until the smog became unbearable, China burnt in one of its power stations.[10] The world has an insatiable demand for energy (notwithstanding the temporary oil price collapse caused, in part, by misunderstood GDP growth figures from China). And while energy efficiency is all well and good, there always comes the 'rebound effect'. As costs go down, more and more participants join the market. This has been true ever since 1775, when James Watt massively improved Newcomen's steam engine.[11] Yet, in captive markets, such as the American auto-industry, politicians block fuel efficiency targets and thereby protect out-of-date motorcar designs.[12]

As the global middle class will expand to 4 billion,[13] says economist Professor Nicholas Stern, we have to hope that decarbonisation will progress steadily, as it had for over 100 years[14] until globalisation came along. China has had to learn, or re-learn, most of its manufacturing processes during the

Figure 2.1. *Mis-LED? An artificial sun for Chinese workers.*[15] *(© Getty Images.)*

Figure 2.2. *Seagulls swarm at a UK landfill site.*[16] *(© Shutterstock.)*

last twenty years. Did no one in America or Europe think of that as millions of manufacturing jobs were exported to China? Yet, as in America in the 1960s, it is local air pollution, finally, that is driving change in China (Figure 2.1).[17] Although there has always been the obligation on business owners and local officials in China to prevent pollution, few have had the authority to do so.[18]

Globally, however, energy per unit GDP is now increasing.[19] The policy problem here is that there are not enough wedges (big chunks of energy supply from non-fossil sources) to offset the contribution from fossil fuels.[20] Alas, what do we do with all this stuff that China makes? Incredibly, it seems that 99% of it sooner or later ends up in landfill (Figure 2.2).[21]

We should not forget, however, the astonishing reality that – for the time being at least – fossil fuels (and capitalism) have played a major part in lifting billions of people out of poverty in the last 30 years.[22]

Government climate-change policies plough on regardless. Huge sums of taxpayers' money across Europe have been spent on programmes aimed at the introduction of renewables, such as wind turbines and solar panels. Many are made in China. They use exotic processes and materials and masses of energy during manufacturing. Rare earth element (REE) disputes have arisen, as China has many of these precious resources.[23] Why is it cheaper to make all these things in China? It is because little account is taken of the environmental impacts of imported goods. Ironically, it was Margaret Thatcher, the British Prime Minister, who first grasped the seriousness of climate change, but she was also among the first to initiate globalisation.

If Lord Stern is right about the emerging global middle class, then we should expect 'a wall of demand' in the developing world, says Oxford economist Dieter Helm.[24] Like the 1990s, there may be a 'dash to gas' or coal. In a world of uncertain oil prices it is renewable-energy projects that will drop out first. It happened in the 1980s[25] and it happened again in 2014–2015. Meanwhile in coal-exporting nations, such as Australia and Indonesia, climate-change policy fails to find traction. There are simply too many vested interests at stake.

Perhaps we should start with the past. UCLA Professor Jared Diamond's book *Collapse: How Societies Choose to Fail or Survive* tells the astonishing story of how and why societies collapse. We are not special because we are technological. No, we are similar because the centres of power – governments – are not up to the challenges that climate change, water stress, globalisation and migration present. The BBC's Andrew Marr touched on this idea at the end of his 2007 television series *The History of Modern Britain*.[26]

Our Climate

Has there ever been 'normal weather'?[27] The climate is erratic.[28] In winter 2013–2014 Dallas airport closed under freak snow conditions as, naturally, there were no snowploughs in Texas. Natural gas prices spiked at over $1 per cubic foot as New England froze in bizarre arctic conditions that ultimately led to once-in-200-year floods in England.[29] Our weather appears to be more and more extreme.[30] Some events have been greater than 3 SD[31] (standard deviation) from the norm. This is extreme.[32] Should we expect more of this?

All this fossil-fuel burning is putting the world on course to reach 4°C of warming, according to the Pottsdam Climate Institute.[33] We are getting an early taste of what that could bring: heatwaves in China and India, submerging Pacific islands, drought-driven conflict.[34] One of the culprits identified in the 2013–2014 weather events was the slackened jet stream that normally circles the Arctic.[35] Has the warming of the Arctic led to less temperature difference between the pole and the equator? Is that why we now see persistent high- and low-pressure weather systems locking-in over whole regions, such as the 'ridiculously resilient [high pressure] ridge' in California that has been associated with the worst drought in millennia?

It appears that stuck or persistent weather systems do occur (Figure 2.3) and, in the past, may have been associated with cataclysmic events such as the collapse of the Mayan empire.[36] These extremes appear throughout human history. But the ancients did not have Met Offices. We do. What would be of more concern for us is some more permanent change, or 'tipping point', such as the ending or diversion of the North Atlantic thermohaline system, or Gulf Stream, which brings warm tropical water to the cold north and gives the UK its temperate climate.[37] Then there are the 'fat tails', but more of that later.

One of the things the 2014 Ebola crisis has taught (some) scientists to do is listen – listen, that is, to sources they might normally ignore.[38] In the case of Ebola, it turns out that burial practices are a key vector. With this in mind, do the sceptics have anything to add to the question of the global warming 'pause' that has so vexed the scientists in the last few years? Maybe. One argument is that the Earth's temperature is always in some pattern of complex, sinusoidal variation due to planetary motion (these wobbles are called Milankovich cycles).[39]

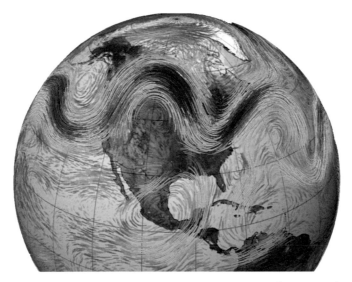

Figure 2.3. *Stuck fast jet stream: US frozen, UK flooded.*[40] *(© NASA.)*

The sceptics argue that, yes, there is some climate change effect but much less than is claimed by the IPCC (the UN's Intergovernmental Panel on Climate Change). The main driver is the Sun–Earth interaction. In the next few years it will be clear, they say, and then we can fine-tune policy appropriately. The point to make here is that both data and models are important. We should respond according to actual impacts (damage) and actual emissions. The models are very useful for interpretation and interpolation of data, not so much for multi-decadal projections (extrapolation) into the future.

A further complication – there are so many – is the effect of ash, dust and clouds on solar input to the Earth. Volcanoes are an obvious source of ash. There is some evidence that the largest events, such as Pinatubo (1991) and El Chichón (1982), both of which had high VEI[41] numbers, did impact global climate in ways that the climate models have been able to accurately capture.

As the world heats up, some lose and some gain: construction worker productivity falls markedly as temperatures exceed 45°C,[42] whereas Nordic grape growers welcome the changing weather.[43] Other, rare, positive effects include the iron-rich glacial run-off from Greenland that stimulates microbial conversion of CO_2 to life forms that sink to the ocean floor when they die. For all that, it is the northern communities – Iceland, Greenland, Arctic Canadians – who are at the front line of climate change.[44] As the permafrost melts, most of what was certain becomes uncertain, from the ground up. For example, pine saplings that started growing over permafrost are now keeling over as the solid ground melts – this is the 'drunken forest' syndrome (Figure 2.4).

Even in the south, many of Canada's cities have been battered[45] by climate change and the wildlife is utterly perplexed as their habitat zones move north several miles a year. In the US, President Obama's National Climate Assessment commission reported 'wide impacts of climate change already in the US'.[46] As with most aspects of climate science, there are always conundrums – e.g. why has tornado intensity declined in the US?[47]

Singular events, such as tornadoes and hurricanes, have been much scrutinised for signs of climate change, not least by Professor Roger Pielke Jr, who has extensively studied hurricane impacts in the US and has found no correlation other than that insurance losses increase as coastal cities become larger. The insurance industry, particularly the reinsurance company Munich RE, says it

Figure 2.4. *A 'drunken forest' in Alaska, where trees adapt to the melting permafrost.*[48] *(© Shutterstock.)*

does see a climate-change impact in disasters.[49] This is a contentious area,[50] but one in which Predict Ability Ltd has made a breakthrough. We now have some real insight into when, where and why disasters happen.

Rhetoric

Many people have made a transition in their beliefs about climate change. It is hard to comprehend something that lies outside our range of experience. This author's 'moment' occurred during a BBC/PBS Horizon/Nova programme on the new science of climate change. People baulked at the word 'pollutant' in connection with CO_2. The year was 1988.[51]

The debate continued a quarter of a century later. In 2013, during Al Jazeera's *Head to Head* programme, Mehdi Hasan quizzed a panel of leading climate scientists about our ongoing struggle to even define 'global warming'.[52] If CO_2 causes heating, why does the temperature go up and down? Of course, heating is energy and air temperature is just one aspect of that, particularly in a dynamic change such as is being imposed on the Earth. Most (93%) of the excess heat is going into the oceans.[53] This is where reasonable points, such as why are we spending so much on renewables, get lost if the speaker then says – as Lord Nigel Lawson did on BBC Radio's flagship programme[54] – that the world is not warming. After that, the BBC mandarins decided that set-piece, highly polarised interviews on climate change had to be avoided, since most climate scientists believe the science is settled to this extent: the world is warming and CO_2 is the main the cause.[55] Astronomer Royal Sir Martin Rees's dictum comes to mind: 'the absence of evidence is not evidence of absence'.[56] No wonder the public is confused, annoyed or detached. People have more important things to worry about and would rather someone else sort 'it' out.

A favourite analogy often used by climate scientists is the overflowing bathtub. It goes like this. We are filling up the atmosphere with CO_2. One day it will be 'full' and something nasty will happen, akin to water pouring onto the bathroom floor. What will happen? Sudden sea-level rise? Let us get this in proportion. There is a plausible worst-case scenario of a one metre rise by 2100, caused by a massive meltdown in the Antarctic, where ice is currently accruing in parts at a huge rate. However, even this would have less impact on coastal megacities than their own sinking effect caused by borehole water extraction.[57] Venice in Italy is a classic example.

If this sea-level rise scenario did happen, many cities would be in jeopardy. However, as this would evolve over a century, there should be sufficient time for city infrastructures to be adapted or rebuilt elsewhere if necessary. The bathtub analogy only works if something truly unexpected were to happen. We should act cautiously. Do we know if the effects we are seeing today relate to current or historic CO_2 levels? And yet there does appear to be evidence that there will be significant degassing of methane from northern tundra that, as methane or CO_2, could provide a significant feedback.[58] Then along comes another George Monbiot column: 'We were wrong about peak oil: there's enough in the ground to deep-fry the planet'.[59]

'Years of living dangerously', broadcast in the US in 2014,[60] was a huge TV production that aimed to connect the public's imagination with those who had experienced climate change first hand. Although it was not always clear if the cause of the devastation was anthropogenic (man-made) CO_2 emissions, the programme clearly illustrated that it is stressed (poor) communities that are most vulnerable to extreme weather. It is they who are likely to reach a tipping point where whole neighbourhoods break down. The immediate problem, again, is their ability or inability to adapt. And for that, government and international protection schemes or other insurance-like mechanisms are vital.

What is the demarcation that divides 'warmists' and 'sceptics'? It seems that a sceptic can believe in climate change or even be a climate-change researcher. What marks them out is that they are not 'on message' with the current (IPCC) viewpoint. Such was the case with Richard Lindzen, an atmospheric physicist, who criticised the scientific consensus on climate change. He appeared on Al Jazeera's *Head to Head* programme[61] at the Oxford Union's climate change debate under the guise of 'climate change denier'. Lindzen's conjecture is that CO_2 is not as potent as the IPCC would have us believe, that its greenhouse gas effect is about one-third of what the Panel expects. He proposes that heat in the equatorial and tropical zones is trapped and must therefore work its way towards the poles, where it will re-radiate into space. Few agree with Lindzen's hypothesis. In most other scientific fields, a minority theory like his would not garner much interest, but in the climate community he is attacked, debate is stifled and there is the danger of 'group think'. Astonishingly, this is not an argument about what to do about the warming, as that involves spending money. No, it is an argument about a theory, a prediction. Climate scientists can be on message and be 'in' or they can be 'tossed out of the tribe', as Georgia Institute of Technology climatologist Professor Judith Curry found.[62]

Nearly all the debate in climate science is centred on the idea that 2°C of warming is the threshold we must not cross. Why 2°C?[63] 'Two degrees is not a magical limit – it is clearly a political goal', says Hans Joachim Schellnhuber, Director of the Pottsdam Institute for Climate Impact (PIK). What happens if we cross the threshold, as we did with CO_2 concentration in 1988? The website http://www.350.org states that 350 ppm is the ideal concentration, yet we are now at 408 ppm. Nothing happened. The campaign continues, but the credibility of other targets is in doubt. The World Bank expects the mean temperature to rise by 4°C.[64] The other aspect of any such target is that it implies it is safe to remain below it. Try telling that to the communities, governments and insurance companies now dealing with the effects of climate change, even though there has been just 1°C of warming so far. This is why vulnerable countries demanded a 1.5°C limit in the Paris 2015 climate negotiations.[65]

There is a temptation, as with the bathtub analogy, to invoke demons. A frequent argument is that, with global warming, heatwaves will be more common and that, as a result, more people will die. Firstly, mortality data requires very careful interpretation.[66] The total number of deaths may not change, but the elderly and the very young may die earlier due to the heat.[67] Secondly, it is again a question of vulnerability. Anyone who can afford it will obtain air conditioning – arguably one of the most important tools for living in hot countries. Conversely, warming may reduce winter hypothermia deaths but wild weather may increase the number.

In the US, assessments of the future impact of climate change suggest that at its worst, in southeastern US, there will be a 20% reduction in agricultural productivity.[68] Maize yields will increase up until 29°C but fall 6% by 40°C, even assuming there is enough rainfall. A bipartisan report on climate change accepts that there is already a 'high toll' on the US economy.[69]

Part of that toll is related to flooding, particularly coastal flooding. There have been some strange and alarming spikes in the financial losses that have had to be covered by the NFIP (National Flood Insurance Program, a US government scheme). This is where the idea of 'fat tails' in the probability curve comes in. James Hansen, a leading climatologist and formerly head of NASA's Goddard Institute for Space Studies, proposes that in these cases our safest strategy is to assume that the probability of certain extreme events is already *unity* (i.e. they will happen) and make our plans accordingly.[70] The danger here is that this generates a 'game over'[71] mentality, which may reinforce the very behaviour the climate scientists implore us to avoid.

Currently – it may pass – we live with the idea that there are flaws with the climate science and that adaptation needs to be included. Add in 'peak oil' – the notion that oil-production rates are peaking – and perhaps we have 'peak anxiety'. This suggests that, as a society, we can only maintain a level of concern about a threat for a certain time span. Either it comes or it does not, in which case we tend to move on to something else, such as the economy and jobs. The 2009 IPCC climate conference in Copenhagen did much to damage the public's confidence in the inter-governmental process. There was a huge build-up and then an empty disappointment. Such dismay was still evident at the Rio+20 conference. The top-down approach is failing,[72] or, as the science writer Fred Pearce puts it, 'the sky did not fall in' as the IPCC implied. There were factual errors, about ice melt in the Himalayas, and the whole process led to a '*cul de sac* of inaction'.[73] Indefatigable, the IPCC bounced back. Climate change is real, it is dangerous, but, they said, it can be paid for with a modest 0.06% impact on global GDP.[74] Why is it that only under duress does the IPCC start being pragmatic? It highlights the fundamental gulf that exists between scientists and politicians. The protracted, ugly and often unscientific process of climate negotiations taints both now. Through extraordinary diplomacy the 2015 climate-change agreement in Paris has, at least, reset the mood for now.

The 2008 banking crisis and the recession that followed it received far more attention than climate change. The latter may end up doing far more damage, but the 'discount rate' ensures that the value or, rather, impact of the recession is given more weight, more NPV (net present value). Economist Lord Nicholas Stern's climate report assumed a 1.4% depreciation rate, unheard of by any bank or business.[75] Ironically, climate change (globally) may have been a trigger for the recession, food riots in Tunisia and the subsequent so-called Arab Spring, not to mention the tragedy still engulfing Syria.[76] India, Columbia and Nigeria head a grim league: they have the most climate-related conflicts in the world.[77]

In the UK, interest in climate change,[78] outside the sacred circles, briefly peaked again in early 2014, when the public wanted to know who or what was responsible for the floods on the Somerset Levels. Yet neither climate change nor energy was a central debate in the UK general election of 2015. What was highlighted was the threat of rolling power cuts due to the recent closure of old coal-fired power stations. If these blackouts had occurred, there are certain fringe politicians who would have placed the blame squarely on our renewables policies. Ministers find grappling with UK energy policies hard enough, even without the climate-change dimension.

Nevertheless, in the 2015 UK general election, the main parties jointly pledged to tackle climate change.[79] The danger here is that there may be insufficient scrutiny of policy. For example, in the UK, the carbon 'omissions' (*sic*) campaign points out that, in real terms (the molecules for which we are responsible), carbon emissions reductions have been completely offset by the increased consumption of imported goods. In China, huge emissions occur during the manufacture of a

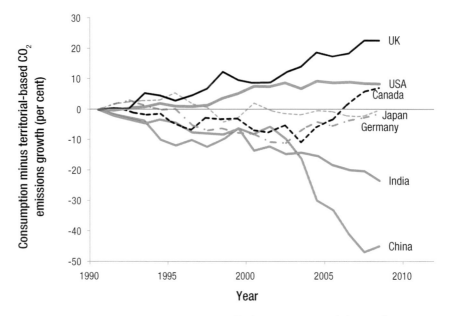

Figure 2.5. *Consumption CO₂ accounting.*[80] *Three-quarters of the UK's increase is due to reduced emissions at home. (© Predict Ability Ltd, with thanks to Glen Peters.)*

major fraction of the world's goods[81] (Figure 2.5). By this measure China is not the bad actor, merely the victim of bad carbon accounting.

Most green-energy projects are held together with government subsidies. The public's climate fatigue and the long-stalled UN–IPCC process forced politicians to become wary of further green-energy support. Even before the 2014 oil price slump, green energy in the US was in trouble. Although there were notable exceptions, such as wind power in the mid-west,[82] the *Financial Times* aptly wrote, 'Oil drop burns green energy'.[83]

If carbon taxation is an answer to this, we must bear in mind the public's limited willingness to pay, the more so if such a tax is administered by an elected government.[84] All this rhetoric suggests that we need to proceed in a less political, more open way. Climate change action needs to be wrested from the politicians. Business and the public need to be much more engaged.

Connecting

Jakob Bronowski is probably best remembered for his 1973 TV series *The Ascent of Man*. He clearly makes the point that where there is accumulation there will be disputes. War is theft. In ancient times it was about food harvested by settled peoples. Today it is about resources, water, oil and rare earth minerals. On top of theft there are the burdens of waste and pollution imposed by one society on another,[85] both in space and time. The day-by-day impact may be small, but the accumulated impact is huge. It is beyond our comprehension, and it may be our undoing.[86]

We live on one small planet, Earth Inc., as Al Gore puts it.[87] We have one world, one chance. Moreover, we are smart, ingenious beings. We have an interconnected electronic mind as never before. We have biotechnology. We could grow without destroying nature. But climate change, Gore says, is a huge issue. He warns us of tipping points. The collapse of the Berlin Wall was a major 20th-century tipping point. No one saw it coming and yet its effects were politically seismic. Does the weather have a climatological wall in store for us?

Collectively we live dangerously. Individually we are often fearful and risk-averse. But make no mistake, we live in the era of HIPPO[88] – habitat loss, invasive species, pollution, population growth and over-harvesting. Ask any child about the bees. . .

Evidence is everything.[89] Seeing is believing. An awe-inspiring event was captured in James Balog's amazing film *Chasing Ice*.[90] A Manhattan-sized slab of blue ice carves away from the Arctic ice sheet and slowly keels over into the sea with an eerie cracking sound and a subsonic roar. Balog and his team had captured a climatic event as it unfolded.

The best way to know the Earth is from space imaging. NASA has finally given us the OCO-2 (orbiting carbon observatory).[91] The original OCO failed after launching. The job of OCO-2 is to precisely map the sources and sinks of CO_2 in the atmosphere. The first images are as awe-inspiring as Balog's ice. We see in Figure 2.6 the lungs of the Earth, still thriving in the Amazon, DR Congo and Myanmar (Burma). And then we see where the CO_2 is being emitted: from deforestation and bush burning in South America, South Africa and South East Asia, particularly China, of course (Figure 2.7). Strangely, India seems to be carbon neutral and Myanmar shines like a beacon of sustainable development. But of course, this is just a snapshot – the picture is ever-changing. And what about tipping points? There is one worrying signature, just east of

Lake Hudson, Canada. And, sure enough, we find microbial action is causing massive degassing of melted tundra.[92] Perhaps these microbial sleeper cells will push the world back into a steamy Eocene epoch? We just don't know.

Temperature measurement, a fundamental indicator of climate change,

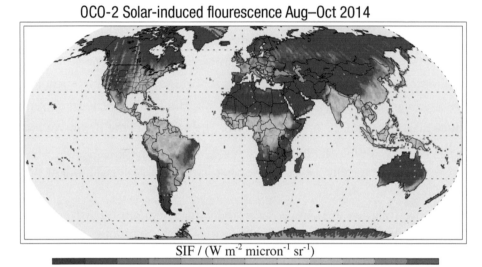

Figure 2.6. *OCO-2: the Earth's lungs. (© NASA/JPL-Caltech.)*

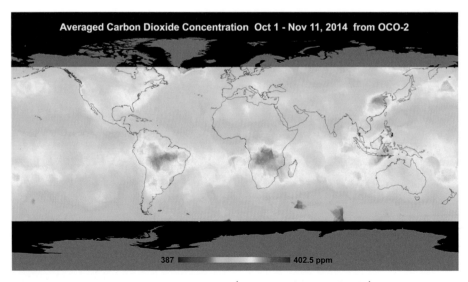

Figure 2.7. *OCO-2: new CO$_2$ surprises. (© NASA/JPL-Caltech.)*

is very challenging. Unreliable readings are caused by inconsistent methods and urbanisation.[93] We need other indicators too, such as ice cores and pollen counts (they are soaring in Japan and elsewhere).[94] However, there will always be uncertainty in measurement, but that should not stop us from taking appropriate actions.

Perhaps Hollywood gets it. Audiences seem to be uncomfortable with climate change. The film *Interstellar* is all about humanity escaping to other worlds and dimensions and alludes to global warming but dares not mention its name. A marvellous production it is, but perplexing nonetheless. Why do we not celebrate the amazing things we have on Earth, and focus on keeping them, as in *Independence Day*? Disney Studios seem to have opted to prepare us for what they expect to come. In *WALL-E*, set in the not-too-distant future, an Earth piled high with trash is brought back from a consumer-induced doom by an inquisitive robot, the last 'living being' on the planet.

The 'stock problem' is perhaps the most difficult aspect of connecting the public and politicians to climate science (Figure 2.8). The harm arises from the accumulated stock of excess CO_2 in the atmosphere, not the rate at which we put it there. *New Scientist* magazine grappled with this and suggested that a UN deal was no longer needed.[95] This ties in with policies such as the UK's Climate Change Act, which mandates that the country should reduce its emissions (with respect to 1990) by 80% by 2050.[96] However, as the UK politicians are frequently reminded by their Committee on Climate Change, delayed action will only mean more pain, as emissions will have to be reduced faster, later.[97] These inconvenient facts about current climate policies will not go away,[98] any more than climate change itself. 'Don't panic, but it is here to stay', says *The Economist*.[99]

Bronowski's premise, that theft cannot be sustained in the long run, leaves communicators with a problem. The public has become weary of disasters. They are doom-averse. People want to hear positive, inspirational ideas. They are there, of course, but can be more complex and subtle, e.g. peak environmental impact sounds bad but is actually a piece of good news.[100]

Without falling into the 'science is settled' trap, it is becoming clear that we know enough to act – proportionately at least. A key problem for the scientists is that 'climate sensitivity' is still an open question.[101] We need to be more open to managed retreat. In other words, we need to assign value to the natural and

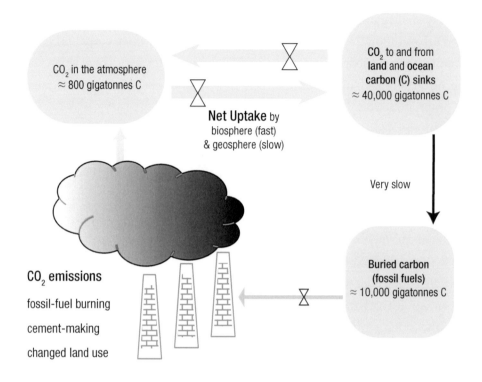

Rate of Accumulation of CO_2 in the atmosphere = CO_2 emissions − Net uptake

Stock = Total Accumulation (from 1750 onwards)

Figure 2.8. *This diagram highlights the CO_2 stock problem: often there is confusion between stocks and flows. (© Predict Ability Ltd.)*

physical stock and make decisions, not lightly but carefully, about what we want to sustain. This is adaptation again: a weather incident should be followed by a dispassionately considered response – some correction or adaptation or retreat – so that we evolve.

It is a 'wicked problem', as climate scientist Professor Mike Hulme puts it. Fossilised carbon has become central to our lifestyle, as well as the planet's biology. We are hooked on it. Most of us do not want to abandon capitalism, even though it constantly challenges us. We do not want to, we cannot, return to some former age of low technology. The only way forward is to exploit the systems and knowledge we have. Science and technology led us here. We need it more than ever to move forward, to survive. Will governments and business keep up, or will the world's elites pull up the drawbridge and leave the rest of us to our fate? At present, the world has not decided collectively that climate change needs to be properly addressed, although the Paris climate change agreement has set the challenge. Will there be a moment, as with slavery, when we decide that emitting CO_2 for free is wrong? The tide turned on slavery some time before it was abolished, but, when that day came in 1807, things moved quickly, yet the threat of its return is ever-present.[102]

Chicken or Egg?

The chicken or the egg: which came first? In the geological past, did CO_2 or temperature rise first?[103,104] Glacial ice core samples show that they rose together but until recently[105] scientists could not definitively determine which came first. For the climate sceptics it would have been a smoking gun. If temperature rise caused CO_2 to be released, then, they argue, climate science is dead. The evidence is now coming in: it was CO_2 that ended the ice ages. In the natural world (excluding massive volcanic eruptions) it is quite possible that CO_2 led or lagged temperature, until some other force – animate or inanimate – took over. This is at the heart of James Lovelock's *Gaia Hypothesis*.[106] Scientists have clearly known, since John Tyndall's seminal work in 1859[107] on absorption

Figure 2.9. *Imprisoned? Credit card debt and CO_2 debt are not 'cool'.*[108] *(© Shutterstock.)*

spectroscopy, that certain gases, including CO_2, water vapour and methane, trap heat in the atmosphere. That is what we now call the 'greenhouse effect', as Svante Arrhenius showed in 1896.[109] Knowing all this, why are we releasing nearly 40 billion tonnes of CO_2 a year into the atmosphere? There will be a significant temperature rise, sooner or later. It is a time bomb. We are building up the debt like a giant credit card, except in the physical world the debt is not cancelled in death. It is left as a legacy for the next generations. Actually, it is obvious that credit card debt is 'socialised' too; we all pay for the behaviour of the most feckless in the end (Figure 2.9).

Notes to Chapter Two

1   Helm, D., *The Carbon Crunch*, pp. 48–49, Yale University Press (2012).

2   Post Carbon Institute, '300 years of fossil fuels in 300 seconds' (2010), http://www.postcarbon.org/videos/

3   Schmidt, J., 'Phasing-out fossil fuel subsidies must be one of the major outcomes of Rio+20', *Huffington Post* (15 August 2012), http://www.huffingtonpost.com/jake-schmidt/phasingout-fossil-fuel-su_b_1600300.html

4   Tomlinson, S., 'How migrants are sending £335 BILLION to their struggling families back home . . . more than three times the world's total aid budget', *Mail Online* (1 February 2013), http://www.dailymail.co.uk/news/article-2271320/How-migrants-sending-335BILLION-struggling-families-home–times-worlds-total-aid-budget.html

5   Allen, M., 'Trillion-tonne budget means carbon capture is not optional', *The Conversation* (10 October 2013), http://theconversation.com/trillion-tonne-budget-means-carbon-capture-is-not-optional-18968

6   Buckley, T., 'Global energy markets transition drives thermal coal into structural decline', *Institute for Energy, Economics and Financial Analysis* (14 January 2015), http://ieefa.org/global-energy-markets/

7   Carrington, D., 'Is it too late to stop Turkey's coal rush?', *The Guardian* (6 August 2015), http://www.theguardian.com/environment/2015/aug/06/is-it-too-late-to-stop-turkeys-coal-rush

8   Slezak, M., 'Coal plants use as much water as 1 billion people and consumption set to double: Report', *The Guardian* (22 March 2016), http://www.theguardian.com/environment/2016/mar/22/world-water-day-coal-plants-use-as-much-water-as-1-billion-people-and-its-set-to-double/

9   Pielke Jr, R., *The Climate Fix*, p. 9, Basic Books, New York (2010).

10   Allen, M.R., 'The people's planet'.

11   Helm, D., *The Carbon Crunch*, p. 103.

12   Ibid., p. 118.

13   Lamy, P., et al., 'Now for the long term', Report of the Oxford Martin Commission for Future Generations (October 2013), http://www.oxfordmartin.ox.ac.uk/downloads/commission/Oxford_Martin_Now_for_the_Long_Term.pdf

14   Pielke Jr, R., *The Climate Fix*, p. 3, Basic Books, New York (2010).

15   http://media.gettyimages.com/photos/the-led-screen-shows-the-rising-sun-on-the-tiananmen-square-which-is-picture-id462905499

16   http://www.shutterstock.com/pic-166556393/stock-photo-bulldozer-working-on-landfill-with-birds-in-the-sky.html

17   'Climate change: An opportunity', Oxford Climate Forum, Spring 2014 (Saïd Business School Oxford, 7–8 February 2014), http://www.oxfordclimateforum.org/oxford-climate-forum-spring-2014.html

18   Hatton, C., 'Under the dome: The smog film taking China by storm', BBC News Beijing (2 March 2015), http://www.bbc.co.uk/news/blogs-china-blog-31689232

19   Helm, D., *The Carbon Crunch*, p. 111.

20   Pielke Jr, R., *The Climate Fix*, p. 53.

21   Leonard, A., 'Story of stuff – referenced and annotated script', storyofstuff.org (Fall 2002), http://storyofstuff.org/wp-content/uploads/movies/scripts/Story%20of%20Stuff.pdf

22   Rogoff, K., 'Where Is the Inequality Problem?', *Project Syndicate* (8 May 2014), https://www.project-syndicate.org/commentary/kenneth-rogoff-says-that-thomas-piketty-is-right-about-rich-countries--but-wrong-about-the-world?barrier=true

23   Helm, D., *The Carbon Crunch*, p. 87.

24   Ibid., p. 112

25   Ibid., p. 49

26   Marr, A., 'Andrew Marr's history of modern Britain', BBC 2 (19 December 2014), http://www.bbc.co.uk/programmes/b007xcfc/episodes/guide

27   Monbiot, G., 'Empty promise: Could scientists have got the impacts of climate change on food supply wildly wrong?' Monbiot.com (15 October 2012), http://www.monbiot.com/2012/10/15/empty-promise/

28   Kelly, M., 'Erratic, extreme day-to-day weather puts climate change in new light', *News at Princeton* (15 November 2011), http://www.princeton.edu/main/news/archive/S32/13/25I02/index.xml

29   Siegel, J., 'How to profit from natural gas shortages – natural gas just hit $100!', *Energyandcapital.com* (12 February 2014), http://www.energyandcapital.com/articles/how-to-profit-from-natural-gas-shortages/4222

30   Jordan, D., et al., 'Climate: Public understanding and policy implications', House of Commons Science and Technology Select Committee (uncorrected transcript, 17 July 2013), http://www.publications.parliament.uk/pa/cm201314/cmselect/cmsctech/uc254-iii/uc25401.htm

31   SD is a measure of how far away from the average an event is; only 0.3% of events lie 3 standard deviations from the average.

32   Victor, D.G, Kennel, C.F., 'Climate policy: Ditch the 2°C warming goal', *Nature Comment*, 514, 30–31 (2 October 2014), http://www.nature.com/news/climate-policy-ditch-the-2-c-warming-goal-1.16018

33   Schellnhuber, J., et al., '4-degrees briefing for the World Bank: The risks of a future without climate policy', Potsdam Institute for Climate Impact Research (19 November 2012), https://www.pik-potsdam.de/news/press-releases/archive/2012/4-degrees-briefing-for-the-world-bank-the-risks-of-a-future-without-climate-policy

34   Connor, S., 'Fewer resources, greater stress, more disasters: Climate change linked to violence among people and societies', *Independent* (1 August 2013), http://www.independent.co.uk/news/science/fewer-resources-greater-stress-more-disasters-climate-change-linked-to-violence-among-people-and-8742512.html

35   Francis, J., 'Weird winter weather plot thickens as arctic swiftly warms', *Scientific American* (19 February 2015), http://www.scientificamerican.com/article/weird-winter-weather-plot-thickens-as-arctic-swiftly-warms/

36   Moyer, J.W., 'More evidence Mayan civilization collapsed because of drought', *The Washington Post* (30 December 2014), http://www.washingtonpost.com/news/morning-mix/wp/2014/12/30/more-evidence-mayan-civilization-collapsed-because-of-drought/

37   Kolbert, E., *Field Notes from a Catastrophe*, p. 56, Bloomsbury (2007).

38   Walker, M., *Ebola*, BBC Radio 4 Drama (18 December 2014), http://www.bbc.co.uk/programmes/b04v5fjr

39   Department of Geography, 'Milankovitch cycles and glaciation', Univerisity of Indiana at Bloomington (accessed 17 April 2016), http://www.indiana.edu/~geol105/images/gaia_chapter_4/milankovitch.htm

40   Pearce, F., 'Is weird weather related to climate change', *Yale Environment 360* (24 February 2014), http://e360.yale.edu/feature/is_weird_winter_weather_related_to_climate_change/2742/

41   'Volcanic explosivity index', Wikipedia (accessed 17 April 2016), https://en.wikipedia.org/wiki/Volcanic_explosivity_index

42   Sharp, P., et al., 'A discussion of the independent risk assessment for risky business: The economic risks of climate change in the United States', Resources for the Future (26 June 2014), http://www.rff.org/events/event/2014–06/discussion-independent-risk-assessment-risky-business-economic-risks-climate

43 Doyle, A., Scrutton, A., 'Climate change a boon for Nordic grape growers', *Business Day* (25 November 2014), http://www.bdlive.co.za/life/travel/2014/11/25/climate-change-a-boon-for-nordic-grape-growers

44 Kolbert, E., *Field Notes from a Catastrophe*, p. 65, Bloomsbury (2007).

45 Chung, E., 'Birds migrating at wrong time for warmer climate', CBC News (4 June 2013), http://www.cbc.ca/news/technology/birds-migrating-at-wrong-time-for-warmer-climate-1.1337461

46 Gillis, J., 'US climate has already changed, study finds citing heat and floods', *The New York Times* (6 May 2014), http://www.nytimes.com/2014/05/07/science/earth/climate-change-report.html

47 Pielke Jr, R.A., 'The decline of tornado devastation', *The Wall Street Journal* (24 April 2014), http://www.wsj.com/news/articles/SB10001424052702303603904579495581998804074

48 Foster, J.M., 'Around the Arctic, frozen earth is thawing and creating "drunken forests"', *Climate Progress* (9 October 2013), http://thinkprogress.org/climate/2013/10/09/2759181/alaska-permafrost-arctic-hudson-bay/

49 Robbins, D., 'Five insurance companies debunk Fox on extreme weather', *MediaMatters* (4 November 2013), http://mediamatters.org/blog/2013/11/04/five-insurance-companies-debunk-fox-on-extreme/196734

50 Davidson, S., 'Climate change: Where theorists and skeptics agree and disagree', *Communities Digital News* (30 May 2014), http://www.commdiginews.com/health-science/climate-change-where-theorists-and-skeptics-agree-and-disagree-18567/

51 Brightwell, R., et al., 'The greenhouse effect', BBC 2 England (8 February 1988), http://genome.ch.bbc.co.uk/983c36698c8241bd9ebd94ff5b1759a8

52 Hasan, M., 'Climate change: Fact or fiction?', Al Jazeera (*Head to Head*, 13 June 2013), http://www.aljazeera.com/programmes/headtohead/2013/06/201361311721241956.html

53 'Effects of global warming on oceans', Wikipedia (accessed 17 April 2016), https://en.wikipedia.org/wiki/Effects_of_global_warming_on_oceans

54 'Hoskins vs. Lawson: The climate debate the BBC wants to censor', The Global Warming Policy Forum (29 June 2014), http://www.thegwpf.com/hoskins-vs-lawson-the-climate-debate-the-bbc-wants-to-censor/

55 Pielke Jr, R., *The Climate Fix*, p. 7

56 Morris, E., 'The certainty of Donald Rumsfeld (Part 4)', *The New York Times* (Opinionator, 28 March 2014), http://opinionator.blogs.nytimes.com/2014/03/28/the-certainty-of-donald-rumsfeld-part-4/

57 Stiles, D., 'Groundwater extraction blamed for cities sinking', *Water & Wastewater Treatment* (1 May 2014), http://wwtonline.co.uk/news/groundwater-extraction-blamed-for-cities-sinking

58 'An Arctic methane worst-case scenario', *Real Climate* (7 January 2012), http://www.realclimate.org/index.php/archives/2012/01/an-arctic-methane-worst-case-scenario/

59 Monbiot, G., 'False summit: We were wrong about peak oil: There's enough in the ground to deep-fry the planet', Monbiot.com (2 July 2012), http://www.monbiot.com/2012/07/02/false-summit/

60 Cameron, J., et al., 'Years of living dangerously', *Showtime* (accessed 17 April 2016), http://yearsoflivingdangerously.com/

61 Hasan, M., 'Climate change: Fact or fiction?', Al Jazeera (*Head to Head*, 13 June 2013), http://www.aljazeera.com/programmes/headtohead/2013/06/201361311721241956.html

62 Rose, D., 'I was tossed out of the tribe': Climate scientist Judith Curry interviewed', *The Spectator* (28 November 2015), http://www.spectator.co.uk/2015/11/i-was-tossed-out-of-the-tribe-climate-scientist-judith-curry-interviewed/

63 Evers, M., 'Climate catastrophe: A superstorm for global warming research. Part 8: The invention of the two-degree target', *Spiegel Online International* (1 April 2010), http://www.spiegel.de/international/world/climate-catastrophe-a-superstorm-for-global-warming-research-a-686697–8.html

64 Tandon, S., 'World Bank fears devastating 4.0 degree warming', *Global Energy World* (19 November 2012), http://www.globalenergyworld.com/news/6639/World_Bank_Fears_Devastating_40_Degree_Warming.htm

65 'Climate impact at 1.5°C and 2°C – a Pacific perspective', Climateanalytics.org (October 2015), http://climateanalytics.org/files/1p5_vs_2_impacts_pacific_islands.pdf

66 Knappenberger, P.C., Michaels, P.J., 'Climate change, heat waves, and adaptation', Cato Institute (20 June 2014), http://www.cato.org/blog/climate-change-heat-waves-adaptation

67 Sharp, P., et al., 'A discussion of the independent risk assessment for risky business', Resources for the Future (26 June 2014), http://www.rff.org/events/event/2014–06/discussion-independent-risk-assessment-risky-business-economic-risks-climate

68 Loc. cit.

69 Gillis, J., 'Bipartisan report tallies high toll on economy from global warming', *The New York Times* (24 June 2014), http://www.nytimes.com/2014/06/24/science/report-tallies-toll-on-economy-from-global-warming.html

70 Than, K., 'Heatwaves "almost certainly" due to global warming?', *National Geographic News* (6 August 2012), http://news.nationalgeographic.com/news/2012/08/120803-global-warming-hansen-nasa-heat-waves-science/

71 Oxford Climate Forum 2013 (Saïd Business School Oxford, 25–26 January 2013), http://www.oxfordclimateforum.org/uploads/3/2/6/4/3264162/_oxford_climate_forum_2013_-_programme.pdf

72 Blok, K., Höhne, N., van der Leun, K., Harrison, N., 'Bridging the greenhouse-gas emissions gap', *Nature Climate Change*, 2, 471–474 (17 June 2012), http://www.nature.com/nclimate/journal/v2/n7/full/nclimate1602.html

73 Demenocal, P., 'After tomorrow', *Orion Magazine* (2004), https://orionmagazine.org/article/after-tomorrow1/

74 Hope, M., 'Tackling global warming could slow global growth – by 0.06 per cent, IPCC predicts', *CarbonBrief* (16 April 2014), http://www.carbonbrief.org/blog/2014/04/tackling-global-warming-could-mean-slowing-economic-growth-by-006-per-cent/

75 Oxford Climate Forum Spring 2014 (Saïd Business School Oxford, 7–8 February 2014), http://www.oxfordclimateforum.org/uploads/3/2/6/4/3264162/spring_2014_oxford_climate_forum_programme.pdf

76 Westcott, L., 'Climate change helped create conditions for war in Syria, study suggests', *Newsweek* (4 March 2015), http://www.newsweek.com/climate-change-helped-create-conditions-war-syria-study-suggests-311199

77 Singh, S., 'Map shows India at top of climate violence', *SciDevNet* (27 January 2016), http://www.scidev.net/global/conflict/news/map-india-climate-violence-injustice.html

78 Gayle, D., 'Green lobby loses the public: Most people no longer consider global warming a serious issue in a recession', *Mail Online* (28 February 2013), http://www.dailymail.co.uk/sciencetech/article-2285812/Most-people-longer-consider-global-warming-issue-financial-crisis-changes-priorities.html

79 Carrington, D., 'Cameron, Clegg and Miliband sign joint climate pledge', *The Guardian* (14 February 2015), http://www.theguardian.com/environment/2015/feb/14/cameron-clegg-and-miliband-sign-joint-climate-pledge

80 Barrett, J., et al., 'Memorandum submitted by UKERC', UK Parliament Energy and Climate Change Select Committee (17 April 2012),

http://www.publications.parliament.uk/pa/cm201012/cmselect/cmenergy/1646/1646vw13.htm

81 Helm, D., *The Carbon Crunch'*, p. 70.

82 Dinan, S., 'Obama clean energy loans leave taxpayers in \$2.2 billion hole', *The Washington Times* (27 April 2015), http://www.washingtontimes.com/news/2015/apr/27/obama-backed-green-energy-failures-leave-taxpayers

83 Clark, P., 'The big drop: Cheap oil burns green energy', *Financial Times* (17 December 2014), http://www.ft.com/cms/s/0/d328ee8a-8605-11e4-a105-00144feabdc0.html

84 Pielke Jr, R., *The Climate Fix*, p. 221

85 Amos, J., 'Polluted air causes 5.5 million deaths a year, new research says', BBC Science and Environment (13 February 2016), http://www.bbc.co.uk/news/science-environment-35568249

86 Bronowski, J., *The Ascent of Man*, BBC *Time Life* (13 part television documentary, 1973), https://en.wikipedia.org/wiki/The_Ascent_of_Man

87 Gore, A., 'The future: Six drivers of global change', Oxford Martin School, Oxford University (31 October 2013), http://www.oxfordmartin.ox.ac.uk/event/1667

88 Wilson, E.O., 'The loss of biodiversity is a tragedy', UNESCO Media Services (9 February 2010), http://www.unesco.org/new/en/media-services/single-view/news/edward_o_wilson_the_loss_of_biodiversity_is_a_tragedy

89 Measurements are crucial: CO_2 levels, emissions data, sea levels, ice extent, insured and uninsured losses, habitat loss, etc.

90 Balog, J., *Chasing Ice*, Chasingice.com (2014), https://chasingice.com/about-the-film/synopsis/

91 Granat, R., 'CO_2 virtual science data environment', NASA Jet Propulsion Laboratory (accessed 17 April 2016), https://co2.jpl.nasa.gov/

92 Vincent, W.F., 'Freshwater resources in a changing environment', in Allard, M., Lemay, M. (eds.), *Nunavik and Nunatsiavut: From Science to Policy. An Integrated Regional Impact Study (IRIS) of Climate Change and Modernization*, pp. 137–155 (2012). ArcticNet Inc., Quebec City, Canada, http://www.cen.ulaval.ca/warwickvincent/PDFfiles/293.pdf

93 Helm, D., *The Carbon Crunch*, p. 23.

94 Radford, T., 'Climate change will send pollen count soaring', *Climate News Network* (9 November 2014), http://climatenewsnetwork.net/climate-change-will-send-pollen-count-soaring/

95   Pearce, F., 'First sign that humanity is slowing its carbon surge', *New Scientist* (6 November 2013), https://www.newscientist.com/article/mg22029422-800-first-sign-that-humanity-is-slowing-its-carbon-surge/

96   'How the UK is progressing', UK Parliament Committee on Climate Change (2015),   https://www.theccc.org.uk/tackling-climate-change/reducing-carbon-emissions/how-the-uk-is-progressing/

97   Fogarty, D., Doyle, A., 'As nations haggle, global carbon cuts get impossibly deep', Reuters UK (28 November 2012), http://uk.reuters.com/article/2012/11/28/us-climate-talks-targets-idUKBRE8AR14T20121128

98   Rapier, R., 'Global carbon dioxide emissions – facts and figures', The Energy Collective (2 July 2012), http://www.theenergycollective.com/robertrapier/89616/global-carbon-dioxide-emissions-facts-and-figures

99   'A sensitive matter', *The Economist* (30 March 2013), http://www.economist.com/news/science-and-technology/21574461-climate-may-be-heating-up-less-response-greenhouse-gas-emissions

100   Boyd, J.W., et al., 'Reforming today's conservation and environmental policies for tomorrow's scarcity', Resources for the Future (9 September 2015), http://www.rff.org/events/event/2015–09/reforming-today-s-conservation-and-environmental-policies-tomorrow-s-scarcity

101   Hasan, M., 'Climate change: Fact or fiction?'

102   Kolbert, E., *Field Notes from a Catastrophe*, p. 143

103   Helm, D., '*The Carbon Crunch*, p. 21

104   Ferguson, W., 'Ice core data help solve a global warming mystery', *Scientific American* (1 March 2013), http://www.scientificamerican.com/article/ice-core-data-help-solve/

105   Hood, M., 'Case closed, says study: CO_2 melted ice age glaciers', *Agence France-Presse* (22 August 2015), http://www.interaksyon.com/article/116410/case-closed-says-study-c02-melted-ice-age-glaciers

106   'Gaia Theory: Model and metaphor for the 21st century', gaiatheory.org (accessed 17 April 2016), http://www.gaiatheory.org/overview/

107   Hulme, M., 'On the origin of the "greenhouse effect": John Tyndall's 1859 interrogation of nature', *Weather*, 64 (5), pp. 121–123 (27 April 2009), http://onlinelibrary.wiley.com/doi/10.1002/wea.386/pdf

108   http://www.shutterstock.com/pic-232804810/stock-photo-gorgeous-girl-using-her-tablet-computer-and-credit-card-to-buy-some-stuff-online.html

109   'Svante Arrhenius (1859–1927)', NASA Earth Observatory (accessed 17 April 2016), http://earthobservatory.nasa.gov/Features/Arrhenius/arrhenius_2.php

Climate change is one of the greatest risks facing humankind this century.

Through a part of its core business, the insurance industry is directly affected

and therefore assumes a leading role in devising solutions for climate protection

and adaptation to the inevitable changes.

Professor Peter Höppe,
Head of Munich Re's Geo Risks
Research/Corporate Climate Centre

CHAPTER THREE

DISASTERS AND CLIMATE CHANGE

Is there a signal in the noise?

A link between climate change and natural disasters – cyclones, floods and droughts – might be expected, but the trends are complex. Unless there is no link, even a small influence from climate change today may have exponential impacts as the world warms. A simple model illustrates what may happen in our changing climate.

Predictions

Climate prediction gets more challenging the more localised it becomes. The climate is a very complex system. It is a probabilistic, non-linear system.[1] At the macro-scale it is much easier to make straightforward claims, such as there will be a 1°C rise for every 125 ppm increase in CO_2 concentration in the atmosphere.[2] But the climate sensitivity of complex models has been called into question since the rate of warming has apparently paused, or flattened, since 2003.[3] Some sectors of the media relish this embarrassment.[4] By reporting atmospheric temperature as the principal indicator of warming, the scientists become a hostage to fortune. If wind shear in the Pacific increases, the air temperature goes down, or, if there is more melting of Greenland's ice sheet, then the latent heat of melting ice has an effect. These things are of course worked into the models as soon as they are apparent or can be quantified. To the public this looks like 'tweaking' or suspicious fine-tuning. It may be justifiable if the scientists want to interpolate data, or to make short-term predictions, but not for long-term predictions. There is elegance in simplicity.

By 2015, the story and science had moved on. The global warming pause had not happened, it appears. There were a number of possible factors, such as faulty seawater temperatures,[5] and the action of natural weather cycles with exotic names: the El Niño-Southern Oscillation (ENSO), the Pacific Decadal Oscillation (PDO) and the Atlantic Multi-decadal Oscillation (AMO). Now, it seems, the period 2015–2016 has set new records.[6]

A more realistic measure of warming is energy (specifically heat or enthalpy). Over 90% of the excess warming ends up in the oceans.[7] But the numbers are quite mind-boggling. What does $\sim 10^{23}$ J mean to physicists, let alone the general public? 10^{23} J is 100,000,000,000,000,000,000,000 joules. It is millions of atomic bombs. Oh heck.

Natural and anthropogenic climate variability gives climate scientists wriggle room (and a media headache). Professor Allen[8] explained all about variability in a talk he wanted to rehearse before attending a UK Parliament's Environmental Audit Committee on climate change. He illustrated his point with a case of flooding at Shillingford Bridge on the River Thames. Extreme weather and flooding are not new (Figure 3.1).

Figure 3.1. *Mail Coach in a Flood, c. 1827 (after James Pollard).*[9] *(© Diomedia.)*

What Myles Allen was explaining to the MPs was event attribution, the new science he helped to create to determine to what extent extreme weather events are man-made. It is as complex as planetary dynamics. The classical 'three body problem' has given rise to exotic and exquisite mathematics since Sir Isaac Newton first posed it in 1687. Henri Poincaré, the father of chaos theory, showed that there was no general analytical solution for certain planetary motions. Climate predictions, too, are chaotic and extremely sensitive to the starting assumptions. This is the 'initial value problem' or, more poetically, the 'butterfly effect'. Yes, a butterfly could flap its wings and later cause a hurricane, but it is highly improbable. For Allen, probability is what it is all about. To get anywhere you have to run complex computer models over and over again. It is very computing-intensive. Use is made of the computing power of idle PCs.

Take the great storm that swept through southern England in October 1987. What we know from nature (and the Met Office) is that there was one fixed starting condition, i.e. the weather pattern the day before the storm. And there was one outcome: the storm of the century. The weather forecasters could see that it was possible but thought it improbable (forecaster Michael Fish said as much on TV, but what else could he do?). In the weather system that day there were many possible outcomes. There was just no way of communicating the risk to the public in any helpful way. On most days, the weather forecast is much more deterministic – the range of expected outcomes is quite small. Superstorm Sandy (New York, October 2012) is another example.[10] It was very improbable, but it happened. It was hugely disruptive and expensive – the New York Subway flooded, city power transformers were destroyed, oil refineries were incapacitated and 159 people died – 44 of them in New York City.

Antarctic ice accumulation is another example where climate scientists have found themselves in hot water.[11] Mainland Antarctica ice thickness reached an all-time high in 2014. It was 4 standard deviations away from the predictions of accepted climatological models, i.e. there was 1 chance in 15,000 of the ice reaching that thickness. Of course, that does not disprove climate change, but it does suggest that policies based on climate models should not be relied on to give exact outcomes for 2025, let alone 2100. Why? For every plus point, there is a minus: it seems that violent waves in the Southern Ocean are in part responsible for the accelerated break-up of the outer Antarctic ice sheet.[12]

Sea-Level Rise

Sea-level rise is the most obvious and tractable outcome of climate change. It has been going on for a long time, since the last ice age, and it matters to hundreds of millions of people. Nowhere more so than in Small Island states, where around 5% of the world's population live.[13] To where will they retreat? And why should they retreat?

An intriguing aspect of sea-level rise is that, although subject to

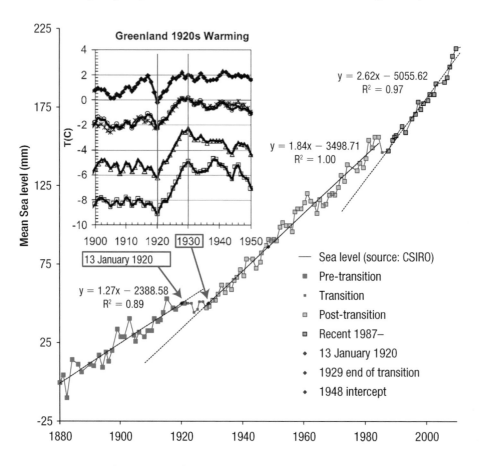

Figure 3.2. *Accelerating sea-level rise: was 13 January 1920 the start of the Anthropocene epoch? It was the day Robert H. Goddard, the father of space rocketry, published his revolutionary ideas. They were mocked*[14] *by* The New York Times *but, 49 years later, that paper quietly published 'a correction' the day after Apollo 11 launched. (Inset: Greenland temperatures, Chylek, P., et al.*[15]*) (© Predict Ability Ltd.)*

measurement errors, there seems to have been three distinct periods in the 20th century: before 1920 the global rate was about 2mm per year but after 1929 ~3mm per year (Figure 3.2). And in between? A pause. 1920–1929 was a period of exceptional Arctic warming.[16] It also marked the onset of industrial-scale carbon emissions with which we are now so concerned. Perhaps this was a tipping point, the start of the Anthropocene (the human epoch)?[17]

Today, sea levels are rising at their fastest rate since Roman times.[18] Because of the heat capacity of the oceans there is a lag – today's sea-level rise relates to the CO_2 emissions of the past. Sea levels will continue to rise for centuries.[19]

Small Island states have sought justice through the US legal system, to seek redress from the energy majors for causing sea-level rise through the emission of pollutants. The case of Kivalina, Alaska (Figure 3.3), is significant. The suit was dismissed by a United States District Court on 30 September 2009, on the grounds that regulating greenhouse emissions was a political rather than a legal issue and one that needed to be resolved by Congress and the Administration, rather than by the courts.[20] In 2013 the US Supreme Court refused to hear the case, effectively ending the legal claim. If Greenland's ice melts, local sea levels may fall as the body of ice exerts gravitational pull on the sea. In mid latitudes,

Figure 3.3. *Alaska: native village of the Kivalina tribe.*[21] (© *Reuters Pictures.*)

the sea level may rise significantly. The oceans are not flat like water in a bathtub.[22] In other areas, like Finland, the land mass has been rising since the last ice age; the Earth's crust was depressed by the weight of ice.

While Small Islands make up 5% of the world's population, there are mainland areas such as Florida where millions of properties will be overwhelmed by the combined effects of sea-level rise and storm surge.[23] How should the cost[24] of this inundation be factored into carbon pricing, for example? With so many coastal cities at risk, it is encouraging that the problem is now receiving the attention it needs at national and international levels.[25]

If the gravitational effect of melting ice masses causes the local sea level to fall, then there needs to be a plan for every kilometre of coast near populated regions. This is a huge undertaking, but it should not be overlooked. The impact may vary in a highly non-linear way, as climate scientists Boettle et al. show.[26]

Floods and Storms

In 1953 coastal communities in England and the Netherlands were devastated by an unexpected storm surge.[27] In bungalows, hundreds drowned in their beds. There was widespread flooding. In 2013 a surge of greater magnitude caused much less damage and three deaths. A combination of sea-wall defences and early-warning systems had been installed. This is an example of where adaptation can be very effective: thousands of lives were saved and people are able to live well in an imperilled area.

At a more local level, a community in rural Oxfordshire, UK, has been grappling with flooding for some time. As the little village of Cholsey[28] develops, there is a concern about the trade-off between drainage systems and the need for industrial or business space. The aim is to make each new site have zero rainwater run-off. It has proven extremely difficult to justify flood defences. One year there is extreme drought and in the next there is flooding. All councils can do is adopt good practice, so far as the budget will allow. There will always be incidents and the hope is that insurance premiums will be reasonable and available, but in future that may not be a sound business assumption.

Such uncertainty is frustrating for government departments charged with flooding policy implementation.[29,30] Naturally there will tend to be a bias towards saving lives, and homes – and most homes are situated in towns and cities. This leaves farmland and rural properties and villages in a vulnerable situation. Combined with the downward pressures on farm prices and outbreaks of infections, such as foot and mouth disease, many British farms face ruin.[31] Here, the dialogue between governments and the insurance industry is very important. We need long-term strategies and leadership. A good example is a flood-specific insurance scheme called Flood Re.[32]

On a larger scale, storms and hurricanes can have devastating impacts that catch even the largest administrations off-guard. The most extreme case was Hurricane Katrina, that in 2005 devastated New Orleans. The disaster response was haphazard or ill-conceived and maintenance of the levees had been unsatisfactory.[33] Even today, large sections of the city's 9th Ward remain derelict in the richest nation on Earth. Although some new housing has been erected, local communities worry about 'gentrification'.[34] Some 60km southwest of New Orleans lies Isle de Jean Charles, long-time home of the Biloxi-Chitimacha-Choctaw, a Native American tribe. They have to move. Over 98% of their land has been lost since the 1950s. 'This is the first time an entire community has had to be relocated due in part to rising sea levels', said Marion McFadden, a spokeswoman for the US Department of Housing and Urban Development.[35]

What still remains hotly contested is whether climate change had a hand in Hurricane Katrina. Professor Roger Pielke Jr has studied this closely.[36] Insurance companies and flood response programmes run by the US government have racked up huge losses during the last two decades, but Pielke attributes this predominantly to economic growth.

To illustrate the point, Pielke Jr cites the city of Miami, where our story began. In 1926 there was a terrible hurricane there.[37] Perhaps it was even a Cat 5 storm, until now the worst kind. So why is the 'Great Storm of '26' not part of popular folklore, whilst the 1906 San Francisco earthquake and fire is seared into the American memory? The reason is simple. In 1926 Miami was one hotel, a small town and a beach. If a storm surge hit today, what would happen? An $80 billion disaster, says a report from insurance risk specialists Karen Clark & Co.[38] Their estimates were made using their insurance-loss tool *RiskInsight*. Miami's risk is topped by New York ($100 billion), New Orleans ($130 billion) and, surprisingly perhaps, Tampa, Florida ($175 billion).

While the economic factors are dominant, they are not the whole story. Predict Ability Ltd has found *there is a climate change signal* in the Munich RE disaster loss database.[39] In the case of hurricanes it is very hard to detect as MIT's Professor Kerry Emanuel explained in an article countering Professor Pielke Jr's assertion: 'no matter what President Obama and British Prime Minister David Cameron say, recent [2012–2014] costly disasters are not part of a trend driven by climate change'.[40]

For a disaster to happen two things have to be present: people and extreme weather events (Figure 3.4). Increasingly people live in cities, a trend called urbanisation.[41] Half of us live in a city today. By 2030 the population of the world's cities will reach 5 billion.

To illustrate the point, consider Cyclone Pam[42] which struck the Pacific Island chain of Vanuatu in March 2015. In the southern hemisphere hurricanes are called cyclones. For a while Pam was a meteorological event, out at sea, brewing up to Cat 5 with wind speeds exceeding 155mph, but when it hit Vanuatu it became a disaster. The world seemed to expect utter devastation as communications were cut. And there was devastation. It was a huge storm and some suggest that sea-level rise made it worse.[43] Typically, most islanders were resilient, self-reliant and as prepared as they could be. They are used to storms. The cavalry never comes but there were shelters, food and water reserves, etc. Damages were estimated to be $360 million; there were 15 deaths. What Cyclone Pam illustrates is that each storm or disaster has its own characteristics. (Six months later the hardship was compounded by drought, but the world was no longer watching.)[44] Only by understanding disasters can we hope to delve deep enough to find root causes.

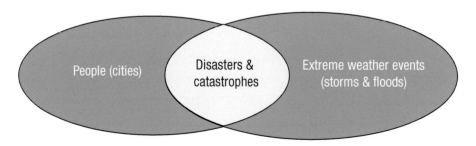

Figure 3.4. *The ingredients for disaster. (© Predict Ability Ltd.)*

Enter Al Gore, US Vice President under President Bill Clinton. Following the debacle of the 2000 US presidential election, Gore devoted himself to his passion: climate change. The result was *An Inconvenient Truth*, the 2006 film[45] and book. For a time it was shown in many schools across the UK, but the US NSTA (National Science Teachers Association) refused free copies of the film. It all got a bit ugly.[46] The cover image suggested a direct relationship between emissions and hurricanes (Figure 3.5), although Al Gore was reportedly very careful not to say there is a direct correlation. It appears no such link exists, or, at least, no such link has been conclusively shown to exist ... so far. Gore is a passionate and persuasive speaker, but if there is one lesson to be learnt from the last thirty years of climate exchanges it is this: your claims about climate change will be challenged. One false step can polarise people's perceptions.

Most researchers focus on the increasing costs of hurricanes, yet inexplicably the number of hurricanes making landfall is currently falling. If the coefficients of climate sensitivity are broadly correct and over 90% of global warming goes into the oceans, why does not more of that energy take the form of hurricanes? Evidently the sea surface temperatures are warming.

Figure 3.5. *An inconvenient question:*[47] *is there a link between emissions and hurricanes? (© Wikipedia, Creative Commons.)*

It may be that the time-constants linking heat input and thermal-hydraulic effects are long – possibly many decades long. Perhaps James Hansen had that in mind when writing his book *Storms of My Grandchildren*.[48] Excess hurricanes may indeed emerge on that timescale.[49]

Returning to the lesser but far more numerous storms that cause flooding, why is it that building codes are so poor? Many homes are built in zones that are known to flood or are predicted to flood, for whatever reason.[50] Of course enhancing building resilience costs money, but why should homeowners and tenants be encumbered with the misery that flooding causes? And that is not to mention the subsequent insurance nightmare. A home should be safe, warm or cool and dry. City authorities across many countries should question their priorities as to whether they build in flood plains or not.[51] Soaking up community charges (or the equivalent housing tax) from vulnerable householders is likely to be a risky strategy from a revenue perspective. It is often those very same city authorities that will have to clear up the mess and re-house these vulnerable householders. In the US, the federal government further complicates the issues. A reform of the US NFIP (National Flood Insurance Program)[52] was attempted, to discourage the practice of rebuilding in flood zones, but it failed (the Biggert-Waters Flood Insurance Reform Act of 2012 was eventually scuppered).[53] City or local authorities tend to be more pragmatic – solution-driven and less ideological – than governments. However, in the US, there are now at least signs of 'bipartisan' action, e.g. a report entitled *Risky Business: The Economic Risks of Climate Change in the United States*.[54]

Flooding is a key indicator of climate change. Wherever we look, flood claims are increasing,[55] monsoons are more erratic[56] and storms are becoming more intense.[57] Their effects, their damages, are expected to double or even triple before 2100.[58] Event attribution is the new science of determining the extent to which man-made CO_2 emissions are responsible for climate change and extreme weather events (more of this in Chapter Seven). As the science steadily evolves, it is providing clear evidence of increased flood risks worldwide.[59]

Droughts
An insidious low-level, long-term disaster, droughts can have a much greater financial impact than expected. In developed and developing countries alike,

droughts change people's lives. From California, with its luxurious lawns and abandoned almond plantations, to São Paulo, once Brazil's city of Amazonian drizzle, droughts are on the increase too. While storms and flooding can be severe, and mudslides are particularly lethal, droughts are deadly, long-lasting events that can affect whole regions. The ongoing (2012) drought in California appears to be the worst in 1200 years when assessed against the PDSI (Palmer Drought Severity Index).[60] Californians have without doubt made things far worse than they needed to have. There is unregulated water extraction, wasteful uses, and inappropriate water-hungry crops. It is a woeful tale of mismanagement, but for sure Hollywood, Silicon Valley and tourism will roll on.[61] It is the farmers and farm workers in the Central Valley who will be most affected. California is coming to terms with its geography and could learn a lot from Arizona, its nearby desert region neighbour.

Desertification, and our ability to adapt to it, has long been a defining feature of human development.[62] The 'spread of deserts costs trillions [and] spurs migrants', reports Reuter's Alister Doyle.[63]

There is a certain irony about drought-affected regions in that they are rather prone to flooding. Suddenly the weather changes, and there is a massive precipitation event. The people of São Paulo know this and so do Californians. Their Governor, Jerry Brown, has spent half of a $1.1 billion drought fund on *flood defences.*[64] This probably makes sense: it is the way things are now. No one can be sure what will happen next.

Droughts could be easily designated as climate-change events. Surely, if the world is warming, droughts become more likely? Well, yes and no. The 2012 heatwaves and droughts that affected the central US states were possibly within the realms of 'normal' weather.[65] This ambiguity may have as much to do with our current level of understanding about event attribution as the weather itself. Some authors think that US droughts have remained steady since the 1950s.[66]

Droughts are widespread. In Africa – Ethiopia for example – they have made world headlines.[67] As a consequence of the 1984 catastrophe, today Ethiopia is much more resilient. Farming methods have been made more drought-tolerant and the economy has grown and diversified. But still, in many areas, drought saps subsistence farmers, who are, at the best of times, vulnerable.[68] In 2015 severe drought again struck, possibly linked with a growing El Niño event.[69] Disease (vector or insect-borne, like the Zika virus)[70] is another threat that appears to increase with climate change and this profoundly impacts income.[71] Elsewhere, both droughts and deluges are expected to increase and the implications for conflict are clear.[72,73] There is compelling evidence that one of the root causes of the ongoing Syrian War (2011 . . .) was the drought of 2007–2010[74] and that the drought was enhanced by climate change.[75] Other causes include changes to farming subsidies by President Bashar al-Assad and an influx of ~1 million Iraqi citizens displaced during the wars in Iraq.[76]

Even if there is relative peace, it seems that drought is capable of demolishing societies and cultures and has done so for millennia. The reasons for the Mayan Empire's collapse are many: clashes of cultures, the decline of trade, disease, etc., but it was an extended and devastating drought that finally brought an end to a resilient civilisation. And all this happened in a world with a so-called 'pristine' climate.[77] Recognising the vulnerabilities and the factors causing them is an essential first step.[78]

Droughts, water scarcity[79] and urbanisation are interwoven. Along with sea-level rise, droughts are creating the narrative of human movement today. And climate change is part of it.

Deforestation

It looks as though NASA's OCO-2 satellite (see Figures 2.6 and 2.7) will be an invaluable tool in the fight to preserve long-established tropical forests. They are so important to our wellbeing that we have to understand why they are being felled and what can be done to prevent that tragedy. Indonesia has overtaken Brazil on deforestation, despite a moratorium.[80] In the drought that affected São Paulo in 2014, deforestation was implicated.[81] Forest clearance for soybean plantations and beef ranching has broken up the forest-driven-rainfall path of over a thousand miles, from the Atlantic across the Amazon and down the Andes. The UN has highlighted deforestation. It is a top priority and REDD+ (Reducing Emissions from Deforestation and Forest Degradation)[82] is a vital strategy for reducing global, forest-related CO_2 emissions, together with emissions offsetting. It is central to the theme of carbon pricing.

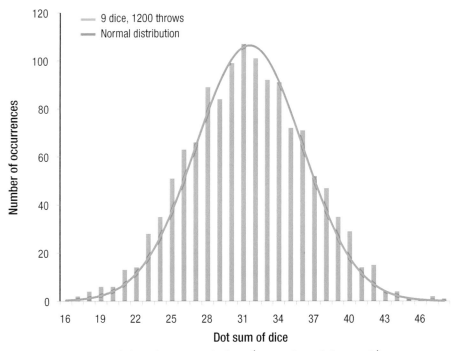

Figure 3.6. *A normal distribution with dice. (© Predict Ability Ltd.)*

Impact Integral

An impact integral? That sounds rather abstract, but it all comes down to this. If the influence of climate change *is* present in the Munich RE Natural Disaster data, then what will be the relative impact – on insurance and government losses – when we have not 0.85°C[83] of warming as we do today, but 2, 3 or even 4°C of warming?

To assess this we need to consider a normal world, even though the world has never stayed 'normal' for long. Consider the rolling of a dice. If rolled enough times, there is an equal chance of any number of dots coming up. But what if there are two, three or more dice? As the number increases, there are ever-more possible outcomes. If we had N dice and we made a graph of the dot sums from $1 \times N$ to $6 \times N$ versus the number of occurrences of each dot sum, a pattern would emerge. As N becomes large, say N = 9, the graph would become 'bell-shaped' (Figure 3.6). This is what statisticians call a normal distribution. And in terms of climate change, this form of statistical distribution of weather-related events could lead to a doubling of impact if the world warmed to 4°C.

Could it be worse? If the dice were loaded for example? If the dice were biased to produce more 6s, hotter weather say, *and always had been*, then the future impact would be less, i.e. extremely hot weather would already be part of normality. Confused? Even climate experts struggle to explain loaded dice and probability.[84]

The worst outcome would be if the weather had a normal distribution to begin with but, as the climate worsened (warmed), it became loaded. Under those conditions, there would be fewer cold events than expected in a normal distribution and more hot events.

There are many forms of statistical distribution, but the so-called 'gamma distribution' can represent the typically asymmetrical and positively skewed distribution of daily rainfall intensities for example.[85] If climate change makes the distribution ever more skewed, then the impact could be much greater than double. It never rains but it pours.

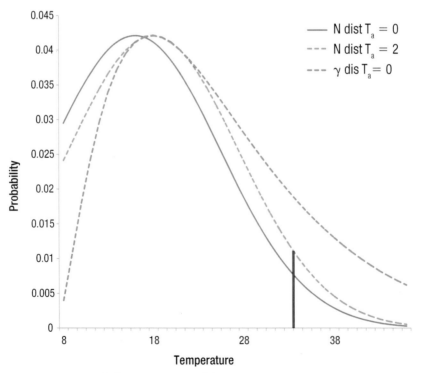

Figure 3.7. *Normal (N) and Gamma (γ) distribution: two possible outcomes for 2°C warming (probability plotted against temperature) for a temperature anomaly of 0°C and 2°C. (© Predict Ability Ltd.)*

Figure 3.7 shows three statistical distributions. The blue lines are normal distributions. The dashed blue line shows what happens if the average temperature anomaly T_a increases by 2°C. The number, or chance, of extremely hot days (over 33°C, say) increases significantly but the number of average days (say 20°C) does not change much. However, if climate change causes the temperature distribution to become skewed as warming proceeds, then it is clear that the number of extremely hot days could vastly increase (gamma distribution, dashed orange curve). We just do not yet know.

If we accept a normal distribution for now, how is it possible to determine that the impact of 4°C of warming is double what it is with no warming? Take, for example, the 33°C day. For this we need to consider three things together:

1. **probability** (without warming): area under the solid indigo curve, right of the red vertical bar;
2. **probability ratio** ('with warming'/'no warming'): area under the dashed blue curve, right of the red vertical bar/area under the solid indigo curve, right of the red vertical bar; and
3. **damage** at 33°C.

By damage we mean the relative human and financial impacts. What matters here is not the relationship between temperature and the amount of damage, but, rather it is the tipping point – the temperature above which there is cataclysmic damage. For example, as a frozen lake starts to melt, ice-skating turns from fun to tragedy in an instant. Cataclysms come in many forms.

So, for the 33°C example, it might be that the number of heat-related deaths rapidly increases, or a crop fails. Or, in the case of storms, the wind speed at which a tree keels over. Nature is highly non-linear, i.e. very resilient until something snaps. And to make matters worse, where people are involved, the perception of damage can vary greatly from one place to another.[86]

The insurance industry knows about risk. Unless the threshold at which damage is deemed to occur is set higher, the impact of climate change could be to *double* weather-related insurance losses if warming reaches 4°C. This would be a huge burden for the insurance industry and the world's nations. This is in line with flooding damage predictions for Europe[87] and 'food shortages, market volatility and price spikes are likely to occur at an exponentially higher rate', according to a joint US–British climate taskforce.[88]

On the other hand, if we consider damage to be something that only occurs when there is a disaster (as defined by international bodies),[89] then 4°C of warming could *treble* global disaster losses. Disaster losses are only a small fraction of all losses (i.e. those that range in magnitude from the everyday claims, right through to disasters). However, we should note that as yet we have little understanding of the extent to which warming is affecting everyday losses. There does seem to be clear evidence that disasters are at least being affected by climate change, as indeed Predict Ability Ltd claims.

Notes to Chapter Three

1   Pielke Jr, R., *The Climate Fix*, p. 15, Basic Books, New York (2010).

2   'What you can('t) do about global warming', World Climate Report (30 April 2009), http://www.worldclimatereport.com/index.php/2009/04/30/what-you-cant-do-about-global-warming/

3   Rojas, J-P.F., 'Global warming at a standstill, new Met Office figures show', *The Telegraph* (8 Jan 2013), http://www.telegraph.co.uk/earth/environment/climatechange/9787662/Global-warming-at-a-standstill-new-Met-Office-figures-show.html

4   Rose, D., 'Global warming stopped 16 years ago, reveals Met Office report quietly released…and here is the chart to prove it', *Mail Online* (16 October 2012), http://www.dailymail.co.uk/sciencetech/article-2217286/Global-warming-stopped-16-years-ago-reveals-Met-Office-report-quietly-released--chart-prove-it.html

5   Mathiesen, K., 'Global warming "pause" didn't happen, study finds', *The Guardian* (4 June 2015), http://www.theguardian.com/environment/2015/jun/04/global-warming-hasnt-paused-study-finds

6   Carrington, D., '2015 and 2016 set to break global heat records, says Met Office', *The Guardian* (14 September 2015), http://www.theguardian.com/environment/2015/sep/14/2015-and-2016-set-to-break-global-heat-records-says-met-office

7   Katz, C., 'How long can oceans continue to absorb Earth's excess heat?', *Yale Environment 360* (30 March 2015), http://e360.yale.edu/feature/how_long_can_oceans_continue_to_absorb_earths_excess_heat/2860/

8   Meyer, A., et al., 'Are changes needed to objectives underpinning carbon budgets?', UK Parliament Environmental Audit Committee (11 June 2013), http://www.parliament.uk/business/committees/committees-a-z/commons-select/environmental-audit-committee/news/progress-on-carbon-budgets-ev-session/

9   http://www.diomedia.com/stock-photo-mail-coach-in-a-flood-c1827-1904-artist-f-rosenbourg-image20164118.html

10   Stephens, E., Science Oxford lecture, Oxford (7 November 2013), https://www.reading.ac.uk/geographyandenvironmentalscience/About/Staff/elisabeth-stephens.aspx

11   Page, L., 'Antarctic ice at ALL TIME RECORD HIGH: We have more to learn, says boffin', *The Register* (9 October 2014), http://www.theregister.co.uk/2014/10/09/we_have_more_to_learn_says_scientist_antarctic_sea_ice_at_all_time_record/

12   Kalaugher, E., 'Big waves cause trouble for sea ice', *Physics World* (10 June 2014), http://physicsworld.com/cws/article/news/2014/jun/10/big-waves-cause-trouble-for-sea-ice

13   Shiller, R.J., 'Buying insurance against climate change', *The New York Times* (24 May 2014), http://www.nytimes.com/2014/05/25/upshot/buying-insurance-against-climate-change.html

14   Byrne, M., '*The New York Times*' 1920 Editorial mocking space travel remains a classic', *Motherboard* (19 July 2015), http://motherboard.vice.com/read/the-new-york-times-1920-editorial-mocking-space-travel-remains-a-classic

15   Chylek, P., Box, J.E., Lesins, G., 'Global warming and the Greenland ice sheet', *Climatic Change*, 63, pp. 201–221 (2004), http://ruby.fgcu.edu/courses/twimberley/EnviroPhilo/GreenlandIce.pdf

16   Bengtsson, L., Semenov, V.A., Johannessen, O., 'The early twentieth-century warming in the Arctic – a possible mechanism', Max-Planck-Institut für Meteorologie Report No. 345 (February 2003), https://www.mpimet.mpg.de/fileadmin/publikationen/Reports/max_scirep_345.pdf

17   Stromberg, J., 'What is the Anthropocene and are we in it?', *Smithsonian Magazine* (January 2013), http://www.smithsonianmag.com/science-nature/what-is-the-anthropocene-and-are-we-in-it-164801414/

18   Cornwall, W., 'Sea levels are rising at their fastest rate in 2000 years', *Science* (22 February 2016), http://www.sciencemag.org/news/2016/02/sea-levels-are-rising-their-fastest-rate-2000-years

19   Gregory, J., 'Projections of sea level rise', Climate Change 2013: The Physical Science Basis, Working Group 1 contribution to IPCC Fifth Assessment Report (November 2013), https://www.ipcc.ch/pdf/unfccc/cop19/3_gregory13sbsta.pdf

20   Beck, S., et al., 'Climate change and the International Court of Justice', Yale Center for Environmental Law & Policy (13 August 2013), http://envirocenter.yale.edu/uploads/publications/Climate%20Change%20ICJ%208.23.13.pdf

21   'Alaska Community Coastal Protection Project: Kivalina project page', State of Alaska Department of Commerce, Community and Economic Development (accessed 17 April 2016), https://www.commerce.alaska.gov/web/dcra/

PlanningLandManagement/AlaskaCommunityCoastalProtectionProject/
Kivalina.aspx

22   'Gravitational attraction of ice sheets on the sea', *Sea Change Science* (2015), http://sealevelstudy.org/sea-change-science/whats-in-a-number/attractive-ice-sheets

23   Editorial, 'The end of Florida?', *Miami Herald* (31 May 2015), http://www.miamiherald.com/opinion/editorials/article22639026.html

24   Hinkel, J., et al., 'Coastal flood damage and adaptation costs under 21st century sea-level rise', *PNAS*, *111* (9), pp. 3292–3297 (4 March 2014), http://www.pnas.org/content/111/9/3292.full.pdf

25   'Preparing for sea-level rise: Plans, actions and resources', *Climate Central* (accessed 17 April 2016), http://sealevel.climatecentral.org/responses/plans

26   Boettle, M., Rybski, D., Kropp, J.P., 'When sea levels rise, damage costs rise even faster', Potsdam Institute for Climate Impact Research (2016), https://www.pik-potsdam.de/news/press-releases/when-sea-levels-rise-damage-costs-rise-even-faster

27   'Storm surge', UK Meteorological Office (accessed 17 April 2016), http://www.metoffice.gov.uk/learning/learn-about-the-weather/weather-phenomena/storm-surge

28   Smart, A., 'From one extreme to the other: Are floods and droughts the new normal?', *Window for Wallingford*, p. 8 (November 2013), http://www.wallingford.co.uk/files/wfw_november_2013-web.pdf

29   Doyle, A., 'Climate uncertainty "frustrating for governments"', *IOL* (19 August 2013), http://www.iol.co.za/scitech/science/environment/climate-uncertainty-frustrating-for-governments-1564313

30   Doyle, A., 'Experts surer of manmade global warming but local predictions elusive', Reuters (16 August 2013), http://www.trust.org/item/20130816133815-ao2wt/

31   Moreton, C., 'The countryside in crisis', *The Telegraph* (17 February 2013), http://www.telegraph.co.uk/earth/countryside/9874680/The-countryside-in-crisis.html

32   'Flood re-explained', Association of British Insurers (8 March 2016), https://www.abi.org.uk/Insurance-and-savings/Topics-and-issues/Flood-Re/Flood-Re-explained

33   Robertson, C., Schwartz, J., 'Decade after Katrina, pointing finger more firmly at Army Corps', *The New York Times* (23 May 2015), http://www.

nytimes.com/2015/05/24/us/decade-after-katrina-pointing-finger-more-firmly-at-army-corps.html

34 Moskowitz, P., 'New Orleans' Lower Ninth Ward targeted for gentrification: "It's going to feel like it belongs to the rich"', *The Guardian* (23 January 2015), http://www.theguardian.com/us-news/2015/jan/23/new-orleans-lower-ninth-ward-condos-gentrification

35 Malo, S., 'Native American tribe to relocate from Louisiana coast as sea levels rise', Reuters (17 March 2016), http://www.reuters.com/article/us-climatechange-usa-displacement-idUSKCN0WJ34D

36 Pielke Jr, R., *The Climate Fix*, p. 175, Basic Books, New York (2010).

37 Pielke Jr, R., *The Rightful Place of Science: Disasters and Climate Change*, Consortium for Science, Policy and Outcomes, Tempe, AZ (2014).

38 Nunes, P., 'News & publications', Karen Clark & Co. (accessed 17 April 2016), http://www.karenclarkandco.com/news/publications/

39 'NatCatSERVICE: Download center for statistics on natural catastrophes', Munich RE (accessed 17 April 2016), http://www.munichre.com/en/reinsurance/business/non-life/natcatservice/index.html

40 Emanuel, K., 'MIT climate scientist responds on disaster costs and climate change', *FiveThirtyEight* (31 March 2014), http://fivethirtyeight.com/features/mit-climate-scientist-responds-on-disaster-costs-and-climate-change/

41 'Urbanization', United Nations Population Fund (accessed 17 April 2016), http://www.unfpa.org/urbanization

42 'Cyclone Pam', Wikipedia (accessed 17 April 2016), https://en.wikipedia.org/wiki/Cyclone_Pam

43 Pidcock, R., 'Cyclone Pam: Untangling the complex science on tropical storms and climate change', *CarbonBrief* (16 March 2016), http://www.carbonbrief.org/cyclone-pam-untangling-the-complex-science-on-tropical-storms-and-climate-change/

44 Mercer, P., 'Drought compounds hardship on cyclone-hit Vanuatu', *Voice of America* (4 November 2015), http://www.voanews.com/content/drought-compounds-hardship-on-cyclone-hit-vanuatu/3036154.html

45 *An Inconvenient Truth* (documentary film), Wikipedia (accessed 17 April 2016), https://en.wikipedia.org/wiki/An_Inconvenient_Truth

46 Mervis, J., 'An Inconvenient DVD', *Science* (30 November 2006), http://news.sciencemag.org/2006/11/inconvenient-dvd

47 Mieszkowski, K., 'Did Al get the science right?', *Salon* (10 June 2006), http://www.salon.com/2006/06/10/truths/

48 Trevisan, L., 'Book review: *Storms of My Grandchildren: The Truth About the Coming Climate Catastrophe and Our Last Chance to Save Humanity* by James Hansen', *Sustainable Development Law & Policy, 10* (2), pp. 55–56 (Winter 2010), http://digitalcommons.wcl.american.edu/cgi/viewcontent. cgi?article=1038&context=sdlp

49 Emanuel, K., 'Downscaling CMIP5 climate models shows increased tropical cyclone activity over the 21st century', *PNAS, 110* (30), pp. 12219–12224 (10 June 2013), http://www.pnas.org/content/110/30/12219.abstract

50 Cuff, M., 'London flood risk set to spike, threatening Flood Re insurance scheme, researchers warn', *BusinessGreen* (8 February 2016), http://www. businessgreen.com/bg/news/2445799/london-flood-risk-set-to-spike-threatening-flood-re-insurance-scheme-researchers-warns

51 Krebs, J., 'Building on flood plains has a long-term cost', Letters to *The Guardian* (29 January 2016), http://www.theguardian.com/ environment/2016/jan/29/building-on-flood-plains-has-a-long-term-cost

52 Theobald, W., 'Report: Climate change could cause massive losses for federal insurance programs', *DailyWorld* (20 November 2014), http://www. dailyworld.com/story/news/2014/11/20/report-climate-change-cause-massive-losses-federal-insurance-programs/70033192/

53 Moore, R., 'The changing climate for flood insurance (Op-Ed)', Yahoo! News (22 August 2013), http://news.yahoo.com/changing-climate-flood-insurance-op-ed-184237745.html

54 Helm, B., 'Climate change's bottom line', *The New York Times* (31 January 2015), http://www.nytimes.com/2015/02/01/business/energy-environment/ climate-changes-bottom-line.html

55 Sherlock, T., 'Global warming a culprit in growth of water-damage insurance claims (Part 3 of 3)', *Vancouver Sun* (9 December 2012), http://www. vancouversun.com/business/economy/Climate+change+culprit+growth +water+damage+insurance/7678156/story.html

56 Doyle, A., 'Indian monsoons may fail more often due to climate change – study', Reuters (6 November 2012), http://uk.reuters.com/ article/2012/11/06/us-climate-monsoon-idUKBRE8A500H20121106

57 Taylor, K., 'Extreme weather forecast for Eastern US', *TG Daily* (18 December 2012), http://www.tgdaily.com/sustainability-features/68156-extreme-weather-forecast-for-eastern-us

58   Pidcock, R., 'Flood damages in Europe to increase 200% by end of century, scientists warm', *CarbonBrief* (15 April 2015), http://www.carbonbrief.org/flood-damages-in-europe-to-increase-200-by-the-end-of-the-century-scientists-warn/

59   Pall, P., 'Anthropogenic greenhouse gas contribution to flood risk in England and Wales in autumn 2000', *Nature*, 470 (7334), pp. 382–385 (17 February 2011), http://www.nature.com/nature/journal/v470/n7334/abs/nature09762.html

60   Worland, J., 'California's drought is now the worst in 1,200 years', *Time* (5 December 2014), http://time.com/3621246/california-drought-study/

61   Howitt, R., Lund, J., 'Five myths about California's drought', *The Washington Post* (29 August 2014), https://www.washingtonpost.com/opinions/five-myths-about-californias-drought/2014/08/29/6a6b8ed4-2c69-11e4-994d-202962a9150c_story.html

62   Stewart, I., *How Earth Made Us: Water*, BBC 2 (6 February 2016), http://www.bbc.co.uk/programmes/b00qhqr8

63   Doyle, A., 'Spread of deserts costs trillions, spurs migrants: Study', Reuters (15 September 2015), http://www.reuters.com/article/us-environment-land-idUSKCN0RF14I20150915

64   Wilde, R., 'Jerry Brown's drought bill leaves farmers dry, quenches thirst of special interests', Breitbart (29 March 2015), http://www.breitbart.com/california/2015/03/29/jerry-browns-drought-bill-spends-660-million-on-flood-control/

65   Bradbury, J., Tompkins, C.F., 'New report connects 2012 extreme weather events to human-caused climate change', World Resources Institute (6 September 2013), http://www.wri.org/blog/2013/09/new-report-connects-2012-extreme-weather-events-human-caused-climate-change

66   Collins, N., 'Droughts steady since 1950', *The Telegraph* (14 November 2012), http://www.telegraph.co.uk/earth/environment/climatechange/9677724/Droughts-steady-since-1950s.html

67   Milner, K., 'Flashback 1984: Portrait of a famine', BBC News (6 April 2000), http://news.bbc.co.uk/1/hi/world/africa/703958.stm

68   Doyle, A., 'African farmers must do more to beat climate change – study', Reuters (7 September 2012), http://uk.reuters.com/article/2012/09/07/uk-climate-africa-farms-idUKBRE88600E20120907

69 'Millions at risk as severe drought hits Ethiopia', Al Jazeera (5 September 2015), http://www.aljazeera.com/news/2015/09/ethiopia-drought-1509050 84538285.html

70 Boseley, S., 'WHO: Zika virus "implicated" in large numbers of brain-damaged babies', *The Guardian* (22 March 2016), http://www.theguardian. com/world/2016/mar/22/who-zika-virus-implicated-in-large-numbers-of-brain-damaged-babies

71 Amorim, L., 'Disease "halves people's incomes" in tropical countries', *SciDevNet* (18 January 2013), http://www.scidev.net/global/health/news/ disease-halves-people-s-incomes-in-tropical-countries-.html

72 Casey, M., 'World Bank: Arab world hit hard by climate change', Yahoo! News (5 December 2012), http://news.yahoo.com/world-bank-arab-world-hit-hard-climate-change-084546406--finance.html

73 Lehner, P., 'Pentagon sees climate change as immediate security risk', The Energy Collective (20 October 2014), http://theenergycollective.com/ peterlehner/2145466/pentagon-sees-climate-change-immediate-security-risk

74 'Syrian civil war', Wikipedia (accessed 17 April 2016), https://en.wikipedia. org/wiki/Syrian_Civil_War

75 Fountain, H., 'Researchers link Syrian conflict to a drought made worse by climate change', *The New York Times* (2nd March 2015), http://www. nytimes.com/2015/03/03/science/earth/study-links-syria-conflict-to-drought-caused-by-climate-change.html

76 Lund, A., 'Drought, corruption, and war: Syria's agricultural crisis', Carnegie Endowment for International Peace (18 April 2014), http:// carnegieendowment.org/syriaincrisis/?fa=55376

77 Moyer, J.W., 'More evidence Mayan civilization collapsed because of drought', *The Washington Post* (30 December 2014), http://www.washingtonpost. com/news/morning-mix/wp/2014/12/30/more-evidence-mayan-civilization-collapsed-because-of-drought/

78 Porzucki, N., Woolf, C., 'Water, water everywhere, in Taiwan today there's just a drop to drink', Public Radio International (8 April 2015), http:// www.pri.org/stories/2015–04-08/water-water-everywhere-taiwan-today-theres-just-drop-drink

79 Pearce, F., 'Mideast water wars: In Iraq, a battle for control of water', *Yale Environment 360* (25 August 2014), http://e360.yale.edu/feature/mideast_ water_wars_in_iraq_a_battle_for_control_of_water/2796/

80   Doyle, A., Beasley, A., Muir, R., Kasolowsky, R., 'Indonesia overtakes Brazil in forest losses despite moratorium', Reuters (29 June 2014), http://in.reuters.com/article/2014/06/29/environment-indonesia-idINKBN0F40RV20140629

81   'Reservoir hogs: São Paulo's water crisis', *The Economist* (20 December 2014), http://www.economist.com/news/americas/21636782-government-responded-late-drought-brazils-industrial-heartland-reservoir-hogs

82   'About REDD+', UN-REDD Programme (accessed 17 April 2016), http://www.un-redd.org/aboutredd

83   'Climate change 2013: The physical science basis', IPCC (accessed 17 April 2016), http://www.ipcc.ch/report/ar5/wg1/

84   'The Myles (Allen) and Mike (Hulme) show', BBC Newsnight, Bishop Hill Blog (18 November 2011), http://www.bishop-hill.net/blog/2011/11/18/the-myles-and-mike-show.html

85   Rana, A., et al., 'Impact of climate change on rainfall over Mumbai using distribution-based scaling of global climate model projections', *J. Hydrology: Regional Studies* 1, pp. 107–128 (July 2014), http://www.sciencedirect.com/science/article/pii/S2214581814000081

86   'Why earthquakes cause more damage than hurricanes: Perception, prediction, people, protection', Actforlibraries.org (accessed 17 April 2016), http://www.actforlibraries.org/why-earthquakes-cause-more-damage-than-hurricanes-2/

87   Pidcock, R., 'Flood damages in Europe to increase 200% by the end of the century, scientists warn', *CarbonBrief* (15 April 2015), http://www.carbonbrief.org/flood-damages-in-europe-to-increase-200-by-the-end-of-the-century-scientists-warn

88   'Climate Change "set to fuel global food crisis"', News24.com (15 August 2015), http://www.news24.com/Green/News/Climate-change-set-to-fuel-global-food-crisis-20150814

89   'Explanatory notes: Classification, criteria, definitions, glossary, guidelines', EM-DAT (accessed 17 April 2016), http://www.emdat.be/explanatory-notes

CHAPTER FOUR

LIFE IN OUR CHANGING CLIMATE

High-tech isolationism and microbes

What if climate change is unstoppable? What if its impacts were ultimately inevitable? What would the world be like and how will we, or should we, respond?

Long Term

In Chapter Two, a short review of the evidence suggests that while some action on climate change is taking place it is either insufficient or, worse, misguided: this is a recurring theme. Yet despite the perils of long-range forecasting we do need to contemplate what might unfold over the next century.[1]

In the long term, what would a world with 4°C of warming be like? To start with, it is probably better to have an over-warm world than one plunged into an ice age.[2] Life on Earth, though not us yet, has survived previous episodes of extreme warming many millions of years ago. The last epoch was the Eocene, which started 55 million years before mankind emerged (Figure 4.1). During that period the sea level was higher and there was almost no ice covering the land. Therefore, if that were to happen again, overall there would be more land available. Much of it would be at northern latitudes, where the agricultural season today is limited by frost. Elsewhere, perhaps drought and heat will be the scourge of the mid-latitudes,[3] as weather systems are disrupted and weakened by the elimination of the Greenland and possibly Antarctic ice masses.[4] Long-established ecosystems are already weakening[5] and eventually plants and soils may become net emitters of carbon dioxide.[6]

Figure 4.1. *Eocene: watery world of persistent warmth?*[7] *(©Wikipedia, Creative Commons.)*[8]

Civilisations are most vulnerable to drought. As with the Mayan civilisation, Akkad, an ancient city in Mesopotamia that thrived in 2200 BC, was decimated by drought[9] (of course, anthropogenic or man-made global warming had not started then). Drought forces migration and, in our world, that will be towards cities and, increasingly, distant places that offer jobs and relative safety. That process is increasingly propelled by the wide availability of smartphones,[10] enabling itinerants to geo-locate themselves, transfer money and utilise social networks.

If we do decide to take action to mitigate (reduce or eliminate) our CO_2 emissions, then it is our great-great-great-grandchildren who will benefit.[11] However, if we continue to emit CO_2 as usual, we will continue to suffer the consequences and, moreover, there is a delay between emissions and the damage they cause. When, or if, the world's climate keels over and flips from one meta-stable state to another, we cannot put it back together or 'fix it' in anything short of eons. As things stand, Asia's young economies are growing fast and it is they that will create most of the new emissions – unless they follow a green path, as Bangladesh is attempting.[12,13] Rightly or wrongly, unfairly or not, it is these emergent economies that have the hardest choices to make. Today, knowledge is abundant and instantly available and, should we choose to use it, technology is our only salvation.[14] Humanity has come too far down the road to go back now, and few want to anyway.

Although Jared Diamond, author of *Collapse*, has wonderfully distilled the key traits of civilisations that survive,[15] the outstanding question for us is whether we can learn from the incredible wealth of knowledge that surrounds us. If we keep arguing about models, then we will be in a mess. In fact we are already in a mess. Models are tools, not ends in themselves.[16] Some NASA scientists take the view that it is elite groups – too many of them – that lead to societal collapse.[17] Increasingly, perhaps because of our digital technology, societal subgroups are retreating into citadels of safety and familiarity. As the tinted glass surrounds the new elites, that sense of oneness and common purpose (to survive, to thrive) evaporates. If it turns into a jungle out there, what the heck, let us just turn up the air conditioning and call down to the security desk for pizza.

And so we come to the monumental and vexing question of global agreements about climate change. Are they the cathedrals of our age, not physical entities but edifices of ideas? Do we have the will to do it? Should we? Do we really expect to agree and adhere to emissions targets in a world ruled by markets and consumerism?

We have been on a path of progress, it is true. Carbon (coal, oil and gas) has helped us humans enormously – we have a carbon inheritance[18] – but we did not pay attention to the carbon debt, we went on spending and spending on our 'carbon credit card'. The consequences of burning carbon are becoming plain to see, and they ravage the most vulnerable people and most vulnerable nations. We really have to come to terms with this!

There is a wide spectrum of options to choose from. The extreme choice would be to change our whole way of life and reject fossil fuels completely, i.e. no planes, trains or automobiles. That would put us in a precarious position, akin to being out on a ridge, far into the mountains (Figure 4.2). On the one hand, we could slide off onto the scree and there will be tough times with the economy. Governments hate recessions. They will do everything for a short-term fix, to get the economy going again. Therein lies the peril: yet more carbon debt. On the

Figure 4.2. *From the once sure ground, the path ahead is precarious: the perils of sliding scree or an icy abyss. (Beinn Eighe in the Western Scottish Highlands was Britain's first National Nature Reserve; © Colin Henderson.)*

other hand, if we do nothing, we may slide off down the other side of the ridge into oblivion. Again, we just do not know. We will have to take a shrewd and well-informed path, and not do anything rash like tampering with the climate.[19] And we will have to hope that the seas do not start fizzing with ancient CO_2 returning to the surface, ice age or no ice age.[20]

We have to adapt and build what is scientifically known as *capacity*: 'the combination of all the strengths, attributes and resources available within a community, society or organisation that can be used to achieve agreed goals' (UNISDR).[21]

What path should we take now? That is the big question. One false step, one chance too many: we need a meaningful, global carbon price and not just a target. The UN's system for pricing carbon is 'cap and trade' (see Chapter Nine). It is based on a premise that the world will agree and follow internationally agreed emissions targets set in Paris[22] in late 2015. In 1945 maybe but, today, that is a huge challenge. For 24 years since the Kyoto Protocol[23] the UN's 'top-down' thinking has driven the process. Markets got us here and, for better or for worse, only a market-led response has the sheer capacity to deliver an effective solution to climate change. Frameworks and science alone are insufficient for the challenge ahead.

When China did its big push into globalisation they knew there would be some negative consequences, but they chose to massively expand trade in order to regain their place in the world[24] and liberate their rural poor[25] and avoid civil strife. Many conurbations in China have excessive pollution, in a transition like every country that has ever industrialised. Within living memory there was smog (deadly, smoke-laden fog) in London. Now Beijing has the same problem. It is the immediate effects of their local pollution that is driving change, more so than the long-term intangible consequences of carbon dioxide.

'The recommendations of the Global Commission on the Economy and Climate, led by former Mexico president Felipe Calderon, include ideas long part of the climate action agenda: build more compact cities with better mass transit, restore degraded land, stop deforestation, phase out fossil-fuel subsidies, set a price on carbon', so reported Marianne Lavelle in the *Daily Climate* in 2014.[26] That in essence is the path we need to take, to couple economic growth with climate-change action, in order to avoid the consequences of the one on the other.

To illustrate this point, the projections of losses caused by climate change made in Chapter Eight were incorporated into a very simple model of the global economy (Figure 4.3). A raw 3.45% compound annual growth rate was assumed (blue dashed line). This drops to 3% if the effects of climate change are included (solid blue line). If the economy weakens ever so slightly, until it reaches a zero-growth equilibrium in 2100 (orange dashed line), then it is probable that the cumulative effects of climate change are sufficient to cause a global economic collapse[27] (solid orange line). And, just in case we are tempted to procrastinate, late action on climate change would not enable us to recover.

The graph shows two projections of the global economy scaled in constant dollar terms from 1980. We seem to be at a point of divergence. This is an example of a tipping point. If we are on the orange line (weakened economy, no action on climate change), we might have no inkling of what is about to unfold until late in the 21st century. By then it would be too late to take evasive action. We need to act now.

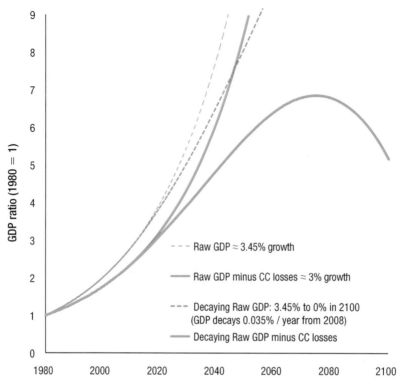

Figure 4.3. *Simplified model of the global economy using 1980 = 1 as a starting point: global growth (GDP) of 3% with effects of climate change (CC) (solid blue line); a slight weakening of the global economy (orange dashed line) may be sufficient to cause the global economy to collapse unless we act on CO$_2$ emissions (solid orange line). (© Predict Ability Ltd.)*

The carbon debt, and the environmental consequences of carbon, would all be in place and we would not have the capacity to respond. Then comes the dystopian future of resources conflicts, diseases and microbes.

Notes to Chapter Four

1   Rees, M., *Is This Our Final Century?*, TED Global 2005 (filmed July 2005), https://www.ted.com/talks/martin_rees_asks_is_this_our_final_century?language=en

2   Helm, D., *The Carbon Crunch*, p. 21.

3   Goldenburg, S., 'US faces worst droughts in 1,000 years, predict scientists', *The Guardian* (12 February 2015), http://www.theguardian.com/environment/2015/feb/12/us-faces-worst-droughts-1000-years-climate-change-predict-scientists

4   McDiarmid, M., 'Melting Arctic ice changing weather patterns, scientists say', CBC News (5 May 2015), http://www.cbc.ca/news/politics/melting-arctic-ice-changing-weather-patterns-scientists-say-1.3061988

5   Rocha, V., Branson-Potts, H., 'Drought kills 12 million trees in California's national forests', *Los Angeles Times* (5 May 2015), http://www.latimes.com/local/lanow/la-me-ln-trees-dying-california-drought-20150505-story.html

6   Kyriakides, R., 'How plants become net emitters of carbon dioxide', Robert Kyriakide's Weblog (22 September 2008), https://robertkyriakides.wordpress.com/2008/09/22/how-plants-become-net-emitters-of-carbon-dioxide/

7   Pross, J., et al., 'Persistent near-tropical warmth on the Antarctic continent during the early Eocene epoch', *Nature*, 488 (7409), pp. 73–77 (2 August 2012), http://www.nature.com/nature/journal/v488/n7409/full/nature11300.html?WT.ec_id=NATURE-20120802

8   http://1.bp.blogspot.com/_kNx32ckJC68/TMgxzb__u3I/AAAAAAAAFic/fZsYIZX4GEU/s1600/baobab_tree_09.jpg

9   Kolbert, E., *Field Notes from a Catastrophe: Man, Nature, and Climate Change*, p. 97, Bloomsbury (2007).

10   Brunwasser, M., 'A 21-century migrant's essentials: Food, shelter, smartphone', *The New York Times* (25 August 2015), http://www.nytimes.com/2015/08/26/world/europe/a-21st-century-migrants-checklist-water-shelter-smartphone.html

11   Palmer, T., 'Climate change uncertainty is no reason for inaction since we can't rule out risk', *The Guardian* (22 March 2010), http://www.theguardian.com/environment/cif-green/2010/mar/22/climate-change-uncertainty

12 Andani, A.A., *Dipal Chandra Barau on How they are Covering 50% of Bangladeshi Population through Innovative Solar Project*, Vimeo (2013), https://vimeo.com/52153229

13 Bharadwaj, R., Bhattacharje, S., 'Greening the brick industry in Bangladesh: Opportunities for South–South cooperation', DevPolicyBlog (18 August 2015), http://devpolicy.org/greening-the-brick-industry-in-bangladesh-opportunities-for-south-south-cooperation-20150818/

14 Broers, A., 'The Triumph of Technology', BBC Reith Lectures (4 May 2005), http://www.bbc.co.uk/programmes/p00ghv8z

15 Diamond, J., *The World Until Yesterday*, pp. 27–47, Allen Lane (2012).

16 Grist, R.L., 'Why the insurance industry won't save us from climate change', Grist (16 October 2011), http://grist.org/climate-change/2011-10-13-free-market-fail-why-the-insurance-industry-wont-save-us-from/

17 Ahmed, N., 'Nasa-funded study: Industrial civilisation headed for "irreversible collapse"?', *The Guardian* (14 March 2014), http://www.theguardian.com/environment/earth-insight/2014/mar/14/nasa-civilisation-irreversible-collapse-study-scientists

18 Webster, A.J., Clarke, R.H., 'An insurance-led response to climate change', arXiv (7 October 2015), http://arxiv.org/abs/1509.01157

19 Editorial Board, 'Geoengineering is good insurance', BloombergView (26 February 2015), http://www.bloombergview.com/articles/2015-02-26/geoengineering-is-good-insurance

20 Martinez-Boti, M.A., et al., 'Boron isotope evidence for oceanic carbon dioxide leakage during the last deglaciation', *Nature*, 518 (7538), pp. 219–222 (12 February 2015), http://www.nature.com/nature/journal/v518/n7538/full/nature14155.html

21 'Terminology', United Nations Office for Disaster Risk Reduction (accessed 17 April 2016), http://www.unisdr.org/we/inform/terminology

22 'United Nations Conference on Climate Change', COP21/CMP11 (30 November–12 December 2015), http://www.cop21.gouv.fr/en

23 'Kyoto Protocol', United Nations Framework Convention on Climate Change (accessed 17 April 2016), http://unfccc.int/kyoto_protocol/items/2830.php

24 Petras, J., 'China: Rise, fall and re-emergence as a global power', Centre for research on Globalization (20 May 2015), http://www.globalresearch.ca/china-rise-fall-and-re-emergence-as-a-global-power/29644

25 Lozada, C., 'Globalization reduces inequality in China' (Shang-Jin Wei, Yi Wu, 'Globalization and inequality: Evidence from within China', NBER Working Paper No. 8611), National Bureau of Economic Research (November 2011), http://www.nber.org/digest/mar02/w8611.html

26 Lavelle, M., 'Challenging the economics of climate solutions', *The Daily Climate* (16 September 2014), http://www.dailyclimate.org/tdc-newsroom/2014/09/economic-impacts

27 Holthaus, E., 'The point of no return: Climate change nightmares are already here', *Rolling Stone* (5 August 2015), http://www.rollingstone.com/politics/news/the-point-of-no-return-climate-change-nightmares-are-already-here-20150805

CHAPTER FIVE

WHY CLIMATE POLICIES DON'T WORK

There is no global treaty and carbon markets are still fragile
The 2015 climate agreement in Paris was a great achievement, yet it may not come into force until 2020, even if all the parties ratify it. In the decades since the Kyoto Treaty on climate change, there has been an explosion of policy and action, mostly by governments and their associated agencies. What are those policies? What works and what does not?

Politics as Usual

In democracies, elections are held every four years – often more frequently. Day-to-day issues dominate.[1] Moreover, since the 1980s, there has been a substantial increase in the machinery and effectiveness of lobbying, the processes whereby powerful interests gain influence over government actions or policy. When it comes to regulation, the politicians are often rendered powerless. Unfortunately the need for campaign funds for re-election, TV political adverts, etc., makes our representatives vulnerable to influence from energy, automotive, banking and other interests.

In the realm of fossil fuels, and oil in particular, the political pressure is intense.[2] In the 2012 US presidential election the question of climate change was considered too 'toxic' to discuss.[3] Although the debate is less polarised in Europe – there are less oil and gas interests – politicians still vacillate over carbon-based taxation. In protests that were triggered by escalating oil prices, UK Prime Minister Gordon Brown had to yield on fuel duty (tax) as a road hauliers' strike brought the country to within days of a national crisis. In 2000, the hauliers had a fair argument: what are the alternatives to diesel trucks? Years later, as oil prices fell, UK Chancellor George Osborne abandoned a scheduled fuel tax increase as prices at the petrol pump had hardly changed, despite a 30% fall in world crude prices.[4] If politicians impose inflexible duties on fuels, sooner or later their schemes will come to grief.

When it comes to nationally designed carbon taxation schemes, the politicians are deadlocked. On the one hand the fossil fuel lobby pushes back, arguing that climate science is uncertain or that there is a 'CO_2 fertilisation effect'[5,6] (i.e. more CO_2 = faster[7] plant growth). On the other, a carbon tax is seen as a valuable source of revenue and a mechanism for reducing CO_2 emissions. In a world where governments have no spare money, what could be better? The trouble is that public opinion about climate change is fickle, often influenced as much by events as any underlying concern.[8] A drawback with most carbon tax schemes is the impact that they have on the energy poor – those who expend more than 10% of their income on energy. The fix often involves means testing and complex workarounds, both of which add insult to injury. There are better strategies, but they involve partnerships. More on that in Chapter Eleven.

Climate-related spending often occurs at a more local level. City politicians have to judge the merits of adaptation schemes, such as flood defences. In Oxford[9] a flood-relief channel has been proposed to protect 1,200 homes at a cost of £120 million, i.e. £100,000 (~$150, 000) per home. This scheme was already in the city's project pipeline when it gained momentum in the wake of the spring 2014 floods that affected several parts of the UK. Linking all these issues, nationally and locally, is the uncertainty of energy prices and the uncertainty of the weather.

When it comes to the longer term, the UK and other countries have managed to commit themselves to a stringent CO_2 emissions reduction law, i.e. to reduce emissions by 80% by 2050. New York has a similar plan.[10] However, in the UK's case, the framing of the legislation coincides with the country's decline in heavy industry. Apparently, the emissions tied up with imported goods do not count. An article[11] in the Financial Times, 'Green groups see red over energy bill', neatly summarises the conflicting energy, tax and political issues at stake. Unsurprisingly, the costs of green energy are passed on to frustrated consumers. At the same time, fracking (the controversial hydraulic fracturing for gas) gets the go-ahead from George Osborne. The lack of an international treaty on CO_2 and other GHGs (greenhouse gases) makes the formulation of coherent energy policy and emissions accounting nigh impossible.

So what is to be done? Economist Nicholas Stern argues for a form of federalism in emissions, to enable individual countries to determine targets but to retain shared goals[12] – principally the decarbonisation pathway the world needs to take. Dieter Helm[13] focuses on the need for countries to recognise and deal with their carbon consumption rather than production, as was discussed in Chapter Two. Leading diplomat Richard N. Haass[14] argues that in an era of supposedly reduced American influence, not least over energy and climate policy, 'efforts to slow climate change, promote trade, set new rules for the digital age, and prevent or contain outbreaks of infectious diseases are inadequate'.

If European countries constrain emissions too hard and electricity prices rise then, over time energy-intensive manufacturers[15] will tend to relocate to more emissions-benign locations like China, or elsewhere in South East Asia. The world's chemical industries are a case in point. The use of subsidies to prevent such a flow seems perverse, except, of course, there are regional and employment factors that have to be considered.[16]

Eventually, climate fatigue sets in and policy reversals start. Even with a global agreement on emissions, national and local aspects may trump long-term goals, no matter how noble or necessary they are. Environmental campaigners and industry then find themselves in the same boat – both become exasperated at the lack of leadership and clear direction. The only certainty, unfortunately, is that CO_2 provides yet another opportunity to raise taxes. And do those taxes end up causing yet more CO_2 emissions? Perhaps they end up in road-building programmes!

Until the Paris climate accord in 2015 there was no global climate agreement, and there is still no prospect of a global carbon price. Some strange policy outcomes are emerging. In Chile, mines are powered by *renewable* energy.[17] In Australian mines, diesel provides most of the off-grid power they need. Mining requires vast amounts of energy. While both countries are fully aware of climate change, it appears the reason for the differing choices of power is China. There's a deal to be done – minerals for power. While Australia doggedly sticks with fossil fuels, Chile imports its solar infrastructure from China.

Not only is renewable energy a large component of the energy mix in China, it has made China a renewable-energy giant[18] overseas too. Where infrastructure developments are needed, and where there are mineral resources that it needs, China has quietly implemented radical changes in solar-energy-rich developing countries across Africa, South America and elsewhere (Figure 5.1).

China has been shrewd in developing renewables. It has created new manufacturing industries and with a vast output comes price competitiveness. As solar panels become cheaper to the point of 'grid parity' – where a kilowatt-hour of solar power costs the same as electricity generated from gas – China is able to penetrate developed economies too. All this has been achieved without a global agreement on emissions and yet China emerges from a classic, energy-intensive and polluted industrialisation as the global green energy giant.

Against this, the parochialism, stagnation and reversals of governments

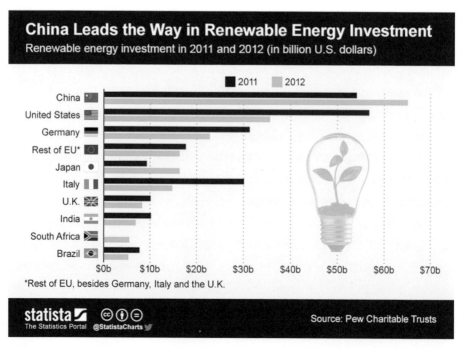

Figure 5.1. *China leads the way in Renewable Energy Investment.* (© *Statista.*)

elsewhere pale into insignificance. Germany once was the exception. It is not now.[19] We are in the midst of an energy revolution. It is 'Made in China'.

The Role of Science in Policy

If science is to play the role in public policy that it should, then scientists need to understand how policy develops and how politics works.[20] Professor Ralph Cicerone, President of the US National Academy of Sciences no less, might have been perplexed[21] at the interrogation he received on the BBC Radio's flagship news and current affairs outlet *Today*. 'You can't absolutely prove, can you, that CO_2 is responsible for global warming?' probed the interviewer, John Humphrys, in July 2012. This is the landscape in which climate policy develops, like it or not. Professor Cicerone, in fact, argued clearly for a proportionate response to climate change.

The central problem is uncertainty about what the climate will do next, but that should not be an excuse for doing nothing.[22] Of course, mitigation – the introduction of clean, green or renewable energy on the planetary scale described earlier – is necessary to contain climate change and thus reduce the uncertainty of what the climate will be like as warming increases. Equally, there is a temptation to put off hard decisions if the evolution of climate change is slower than the often-cited '97% scientific consensus'[23] expects. This has led to a rather unfortunate paradigm in the world of commitment, or pledging, to cut CO_2 emissions: the UN's scheme of pledge-and-review.[24] This is a contradiction in terms! The Cambridge Dictionary states: *pledge* – to make a serious or formal promise to give or do something.

Perhaps an emissions target is the wrong tool, even if we suppose that a 'top-down' international agreement on climate change is the right process. How about innovation targets, suggest Matthew Stepp and Megan Nicholson at the Washington, DC, Center for Clean Energy Innovation (CCEI). They continue:

> The climate community is backing the wrong policy and it's running out of time. New climate leadership is needed, not to try to coax countries into agreeing to emissions targets, but to commit to targets on clean energy innovation. In other words, nations should set goals

to invest a certain amount of money in research, development, and demonstration (RD&D) to make clean energy so cheap that all businesses and consumers will voluntarily replace fossil fuels with clean energy because it makes economic sense to do so.[25]

Let us look again at the Renewable Energy Investment (REI) statistics from Figure 5.1, this time plotted as REI divided by GDP[26] (Figure 5.2).

Again, China stands out as a global leader in terms of its sheer scale of investment. South Africa, a fast developing economy, has grasped the need to harness its rich renewable resource – the sun's energy – to meet energy demand, despite its huge coal deposits. As in China, coal reserves may get used too. On the global report card it might read: 'China is showing leadership but the United States, Japan, Brazil and the Rest of the EU could all do better.' Perhaps there should be a goal for developed countries just as there is on overseas aid: to pledge 0.7% of GDP to REI.[27] (Such measures would enable developed nations to meet their obligations on adaptation and mitigation, as further discussed in Chapters Six and Eleven.)

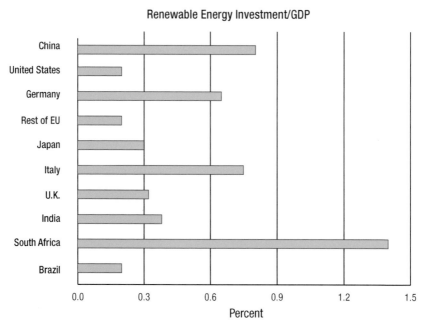

Figure 5.2. *Renewable Energy Investment divided by GDP is dominated by China's capacity.* (© *Predict Ability Ltd.*)

Let us return to the overarching IPCC goal, of limiting global warming to 2°C. In the leading science journal *Nature*, David Victor, a professor of international relations at the University of California, and Charles Kennel, director emeritus at the Scripps Institution of Oceanography, state: 'politically and scientifically, the 2°C goal is wrong-headed'.[28] While it is easy to grasp, temperature anomaly is insufficient at best or positively misleading. There has been no 'global warming pause' since 1998; instead the missing heat is to be found deep in the oceans. The second problem, very much the result of the policy arena, is that the goal is effectively unachievable. Failure to mitigate emissions means that heroic efforts must be made in short order. Flawed it may be, but global warming or, more accurately, temperature anomaly is the simplest and clearest measure we have. It is probably here to stay. And that is why global temperature anomaly T_a is part of the *PALcarbon*[29] pricing tool.

There are three problems with targets. Firstly, to the average person, indeed the average politician, it is not at all clear what they personally should do to help achieve the target. Walk? Cycle? Staycation?[30] Eat less meat (yes, definitely)?[31] How much individual action is enough? Secondly, there is still some time before 2°C arrives, so it is human nature to procrastinate. Thirdly, there is the 'boiled frog syndrome',[32] which supposes we *cannot* act until it is too late, by which time 2°C has come and gone. This happened with the 350 ppm goal (ppm = parts per million of CO_2 in the atmosphere). The figure of 350 ppm, the organisation 350.org[33] argues, is the ideal concentration of CO_2 in the Earth's atmosphere. Sadly for us, if that was the case, 350 ppm came and went. We have already passed 408 ppm. Some argue that, because nothing cataclysmic has happened, these targets are flawed. Tell us we are doomed, plead the civil servants, and then we can put climate change on a war footing.

Unless there is global consensus about the 2°C target, and it seems there is not,[34] how can there be any understanding that to miss it is unacceptable? We need feedback well before then, frequent nudges, not to adjust our pledges but to reinforce action. If we have a global carbon tax, or even an ensemble of regional carbon taxes, the revenue raised will – it surely should – provide the means to innovate in renewable energy, adapt to change and protect the world's ecosystems. A stable, global carbon price will send a strong and clear signal in the energy marketplace.

Treaties

Treaties can work, if the problem is well posed. This was the case with the Montreal Protocol in 1987. It led to the effective phasing out of the chemicals used in old refrigerators. Hydrofluorocarbons (HFCs) were shown to be responsible for partially destroying the ozone layer that protects the Earth's inhabitants from harmful solar radiation. Ozone 'holes' could lead to an increase in skin cancer, particularly in the mountainous regions of South America (Figure 5.3). And, it should be noted, HFCs are very potent greenhouse gases, so cutting their emissions is good for climate change too.

Chemists and chemical engineers were able to come up with viable, less harmful alternatives to HFCs and there has been international agreement on action and implementation. It will take many years for the existing chemicals to break down, but huge progress has been achieved.

The lament now, among diplomats and others linked to the UN process, is why the world is unable to respond to the climate change problem, as it did regarding HFCs? There are two primary reasons: (a) climate change is

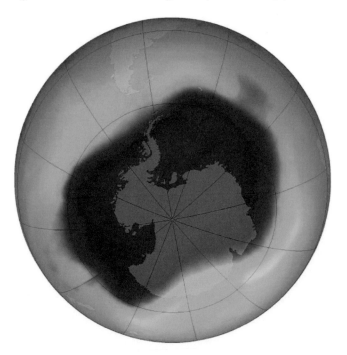

Figure 5.3. *The largest Antarctic ozone hole recorded as of September 2006.* *(© NASA.)*[35]

all-pervasive and (b) until recently there have been no viable, market-ready alternatives to fossil fuels.

One of the reasons the United States never ratified the Kyoto Protocol[36] was because China wanted to burn coal for electricity in order to develop.[37] China said it was growing its economy and it appeared the United States wanted to hinder that. The Kyoto Protocol has nevertheless been a milestone. The existence and cause of climate change were formally recognised, and the Kyoto Treaty has been ratified – accepted into law by national governments – by most other countries across the world.

The United States has not and will not sign[38] the Kyoto Treaty and that has been an impediment, but in many respects there has been progress. Out of Kyoto there have been three major developments:

- International Emissions Trading (IET)
- Clean Development Mechanism (CDM)
- Joint Implementation (JI)

The frameworks for emissions trading (IET) will be explored further in Chapter Nine. In essence, (some of) the Kyoto Treaty's signatories have agreed targets to limit their emissions. Each allowed unit of emission, equivalent to one tonne of CO_2, can then be traded. If a power station wants to emit a tonne of CO_2, it has to buy a permit to do so in one of the carbon markets, such as the EU ETS[39] – the EU emissions trading system.

The Clean Development Mechanism (CDM), defined in Article 12 of the Protocol, allows a country with an emissions-reduction commitment to offset some of its carbon emissions by implementing an emissions-reduction project in a developing country. This process allows the sponsoring country to receive carbon (pollution) permits. The CDM is fiendishly bureaucratic to operate.

Joint Implementation (JI) is where two or more countries collaborate on a CDM project.

Whilst there are many CDM projects worldwide, they have had little impact on the amount of coal burned in China. Historically, developed countries have baulked at the idea of paying substantial sums to fund projects that might prevent China from burning coal. Under the terms of the Kyoto Treaty, much of that funding would have had to come from the United States.

Such is the complexity of these arrangements, it took eight years to implement IET, and CDM took ten years.[40] This is the hallmark of a top-down system. Meanwhile the clock is ticking. The 2°C threshold is looming, perhaps in 2035 or 2040. And the 1.5°C target? We have just five years left!

The tide is beginning to turn, however, and much more emphasis is being directed towards bottom-up approaches, as, for example, the World Resources Institute[41] proposes; e.g. by building grass-roots resilience through trade. Partly this is a response to the bureaucracy, but mainly it is because mitigation (the reduction of emissions) is not enough. The world, and particularly developing nations, needs to adapt to climate change because it is already happening. This requires major funding and the UN and World Bank have begun the huge task of coordinating multi-billion-dollar projects.[42] However, impressive though these schemes are, they are nothing like enough.

Ceres, a US-based not-for-profit organisation that advocates sustainability leadership, argues that the scale of funding for mitigation and adaptation needs

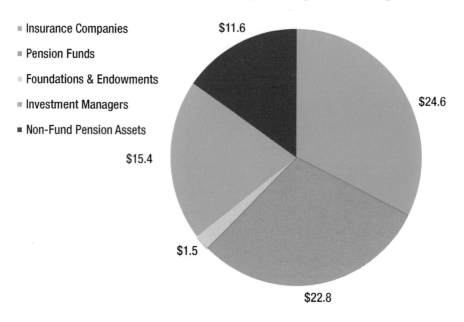

Figure 5.4. *Total assets by type of institutional investor (trillions of 2010 $US). Global total of $75.9 trillion. (© Predict Ability Ltd with thanks to Ceres.)*

to be an order of magnitude bigger than what has so far been committed, i.e. in the region of $1 trillion per year.[43] Ceres suggests that if businesses, investors and policymakers work together, they can meet this challenge. It is, they say, necessary if the world wants to meet the 2°C target.

Ceres has identified over $75 trillion in assets held by various institutional investors (Figure 5.4). These funds are now being asked to question their involvement in fossil-fuel industries by fossil-fuel divestment campaigns,[44] e.g. the Rockefeller Brothers Fund, who state that 'it is our moral duty to divest from fossil fuels'. Until recently, oil and gas companies have been a source of reasonable return over extended timescales. The question then arises: will many fossil-fuel reserves become stranded? This means they exist, but they cannot be used. It is not yet clear which way this will go, but the pressure is mounting on oil industry giants such as Exxon.[45]

Why has the Kyoto Treaty not worked better? The world, and climate change, has moved on from the 1990s when the original framework agreement that led to the Kyoto Protocol was signed. The UNFCCC – the United Nations Framework Convention on Climate Change – properly recognised in 1992, at the Rio Earth Summit, the existence and cause of climate change, but the proposed action was not rooted in the reality that the world depends utterly on fossil fuels (yes, renewables are growing fast, but from a very small base). The first crisis was the embarrassment of the 2009 Copenhagen Conference, where just five countries – the United States, Brazil, South Africa, India and China – made a deal called the Copenhagen Accord. Richard Black, then the BBC's environment correspondent, stated that there were many reasons why Copenhagen failed.[46] The key problem was that the United States and China (who had by this time transitioned from being a developing economy to a major one) would not countenance the idea of a legally binding commitment to pay for the damage caused by their emissions.

Staggeringly, it took until 2012, the 'COP18' in Doha, for the questions of climate change loss and damage to be fully addressed.[47] In 2013, this led to the Warsaw International Mechanism for Loss and Damage associated with Climate Change Impacts.[48] The problem was that the UNFCCC process never had a Plan B.[49] It had assumed that all countries (including the United States) would eventually sign up to and implement the Kyoto process. They did not.

Energy and Policy

The Volkswagen diesel emissions scandal[50] highlights a good (or is it bad?) example of the perils of policymaking on the basis of partially resolved science. Speaking on the BBC Radio's *Costing the Earth* series,[51] former government adviser Stephen Tindale had to admit that the Blair government had got it badly wrong on diesel cars. Ten years ago in the UK diesels were seen, incredibly, as a greener alternative to petrol-engine cars, simply because they had slightly lower CO_2 emissions per kilometre. It is hard to know what persuaded ministers at the time, but 'green' diesels they are not.

The obsession with CO_2 emissions masked the need to seriously probe the other emissions of diesel vehicles – a cocktail of carcinogenic[52] particulates, nitrous and nitric oxides, etc. Today, we can put a price on carbon, but the health cost of diesel emissions is still unknown. In excessively polluted London, some zones[53] have higher parking charges for diesel cars, but still there is no concerted policy. It is very hard to unwind environmental policies, even if they have been entered into with good intentions. The worry is that the CO_2 debate has skewed rational thinking, leading to reversals in environmental progress at the local or regional level.

For example, feed-in tariffs (FiTs) are a funding device used by many governments to encourage the switch to renewable energy. Millions of solar panels on roofs, and fields too, across Western Europe are a testament to FiTs. Are they necessary? Are they just? They encouraged the early, but costly, adoption of solar panels, even though research showed solar panel prices had been plummeting since the 1980s. They have locked in UK government spending for 20 years (as set in law by the Energy Act 2008) and favour those who own property.

Germany led the way with its giant *Energiewende* (energy transformation) programme,[54] which has literally transformed the landscape. And yet, despite the huge investment, Germany's CO_2 emissions are rising and new coal plants are being built.[55] All that the new energy has done is fill a gap left by Germany's abandonment of nuclear power following the Fukushima nuclear accident in Japan, from which no one died. Where is the strategy? Where is the leadership? Not building any new nuclear stations is one thing, but to abandon working, low-carbon energy plants seems extraordinary. It comes down to our vague understanding of risk, nuclear-energy risk in particular.[56]

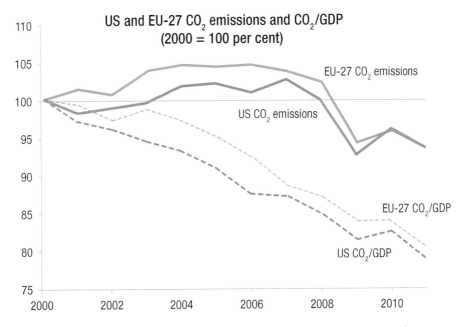

Figure 5.5. *Trends in US and EU emissions and emissions-per-GDP. (© Predict Ability Ltd, with thanks to Roger Pielke Jr.)*

Despite Europe's 'green credentials', the reality is that the United States has achieved more CO_2 reductions per unit of GDP than Europe, even with a deadlocked Congress (Figure 5.5).[57] Admittedly there was some low-hanging fruit in the energy savings market and shale gas has transformed the gas industry.[58] In both continents, however, the marked reduction in overall emissions was caused mainly by the decline in manufacturing. The carbon footprint of goods manufactured in China seems to have been deliberately overlooked by policymakers.

Carbon Capture and Storage (CCS)

The concept is simple enough. The reality is anything but. If we want to reduce our emissions, why not capture the CO_2 from the smokestack of a coal-fired power plant and bury the gas. In that way we can make use of our coal reserves without harming the planet. The reality is that it is expensive and risky and the capture process uses a lot of energy. Then there is the awkward question of where to put the CO_2. Will it be safe? Will the CO_2 remain in the ground or react with the rocks[59] and burst out through 'wormholes'? And should we not make use of the CO_2 anyway?

Norway is a fairly progressive country when it comes to energy policy. They have created a massive social fund using the revenues generated by their serendipitous natural gas reserves in the North Sea. They used $1 billion of it to reduce deforestation in Indonesia, although that has turned out to be harder than expected.[60] They have successfully captured CO_2 at the Snøhvit LNG (liquefied natural gas) facility in the Barents Sea.[61] It seems carbon capture 'works' when (a) CO_2 needs to be removed from natural gas anyway, (b) there is a lot of natural gas that will bring in sizeable revenues and (c) not capturing the CO_2 would result in a large single point source of CO_2 that would stand out, politically, like a sore thumb!

Norway, however, wanted to take carbon capture to the next level, to demonstrate the first full-scale capture plant in Europe at a major oil refinery. It was even dubbed Norway's 'Moon Landing' project, such was its status. The national oil company Statoil had built a pilot-scale capture unit at Mongstad,[62] but a change of government meant the new facility was shelved.[63] The situation has been similar elsewhere. Without a price on carbon there is just not the incentive to capture CO_2 unless the political consequences of not doing so are unacceptable. This has led some to suggest that oil companies should be compelled by law[64] to capture CO_2, but, even if that happened, the scale of carbon capture required is mindboggling. And that is just the power plants. What about vehicle emissions? For now CCS is in the doldrums and the scale of the challenge CCS faces is daunting (Figure 5.6). We need a smarter approach to removing CO_2 from the atmosphere.[65]

Biofuels

Biofuel means growing corn (maize) to turn into ethanol. It seemed like the perfect policy solution: carbon-neutral gasoline or a gasoline additive. In Brazil bio-ethanol production powers much of the country's motorcars, but what are the costs? Where it does not displace food production and cause deforestation, biofuel reduces oil imports and can – but not greatly – reduce emissions. Brazil's ethanol industry has had a chequered history[66] and it is still vulnerable to world oil price fluctuations. In the United States, mid-western

Figure 5.6. *Carbon capture: the scale of the challenge (beige circle) versus projects in place (red and yellow) and projected (blue).*[67] *(© Predict Ability Ltd.)*

farmers have become reliant on biofuel subsidies.[68] Government programmes tend to become entrenched and the US biofuel industry is a prime example. Shale gas has led to some road hauliers switching to compressed natural gas,[69] but there are not many filling stations selling it in the US and there is possibly little incentive to do so. In China, however, natural-gas-powered vehicles are commonplace and the market is growing rapidly,[70] partly because of the giant natural gas deal China and Russia did in 2014.[71]

Fossil-Fuel Subsidies

In developing oil- and gas-producing countries, fossil-fuel consumption subsidies amounted to $523 billion in 2011. The main participants are shown in Figure 5.7. While the problem subsidies cause, in terms of climate change, is internationally recognised, dismantling them is hard. Although it is an inefficient social policy delivery system – only 20% of the subsidy goes

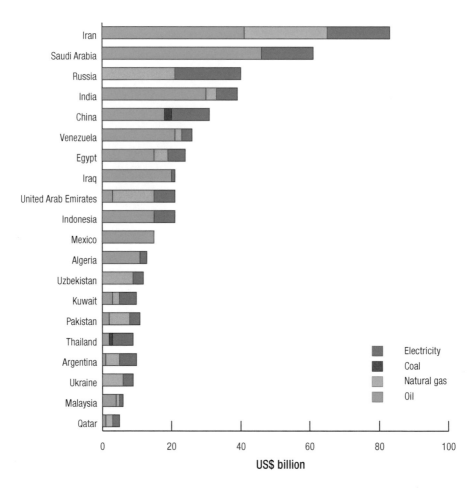

Figure 5.7. *Top twenty countries making fossil-fuel consumption subsidies (Institute for Energy Research).*[72] *(© Predict Ability Ltd.)*

to the poor – attempts to remove subsidies have led to civil unrest. However, Alan Beattie in the *Financial Times*[73] has cited two leaders who are achieving successful reform, Narendra Modi in India and Joko Widodo in Indonesia. Both have made subsidy reform a centrepiece of their respective legislative programmes and they have started successfully.

Economists Gernot Wagner and Martin Weitzman, in their book *Climate Shock: The Economic Consequences of a Hotter Planet,*[74] make a good case against fossil-fuel subsidies. They amount to nearly \$15/tonne CO_2, annihilating the world's carbon-pricing markets. Wagner and Weitzman, however, decline to say what the price of carbon should be.

The *Story of Stuff*

The *Story of Stuff* is a short film[75] showing how today many people have little regard for anything they buy. The bag is often more significant than the product! In no time at all they move on to the next thing, along with yet more packaging. Nearly everything is wasted. Can or should government policy do anything about this woeful state of affairs and the emissions, waste and toxicity they create all along the supply chain? Or did governments collude in this travesty? Why does the UK impose low rates of VAT (value added tax) on energy-related products? This suggests energy consumption is encouraged. Shouldn't we be taxing bad things, e.g. by using carbon-emissions accounting? If applied fairly, a global carbon tax could discourage emissions-creating behaviours, provided the costs were directly passed on to the end user. That, however, is not enough in itself.

Whatever happened to sustainability? Even the word has been corrupted since Gro Harlem Brundtland[76] clearly defined it thus in 1983: *sustainable development* is the kind of development that meets the needs of the present without compromising the ability of future generations to meet their own needs.

In essence, that is the central challenge. How do we have economic growth without consumption? Dear Consumer, try this for size: http://uncached-site.globalcalculator.org

Notes to Chapter Five

1   Helm, D., *The Carbon Crunch*, p. 170.

2   Klare, M.T., 'Fossil-fueled Republicanism: What to expect from the new US Congress', *Energy Post* (25 November 2014), http://www.energypost.eu/fossil-fueled-republicanism-grand-oil-party-takes-washington-storm/

3   Monbiot, G., 'Struck dumb: Why, even now, climate change cannot be mentioned in the US presidential election', monbiot.com (5 November 2012), http://www.monbiot.com/2012/11/05/struck-dumb/

4   Kirkup, J., 'Osborne accused of panic as fuel duty rise is scrapped', *The Telegraph* (26 June 2012), http://www.telegraph.co.uk/news/politics/georgeosborne/9358130/Osborne-accused-of-panic-as-fuel-duty-rise-is-scrapped.html

5   Ridley, M., 'Now here's the good news on global warming', *The Times* (19 October 2015), http://www.thetimes.co.uk/tto/opinion/columnists/article4589359.ece

6   More CO_2 does help plants and we accept the benefits of that (e.g. lower food prices), but those benefits only partially offset the damages caused elsewhere for which there is no proper accounting. If rice grows faster, it becomes less nutritious (see reference 7 below).

7   Wilson, K., 'Food for thought', *China Daily Asia* (6 June 2014), http://www.chinadailyasia.com/asiaweekly/2014–06/06/content_15138937.html

8   Briggs, H., 'Climate concern "linked to floods"', BBC News (29 January 2015), http://www.bbc.co.uk/news/science-environment-31024149

9   'Oxford flood relief channel to protect 1,200 homes', BBC News (7 January 2015), http://www.bbc.co.uk/news/uk-england-oxfordshire-30706748

10   Press Office, 'Mayor de Blasio proposes NYC divestment from coal, comprehensive study of all fossil fuel investments', official website of the City of New York (29 September 2015), http://www1.nyc.gov/office-of-the-mayor/news/655–15/mayor-de-blasio-proposes-nyc-divestment-coal-comprehensive-study-all-fossil-fuel

11   Chazan, G., 'Green groups see red over energy bill', *Financial Times* (23 November 2012), http://www.ft.com/cms/s/0/61f1cb2–3579-11e2-bf77-00144feabdc0.html

12   Hepburn, C., Stern, N., 'A new global deal on climate change', *Oxford Review of Economic Policy*, 24 (2), pp. 259–279 (2008), http://eprints.lse.ac.uk/32938/

13   Helm, D., *The Carbon Crunch*, p. 193.

14   Haass, R.N., 'Era of disorder', Project Syndicate (27 October 2014), https://www.project-syndicate.org/commentary/new-era-of-global-instability-by-richard-n--haass-2014–10

15   Jones, G., 'BIS low carbon economy', Institution of Chemical Engineers, London event (28 March 2012), https://www.icheme.org/communities/special-interest-groups/sustainability/events/2012/bis%20low%20carbon%20economy.aspx

16   Stacey, K., 'Tata Steel and Port Talbot: Five key questions', *Financial Times* (31 March 2016), http://www.ft.com/cms/s/0/4cc97566-f72a-11e5-96db-fc683b5e52db.html

17   Mathews, J., 'Why Chile's mines run on renewables – and Australia's don't', *Energy Post* (19 December 2014), http://www.energypost.eu/chiles-mines-run-renewables-australias-dont/

18   Soria, C., 'China at the top of renewable energy investment', IndexMundi Blog (7 August 2013), http://www.indexmundi.com/blog/index.php/category/topics/energy/

19   Le Blond, J., 'Coal resurgence darkens Germans' green image', *Financial Times* (13 October 2015), http://www.ft.com/cms/s/0/719ea15e-68fa-11e5-a57f-21b88f7d973f.html

20   Pielke Jr, R., *The Climate Fix*, p. 7, Basic Books, New York (2010).

21   '"You can't absolutely prove, can you, that CO_2 is responsible for global warming?" The *Today* programme, out of its depth on climate science', *CarbonBrief* (13 July 2012), http://www.carbonbrief.org/you-cant-absolutely-prove-can-you-that-co2-is-responsible-for-global-warming-the-today-programme-out-of-its-depth-on-climate-science

22   Pancost, R., Lwandowsky, S., 'Why climate "uncertainty" is no excuse for doing nothing', *The Conversation* (16 October 2014), http://theconversation.com/why-climate-uncertainty-is-no-excuse-for-doing-nothing-32924

23   'Scientific consensus: Earth's climate is warming', NASA Global Climate Change (accessed 17 April 2016), http://climate.nasa.gov/scientific-consensus/

24   Buhr, K., Roth, S., Stigson, P., 'Climate change politics through a global pledge-and-review regime: Positions among negotiators and stakeholders',

Sustainability, 6 (2), pp. 794–811 (19 February 2014), http://www.mdpi.com/2071–1050/6/2/794

25   Stepp, M., Nicholson, M., 'Time to focus on innovation targets, not emissions targets, to fight climate change', *Europe's World* (19 January 2015), http://europesworld.org/2015/01/19/time-focus-innovation-targets-emissions-targets-fight-climate-change/

26   GDP in this context means the gross domestic product of a country or group of countries.

27   'The 0.7% target: An in-depth look', UN Millennium Project (accessed 17 April 2016), http://www.unmillenniumproject.org/press/07.htm

28   Victor, D.G., Kennel, C.F., 'Climate policy: Ditch the 2°C warming goal', *Nature*, 514 (7520), pp. 30–31 (2 October 2014), http://www.nature.com/news/climate-policy-ditch-the-2-c-warming-goal-1.16018

29   Coe, E., 'PAL Carbon simply explained', Predict Ability Ltd (accessed 17 April 2016), http://predictability.ltd.uk/palcarbon

30   Staycation: to holiday in one's home country, without getting on an aeroplane.

31   Carrington, D., 'Eating less meat essential to curb climate change, says report', *The Guardian* (3 December 2014), http://www.theguardian.com/environment/2014/dec/03/eating-less-meat-curb-climate-change

32   'Boiling frog – metaphor', Wikipedia (accessed 17 April 2016), https://en.wikipedia.org/wiki/Boiling_frog

33   http://350.org/

34   After the Paris climate change agreement in 2015, there is still not a global consensus about 2°C and there is now a 'stretch target' of 1.5°C (that is four times harder, given that we are at 1°C already: we have half the time and the target is twice as hard).

35   Gurro, R., 'NASA and NOAA announce ozone hole is a double record breaker', NASA (19 October 2006), http://www.nasa.gov/vision/earth/lookingatearth/ozone_record.html

36   'Kyoto Protocol', UN Framework Convention on Climate Change (accessed 17 April 2016), http://unfccc.int/kyoto_protocol/items/2830.php

37   Helm, D., *The Carbon Crunch*, p. 163.

38   The US Congress will not ratify anything that subjects the United States to legally binding international financial obligations.

39 'The EU Emissions Trading System (EU ETS)', European Commission Climate Action (accessed 17 April), http://ec.europa.eu/clima/policies/ets/index_en.htm

40 Hone, D., 'Reaching net-zero emissions', LinkedIn Blog (1 May 2015), https://www.linkedin.com/pulse/reaching-net-zero-emissions-david-hone

41 Dougherty-Choux, L., Terpstra, P., 'Building climate resilience from the bottom up', World Resources Institute (July 2015), http://www.wri.org/resources/presentations/building-climate-resilience-bottom

42 Doyle, A., 'New UN climate fund to take risks to promote green tech', Reuters/WHBL Radio (5 June 2015), http://whbl.com/news/articles/2015/jun/05/new-un-climate-fund-to-take-risks-to-promote-green-tech/

43 'The path to a clean trillion', Ceres (accessed 17 April 2016), http://www.ceres.org/issues/clean-trillion

44 Ansar, A., Caldecott, B., Tilbury, J., 'Stranded assets and the fossil fuel divestment campaign: What does divestment mean for the valuation of fossil fuel assets?', Oxford Smith School Stranded Assets Programme (October 2013), http://www.smithschool.ox.ac.uk/research-programmes/stranded-assets/SAP-divestment-report-final.pdf

45 Evans-Pritchard, A., 'Fossil crisis deepens as Exxon probed on climate cover-up', *The Telegraph* (6 November 2015), http://www.telegraph.co.uk/news/worldnews/northamerica/usa/11980840/Fossil-crisis-deepens-as-Exxon-probed-on-climate-cover-up.html

46 Black, R., 'Why did Copenhagen fail to deliver a climate deal?', BBC News (22 December 2009), http://news.bbc.co.uk/1/hi/sci/tech/8426835.stm

47 Harvey, F., 'Doha climate change deal clears way for "damage aid" to poor nations', *The Guardian* (8 December 2012), http://www.theguardian.com/environment/2012/dec/08/doha-climate-change-deal-nations

48 'Warsaw international mechanism for loss and damage associated with climate change impacts', UN Framework Convention on Climate Change (November 2013), http://unfccc.int/adaptation/workstreams/loss_and_damage/items/8134.php

49 Clark, P., 'Failure in Paris would be grave, warns US climate envoy', *Financial Times* (26 February 2015), http://www.ft.com/cms/s/0/583b18f8-bdee-11e4-9d09-00144feab7de.html

50 Hotten, R., 'Volkswagen: The scandal explained', BBC News (10 December 2015), http://www.bbc.co.uk/news/business-34324772

51 Heap, T., 'Lungs, lies and automobiles', BBC Radio 4 *Costing the Earth* (7 October 2015), http://www.bbc.co.uk/programmes/b06flmf1

52 Scowcroft, H., 'Diesel exhaust fumes "definitely" cause cancer – should we be worried?', Cancer Research UK Science Blog (14 June 2012), http://scienceblog.cancerresearchuk.org/2012/06/14/diesel-fumes-definitely-cause-cancer-should-we-be-worried/

53 Christmas, W., 'End of the road for diesel cars? Owners face additional charges and big depreciation', BT Motoring Blog (1 May 2015), http://home.bt.com/lifestyle/motoring/motoring-news/end-of-the-road-for-diesel-cars-owners-face-additional-charges-and-big-depreciation-11363978817654

54 'Energiewende', *The Economist* (26 July 2012), http://www.economist.com/node/21559667

55 Pearce, F., 'On the road to green energy, Germany detours on dirty coal', *Yale Environment 360* (29 May 2014), http://e360.yale.edu/feature/on_the_road_to_green_energy_germany_detours_on_dirty_coal/2769/

56 Allison, W., 'The Fukushima nuclear accident and the unwarranted fear of low-dose radiation', The Foreign Correspondents' Club of Japan (3 December 2014), https://www.youtube.com/watch?v=A2syXBL8xG0

57 Pielke Jr, R., 'Europe's climate fail', *The Breakthrough* (3 May 2013), http://thebreakthrough.org/index.php/voices/roger-pielke-jr/europes-climate-fail

58 Flower, A., 'LNG: The global liquefied natural gas industry', in: Nuttall, W.J., Clarke, R.H., Glowacki, B.A. (eds.), *The Future of Helium as a Natural Resource*, Routledge (2012), https://www.routledge.com/products/9780415576970

59 Jackson, L., 'Carbon dioxide stored underground can find multiple ways to escape', *Penn State News* (11 February 2016), http://news.psu.edu/story/392047/2016/02/11/research/carbon-dioxide-stored-underground-can-find-multiple-ways-escape

60 Schonhardt, S., 'Indonesia comes up short in $1 billion bid to save forests', *The Wall Street Journal* (13 May 2015), http://www.wsj.com/articles/indonesia-comes-up-short-in-1-billion-bid-to-save-forests-1431536197

61 'Snøhvit', Statoil (accessed 17 April 2016), http://www.statoil.com/en/ouroperations/explorationprod/ncs/snoehvit/pages/default.aspx

62 'Statoil Mongstad fact sheet: Carbon dioxide capture and storage project', Sequestration Technologies at MIT (17 February 2016), https://sequestration.mit.edu/tools/projects/statoil_mongstad.html

63 Holter, M., 'Norway drops "moon landing" as Mongstad carbon capture scrapped', *Bloomberg* (20 September 2013), http://www.bloomberg.com/news/articles/2013–09-20/norway-drops-moon-landing-as-mongstad-carbon-capture-scrapped

64 Macalister, T., 'Fossil fuel companies "should be made to invest in carbon capture and storage" ', *The Guardian* (2 July 2015), http://www.theguardian.com/environment/2015/jul/02/fossil-fuel-companies-should-be-made-to-invest-in-carbon-capture-and-storage

65 Flannery, T., *Atmosphere of Hope*, Chapter 16, Penguin Books (2015).

66 Gallas, D., 'Brazil's biofuel industry finds new sweet spot', BBC News (23 June 2015), http://www.bbc.co.uk/news/business-33114119

67 'The global status of CCS: 2011', Global CCS Institute (accessed 17 April 2016), https://hub.globalccsinstitute.com/sites/default/files/publications/22562/global-status-ccs-2011.pdf

68 Opinion, 'Dirty rotten ethanol scoundrels', *The Wall Street Journal* (7 June 2015), http://www.wsj.com/articles/dirty-rotten-ethanol-scoundrels-1433716070

69 Stafford, J., 'Could natural gas dominate global transportation soon?', oilprice.com (4 June 2015), http://oilprice.com/Energy/Natural-Gas/Could-Natural-Gas-Dominate-Global-Transportation-Soon.html

70 Shauk, Z., 'Natural gas vehicles show "phenomenal growth" in China', *Fuel Fix* (4 March 2014), http://fuelfix.com/blog/2014/03/04/natural-gas-vehicles-show-phenomenal-growth-in-china/

71 Mazneva, E., Kravchenko, S., 'Russia, China sign $400 billion gas deal after decade of talks', *Bloomberg* (21 May 2014), http://www.bloomberg.com/news/articles/2014–05-21/russia-signs-china-gas-deal-after-decade-of-talks

72 'Developing countries subsidize fossil fuels, artificially lowering prices', Institute for Energy Research (3 January 2013), http://instituteforenergyresearch.org/analysis/developing-countries-subsidize-fossil-fuel-consumption-creating-artificially-lower-prices/

73 Beattie, A., 'Getting rid of fuel subsidies', *Financial Times* beyondbrics blog (22 January 2015), http://blogs.ft.com/beyond-brics/2015/01/22/getting-rid-of-fuel-subsidies/

74 Clark, P., 'Review of *Climate Shock: The Economic Consequences of a Hotter Planet*, by Gernot Wagner and Martin Weitzman', *Financial Times* (29

March 2015), http://www.ft.com/cms/s/0/bc2016e2-d320-11e4-9b0a-00144feab7de.html

75   Leonard, A., '*Story of Stuff*, referenced and annotated script', storyofstuff.org (excerpted from: 'Economies for life' by David Korten in *YES! Magazine*, Living Economies Issue, Fall 2002), http://storyofstuff.org/wp-content/uploads/movies/scripts/Story%20of%20Stuff.pdf

76   'Brundtland Commission', Wikipedia (accessed 17 April 2016), https://en.wikipedia.org/wiki/Brundtland_Commission

CHAPTER SIX

STRATEGIES FOR CLIMATE RESILIENCE

Attaining a balance between mitigation and adaptation
What can be distilled from all the policies and climate-change actions now in play? What strategies would work well in conjunction with carbon pricing?

Carbon Decorum

Chapter Five shows there is no shortage of policies relating to climate change. It is also clear that these can become politicised and unfortunately even badly designed policies are hard to shut down. Are these policies addressing the right issues? Are they enough? Governments used to try and 'pick winners', but after many bruising experiences most administrations are now content to implement 'no regrets' policies.[1] At least there is a hint of science and social policy in play.

In corporate circles the motivation may be less noble. Like pupils at a Swiss finishing school, corporate social responsibility (CSR) teams are very adept at delivering environmental messages in a manner acceptable at the Court of King Carbon – a media-centred circus where 'green' appearances are often more important than 'green' realities.[2] King Carbon, however, is unimpressed and merciless. He causes disaster at will. Will we learn to adapt, to protect others in different countries and cultures as well as ourselves, in addition to relentlessly focusing on being seen to be reducing carbon emissions?

Major renewable-energy companies, insurers and learned institutions such as Siemens, Lloyd's of London[3] and the Institution of Chemical Engineers have produced fine videos, hosted conferences and commissioned detailed reports. The underlying theme is that climate change will change everything. They want to show leadership in a frenzied arena and climate-change leadership appears to be good for business. But how will all this translate into real emissions reductions and support for those who are most vulnerable to the effects of climate change?

The December 2015 Paris agreement was surely a testament to French diplomacy. Now, just a few months later, those connected with the process are beginning to wonder how to translate the skilful words into meaningful actions.[4] Yet the things that are distracting governments now – crashing oil prices, Syria, Brexit (the British EU exit referendum) and the militarisation of the South China Sea – are all in some way connected to the very issues the Paris agreement addressed: carbon bubbles, disasters, displaced persons and our addiction to fossil fuels.

In today's febrile atmosphere it is hard to focus on core issues, whether it is about the design of passive buildings, the causes of migration or the ethics of genetically modified (GM) crops. Some major corporations, such as Monsanto, are well placed to react. According to Maggie Severns[5] at *Mother Jones* magazine, the company now provides 'data to help farmers grow crops in a changing climate; insurance for when it's too hot, cold, dry, wet, or otherwise extreme outside; drought-resistant corn; cotton that needs less water to grow and crops for biofuel'. All this data comes at a price. Therefore, the question has to be asked, are these solutions safe, appropriate, ethical or fair to small farmers around the world? The Bill & Melinda Gates Foundation (BMGF)[6] came in for much criticism for buying Monsanto stock and collaborating in some of the company's research into genetically modified crops, even though the project's goals appear to align with the aims of the BMGF.

Where does carbon pricing fit into this picture? According to Oxford University's Myles Allen, one of the reasons he is against a carbon tax is that it looks like 'business as usual', of compensating victims instead of finding solutions.[7] The environmentalists, he says, want justice (legal justice) and the energy corporations will not change their ways over a few cents a gallon. Propositions such as carbon capture and storage are a distraction, some environmentalists argue,[8] focusing on the past, instead of the future. Yet

Professor Allen, citing his physics background and the impact of cumulative CO_2 emissions, has become a strong proponent of CCS.[9] He argues that the oil companies should be compelled to make CCS work. Perhaps, if all goes well, carbon capture could buy us some more time.

Yesteryear's concepts of 'working for the greater good', of utilitarianism,[10] are now discredited by many societies. The pendulum has swung back to the point where appearances predominate – this is the world of 'carbon decorum'. Into such a vacuum, enter the less scrupulous: 'from politicians to profiteers, some people look at the effects of climate change and see dollar signs', writes *The Wall Street Journal's* Philip Delves Broughton in his review of Mackenzie Funk's cleverly entitled book *Windfall*.[11] Funk explores the many and bizarre ways edgy entrepreneurs are gaining handsomely in the unsettled new world of risk and disaster.

After the Fukushima nuclear accidents in 2011 there was much unease about nuclear energy in Europe, and Germany's politicians voted to phase out its atomic power stations. Artist Yann Toma's symbolic installation, Figure 6.1, appeared in response to Japan's tsunami disaster as a gesture of solidarity.

Figure 6.1. *Art installation,* Dynamo Fukushima, *at the Grand Palais, Paris, September 2011.*[12] *(© Reuters Pictures.)*

Dozens of human-powered dynamos were needed to light one bulb. It was intended to raise awareness of sustainable and development issues. However, as a means of powering our world, it is futile. Although well intended, this disconnect with reality is troubling.

No Regrets Strategies

Sentiment is no substitute for strategy. So what strategies should be implemented? For a start, something strong and clear – a predictable carbon-pricing scheme that sends a reliable and future-proofed signal to the energy markets. Of course governments want to, and should, do more than that. Energy and CO_2 cannot be viewed in isolation. Fuel costs and energy security (geopolitics) have to be considered too.

Water shortages (and storms) have been identified as a major threat to energy supplies, says Christoph Frei, Secretary-General at the World Energy Council.[13] Most coal-fired power stations are cooled by river water. In a post-COP21 interview with the EU's *Energy Post*, Frei commented: 'In our latest scenarios report [the WEC said] coal faces great uncertainty, which was not a story the [coal] companies really wanted to hear. We could not support the logic of the industry that coal is needed to provide access to energy for the poor.'[14]

Nuclear stations, to prevent the core from overheating, use ever-abundant seawater for cooling. Even then, as the Japanese utility company Tepco[15] found on 11 March 2011, a huge tsunami can overwhelm the cooling systems. There is much we should learn from the Fukushima disaster and evacuations, both from an engineering and social perspective.

The World Economic Forum considers threats to the world economy at its annual meetings in Davos, Switzerland. In 2015[16] four topics appeared in the agenda: state conflicts (e.g. EU–Ukraine–Russia), the global access-to-water crisis, state collapse (e.g. Syria) and unemployment (the overhang from the 2009 banking crisis). While climate change was acknowledged, it is politically a slow-burning issue. This is a real challenge for democracies – how to keep up the momentum needed to address energy and climate-change issues? There needs to be reduced intervention and more strategic thinking.

What governments do best is to provide information, fund research and develop the regulatory frameworks that turn policies into strategies.[17] More challenging than mitigation – the quest for lower emissions – is adaptation: the measures societies, cities and settlements might adopt to reduce their vulnerability to the effects of climate change. These are complex issues and their resolution can create conflicts that only governments or their agencies can resolve.[18] An example is the winter storms of 2015, during which UK Prime Minister David Cameron admitted 'there needs to be a complete rethink on flood defences',[19] i.e. on how to more effectively adapt to the massive rainfall now being pinned on climate change.[20]

Decarbonisation

Roger Pielke Jr addresses the socio-political issues surrounding climate change in his book *The Climate Fix*[21] and stresses the importance of decoupling economic growth from carbon emissions. No matter what the impact of each tonne of CO_2, we need to decarbonise sooner or later. Our current consumption of fossil fuels is unsustainable and is a key factor in world conflicts.

There is, however, a counter-argument akin to accelerating a motorcar round a bend. The logic is this. If we focus on economic growth, carbonised or not, then we will become richer and more able to adapt to the negative impacts of climate change.[22] In their paper *Declining vulnerability to river floods and the benefits of adaptation*, water and climate risk experts Brenden Jongman et al.[23] focus on the susceptibility of different societies, developing and developed, to flooding. The paper makes a good case for adaptation, the poor cousin of mitigation, and clearly much more needs to be done.

Perhaps the central question is whether, globally, we have decided that it is time to end our relationship with fossil fuels. The 2015 Paris climate-change agreement would suggest we have begun to engage with the problem. Yet it seems we are still in the wait-and-see mode, fearing a coming disaster but not acting until we see it for sure (by which time it may be too late to change course, as we saw in Chapter Four). Sheikh Ahmed Zaki Yamani was the Saudi Oil Minister in charge at the time the 1970s oil embargoes were imposed.[24] He asks if we have yet decided to stop using fossil fuels, because, if history is our guide, our oil will not run out before we resolve to get our energy differently. The Stone Age ended not because there was a lack of stone . . .

What the Paris agreement suggests is that governments have indeed heard the science and do understand that a wait-and-see policy is too risky. Carbon pricing and other incentives are good but market mechanisms are not sufficient by themselves.[25] From governments we also need clear, considered strategies – information, research and regulations – to ensure fairness across all sectors of the population.

Some Specific Strategies

Tables 6.1–6.5 (pp. 109–114 with colour key p. 113) outline a selection of interesting or promising strategies for mitigation – energy sources, storage systems and refrigeration – that might develop in due course. The list is not exhaustive. Similarly there is a table of adaptation strategies that might help reduce vulnerability and the impacts of extreme weather.

In Table 6.1, the main contenders are listed along with some that may be unfamiliar, such as the Allam Cycle. In each case a synopsis, benefits and drawbacks are given, together with some background references. In the right-hand column, 'Actions Needed', there is an assessment of what role a reliable carbon-pricing scheme (CP) might have.

In most cases, if fossil-fuel and other subsidies can be removed or worked around, it seems there is no need for particular subsidies – an appropriate carbon price should yield the pricing signals that are required. However, for some options, such as Ultra Supercritical Coal Plants, the carbon price may (correctly) send a warning that more coal is not the solution.[26] It all depends on whether the energy source has a carbon intensity (the amount of CO_2 emitted per unit of useful energy gained) higher or lower than average. In time the average will, or should, fall.

Highlighted in *blue* are the strategies that may be suppressed by the carbon price and, in *green*, those that might be incentivised. In *yellow* are strategies where some of the revenue from carbon-pricing schemes might be selectively used to enhance the development phase. Of course, it can be asserted that this is 'picking winners' and, indeed, it is just the opinion of one chemical engineer. However, in the case of *Biomass: Algae*, it seems that Bill Gates thinks this a good idea too![27]

Table 6.2 deals specifically with nuclear technologies, yet most of them are not what might be termed 'conventional'. The high, upfront capital costs[28] of large nuclear power plants has been prohibitive for nuclear energy's wider development, not to mention the negative impacts of headline-grabbing accidents.[29] In this table the state of fusion energy research was examined together with some promising small-scale nuclear plants with a 50–100 megawatt output that could be produced in modular form. In operation, they could work well with a dynamic, renewable-energy-based power grid. The pebble bed modular reactor has been the focus of a new strategy of localised, city-sized power plants in China. The main drawback has been the rather complex gas turbine technology needed to boost the overall efficiency to 40%.

Vital to a renewable-energy-based electricity grid is storage – the storage or utilisation of the product of combustion (CO_2) and the storage of power from renewable energy sources. In Table 6.3, there are a number of promising candidates and ingenious solutions, such as Natural Gas: Hydrogen, that cross boundaries from power to heat and back to power. A reliable carbon price (CP) would in most cases be enough to incentivise the uptake of carbon capture and storage.[30] However, CCS is a good example of where there needs to be both a price signal and a regulatory framework.

Some energy options are not centralised; they are distributed, e.g. wind turbines are often built in clusters and, if one fails, the others can still continue. Due to their low carbon intensity, both wind power and solar power should benefit from a reliable carbon price. Included in Table 6.4 is energy efficiency, the Cinderella of energy policy – unloved but in the end one of the most attractive options (this has been amply demonstrated in California). Some carbon-pricing revenue is already being directed towards home and business energy efficiency in the United States.[31] This seems very sensible. However, a note of caution here: if home insulation reduces air circulation below a certain limit, then air quality may become so degraded that it becomes a health hazard (asthma etc).[32] Fortunately, there are engineering remedies.[33]

Resilience

It would be encouraging to think that societies that solve their problems survive. The reality is starker, finds Jared Diamond, author of *Collapse: How Societies Choose to Fail or Succeed*.[34] In most cases, if population exceeds the carrying capacity of the society concerned there is great risk of collapse.[35] Moreover, Diamond observes that societies fail 'to perceive a problem in its initial stages, and end up with refusal to address the problem because of conflicts of interests and other reasons'. This sounds familiar. We can help ourselves by 'taking lightly' of the Earth, as noted in Chapter Five; by eating less meat, for example (Figure 6.2).[36] Or, like the ancient Inca people, build food and provisions 'warehouses' in the mountains that, through collective action, allow droughts and other disasters to be weathered.[37]

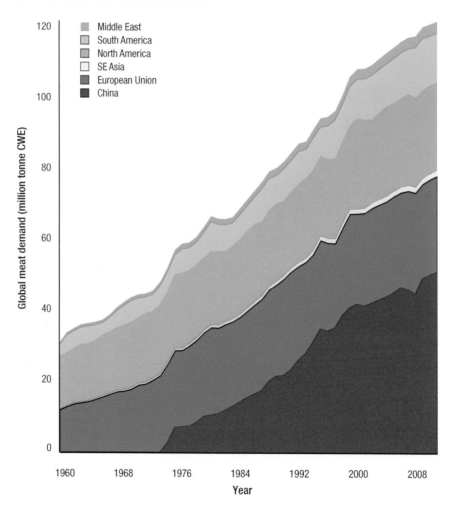

Figure 6.2. *Growing global demand for protein (meat) has a significant impact on climate change. (Source: Kona Haque, Macquarie's outlook for global commodities, São Paulo, May 2012.) (CWE = carcass weight equivalent) (© Predict Ability Ltd.)*

The risk for modern societies is that, if we address climate change at all, we focus almost exclusively on mitigation strategies. But what if mitigation alone fails, asks Nobel Laureate economist Robert J. Shiller, in his *New York Times* piece 'Buying insurance against climate change'.[38] He suggests we need to be more risk aware and use the tools available – insurance and insurance-related bonds and derivatives. With such variability in the pattern of disasters, risk needs to be pooled in ways that the insurance industry understands particularly well.

Cities

Can we realise that the time for mitigation alone has passed, that 'we should give up trying to save the world from climate change and instead retreat to climate controlled cities', suggests the scientist and inventor James Lovelock?[39] Cities need to be much more resilient than most of them are, particularly if governance is poor and climate risk factors are high. New or old, big or small, cities need to become much smarter.

New York, for example, needs to be more resilient. 'Much of the [American] public blamed [Superstorm] Sandy on a warming climate. But the principal reason for Sandy's devastating impact is that millions of people live and work in a place that is inherently dangerous', wrote Greg Ip, Chief Economics Commentator at the *Wall Street Journal*.[40]

Advanced modelling tools are now available to enable city planners to quantify the adaptation task as never before (Figure 6.3). Open minds are needed. There is no room for climate-change belief systems in flood mapping.[41] We cannot afford to keep building and rebuilding un-adapted housing in flood hazard zones, and having to deal with the displacement of thousands of flood victims.[42]

In a 2015 paper[43] by geographers Sanne Muis et al., the authors describe a probabilistic model for examining the impact of climate change on flood risk in growing cities worldwide. They found that climate change amplifies coastal flood risk by 19–37% and that 'adaptation is effective and increasingly urgent, regardless of climate uncertainties'.

It is not just flooding that can be better predicted.[44] The trend with earthquake zones is, of course, to build earthquake-resistant buildings and infrastructure but, increasingly, to adopt earthquake event early-warning

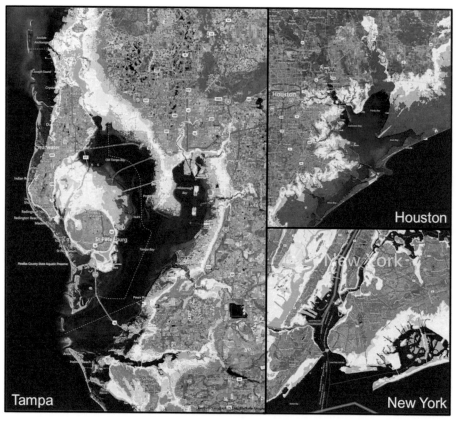

Figure 6.3. *High-resolution flood mapping: flood-risk zones in three cities calculated using the Oak Ridge National Laboratory TITAN supercomputer. (© Katrisk.)*[45]

systems[46] – the near instantaneous transmission of timely and actionable safety information to the general public via smartphones.

If a disaster hits, the use of Twitter (tweets from smartphones) in the disaster zone can provide valuable mapping of needs for emergency responders. Clearly, there must be robust cellular communications infrastructure and charging points for this to work. Maps can be produced within a minute of tweets being posted.[47]

Funding

Adaptation in developed countries is expensive. The Dutch know this very well. They have a plan to spend the equivalent of €2.2billion ($2.5–3 billion) per year on river flood defences with 'room for the river' being a key strategy. The question is whether to adapt or abandon land? It has always been a stark choice, but in the right hands it can be done very well.[48]

In the United States, after President Obama declared his intention in 2013 to tackle climate change (through executive action if necessary). The insurance industry was seen to be well placed to act on adaptation strategies, for example, to see how New York's resilience to storm surge could be improved.[49] The funding will mostly need to come through private, state and federal funding. Similar approaches are under way in other US states:[50] adaptation is, at last, part of the climate change vocabulary.

The World Economic Forum estimates[51] that around $700 billion per year is needed to pay for the effects of climate change. If there were a $15 per tonne CO_2 carbon tax, this would raise, in theory, around $600 billion. Disaster loss data[52] indicates that around 30% of the weather-related losses the WEF identifies is insured. This is a heavy burden for the insurance industry. Even though the necessary funding can be raised in the world's capital markets, there is a lack of transparency about cause (climate change) and effect (the climate-change costs are unaccounted for).

Adaptation in Developing Countries

Developed nations can find the funding needed for adaptation – it is in their interests to do so – but what happens in developing nations?[53] Often the effects of disasters are so devastating that there is little capacity to absorb the impacts, let alone plan to avoid future events.[54] Under these circumstances, infrastructure funding must come from external bodies such as the World Bank or the United Nations.

There is also a convincing case to be made that some of the funds raised by reliable carbon-pricing (CP) schemes worldwide should be directed towards credible adaptation schemes globally. As Table 6.5 indicates, these schemes could cover a wide range of needs, ranging from basic health and crop insurance to food, water and environmental protection.

Worthwhile though it is, we should not expect too much of adaptation. Already it is clear that there are limits to adaptation.[55] While adaptation is vital,[56] a set of skills we must never forget,[57] we must act on mitigation. If we arrive at

4°C of global warming then adaptation will fail. The World Bank's report 'Turn down the heat: Why a 4°C warmer world must be avoided' states that 'a series of recent extreme events worldwide continue to highlight the vulnerability of not only the developing world but even wealthy industrialized countries. No nation will be immune to the impacts of climate change. However, the distribution of impacts is likely to be inherently unequal and tilted against many of the world's poorest regions, which have the least economic, institutional, scientific, and technical capacity to cope and adapt.'[58]

Table 6.1. Mitigation strategies – centralised systems, generation, non-nuclear.

Category	Summary	Benefits	Drawbacks	Actions Needed colour key - see p.113
Coal: ultra supercritical cycles	Ultra-high pressure cycles 40% efficient[59]	Better efficiency than conventional coal	Higher carbon intensity than natural gas	A reliable CP may suppress demand
Natural gas: liquid fuels	GTL[60] (gas to liquids)	Monetise stranded gas to distant markets	Transition fuel, cost v. diesel, particulates?	A reliable CP might incentivise
Natural gas (and coal): Allam Cycle[61]	High-pressure oxy-fuel power generation	60% efficiency with direct CO_2 capture	Scale up, strength of materials?	R&D phase: a reliable CP might incentivise
Natural gas: biogas	Inject cleaned biogas to grid	Avoids methane venting, reduces carbon intensity	Impurities, safety[62]	A reliable CP might incentivise
Biomass: corn (a huge industry)	Bio-ethanol fuel / additive	Use for excess agricultural land	Environmental impact? Land conflicts[63]	A reliable CP may suppress demand
Biomass: wood chip (a huge industry)	Wood chip fuel[64] for power plants	Use for marginal land (non-food)	Environmental impact?	A reliable CP may suppress demand
Biomass: algae[65]	CO_2 from air, sunlight, water to 'crude oil'	Efficient use of land	Control, impact on biosphere? R&D phase[66,67]	CP mitigation funding – short-term goals
Solar: concentrated solar power[68]	Sun's rays concentrated for heat	Use of deserts, thermal storage	Birds,[69] dislocation of supply and demand, clouds	Demonstration phase

Table 6.2. Mitigation strategies – centralised systems, generation, nuclear.

Category	Summary	Benefits	Drawbacks	Actions Needed *colour key - see p.113*
Nuclear: fusion, public funded	ITER project: next step fusion research	International science and collaboration	Slow, expensive, political	How to make project more efficient?
Nuclear: fusion, private funded	Tokamak Energy[70] UK, for example	Dynamic, leading-edge, flexible output	Funding, uncertain RoI	R&D phase
Nuclear: fission, modular[71] (PBMR)	Small scale, repeatable units: China leading[72]	Less upfront capital, flexible power output	Costs per MWh, complexity of gas turbines	A reliable CP might incentivise
Nuclear: fission, LFTR[73]	Molten salt fission reactor	Non-proliferation fuel: thorium, inherent safety	Competing nuclear cycles (uranium)	R&D phase (again, first done in 1960s!)
Nuclear: fission, ion-beam reactor[74]	Thorium[75] accelerator ion beam reactor	Inherent safety, may use nuclear waste as fuel	Concept stage	R&D phase

Table 6.3. Mitigation Strategies – Centralised Systems, Storage.

Category	Summary	Benefits	Drawbacks	Actions Needed colour key - see p.113
CO_2 Capture & Storage[76] (amine absorption)	Collect power plant CO_2, purify and bury it[77]	New generation of coal-fired power plants	Expense, size, storage integrity, huge scale-up, amine toxicity	R&D demonstration phase
CO_2 Capture & Storage (chemical looping)	Bury pure CO_2 from metal oxide + fuel reaction[78]	Avoids nitrogen entering the combustion loop	Solids handling, oxide degrading, huge scale-up	R&D phase: a reliable CP might incentivise
CO_2 Capture & Re-use of CO_2	Make plastics[79] and building materials	Limestone-based buildings avoid cement	Only delays return of carbon to atmosphere	R&D phase: a reliable CP might incentivise
CO_2 Capture: air-capture[80]	Capture CO_2 from atmosphere	Could help reduce CO_2 concentration	Very challenging thermodynamics and costs[81]	Continue at R&D level?[82]
CO_2 Capture: bio-capture[83]	Use bio-fuel, capture CO_2	Negative CO_2 emissions	Negative impacts offset the benefits?	Continue at R&D level?[84]
Natural gas: hydrogen[85]	Convert renewable power to hydrogen	Can have up to 12% H2 injected into gas grid	Cost? Availability of water (for H_2)	A reliable CP might incentivise
Storage: hydro	Pumped storage for demand 'peak shaving'	Well-proven, existing hydro schemes	Drought,[86] dislocation of supply and demand	A reliable CP might incentivise

Table 6.4. Mitigation strategies – distributed systems, various.

Category	Summary	Benefits	Drawbacks	Actions Needed *colour key - see p.113*
Energy Efficiency	Insulation, better building design	Often highest impact per dollar spent[87]	Unglamorous, detailed, how to manage?	CP mitigation funding – short-term goals
Wind: onshore	Wind turbines in Mid-West US for example[88]	Onshore cheaper than offshore	Unsightly, intermittency,[89] REE[90] scarcity?	A reliable CP might incentivise
Wind: offshore	Wind turbines	As onshore, more wind, turbine farms	As onshore, arduous marine environment	A reliable CP might incentivise
Solar: PV	Silicon crystal structures turn light to power	Efficiency (20%), falling costs	Intermittency, need for energy storage	A reliable CP might incentivise storage
Storage: super-capacitors	Store DC power as electric charge	Energy density and costs improving fast	Development stage, cost?	R&D phase
Storage: Li-air battery[91] technology	High-density, high-power lithium batteries	Next generation Li-air advances on Li-ion types	Development stage, chemical instability	R&D phase
Storage: heat[92]	Engine converts electricity to heat and back	Known sub-systems used in machine design	Development stage, cost, plant plot area?	R&D phase
Storage: cryogenic[93]	Energy stored as cryogenic liquid	Distributed, compact energy storage	Efficiency? Couple to waste heat (hard to do)	R&D phase

Table 6.4 (cont.)

Refrigeration: Dearman engine[94]	Liquid air / LiN[95] used as 'engine' working fluid	Efficient, low-carbon intensity, new food-chains	Niche market? Diesel-powered incumbent	R&D demonstration phase
Forests (carbon cycle)	Afforestation (new forests)	Biodiversity, social integration	Return on investment (RoI) much delayed	Reduce RoI delay, e.g. ArBolvia[96]
Sea plants (carbon cycle)	Preservation of seawater ecosystems	Vital impact on carbon and food cycles	None. Alarming decline in sea ecosystems.[97]	International law and education?
Geo-engineering	Aims to reduce symptoms of climate change	Contain costs until better mitigation possible	Many.[98] Makes existing problems worse!	A reliable CP + 'REDD+' help[99] preserve forests
Weathering[100]	CO_2 reacts with rocks, e.g. limestone	Ultimate CO_2 removal process but...	...weathering is very slow.	R&D on accelerated weathering?

Colour key	
Blue	Strategies that may be suppressed by carbon pricing (CP)
Green	Strategies that may be incentivised by carbon pricing
Yellow	Strategies for which some of the carbon pricing revenue could be used

Table 6.5. Adaptation strategies – vulnerability and impact reduction.

Category	Summary	Benefits	Drawbacks	Actions Needed *colour key - see p.113*
Adaptation: farm micro-insurance[101]	Index (data) based small-scale insurance	A way to insure small farmers against CC	Effectiveness? Take-up?	CP adaptation funding – short-term goals
Adaptation: basic health insurance[102]	Combine out- & in-patient health card schemes	Better health outcomes, offset effect of CP	CP still has negative day-to-day impact	CP adaptation funding – short-term goals
Adaptation: flood/drought-resilient crops[103]	Sustainable development of crops (no GM?)	Subsistence farmers gain better resilience	Big agriculture seeks to control seed markets	CP adaptation funding – short-term goals
Adaptation: food waste[104]	Reducing food waste impacts climate change	Financial, social, energy, environmental benefits	Food hygiene, stigma of 'food banks'	Programmes in place, could do more
Adaptation: fog catchers[105]	Capture water from air in arid environments	Helps sustain marginal habitats	Scalability, cost	CP adaptation funding – short-term goals
Adaptation: flooding[106]	Redress upland habitat destruction	Sustainable flood prevention: slows flows	Conflicting policies, land-user interests	CP adaptation funding – short-term goals
Adaptation: forestation/afforestation[107]	Preserve existing forest, plant new?	Forests vital for carbon cycle and biodiversity	Strong legal frameworks + finance together	Programmes in place, could do more.
Adaptation: palm oil[108]	Controlling palm oil production, deforestation	Sustainable palm oil	Corruption, lack of policing	Move to synthetic palm oil? It exists[109]
Adaptation: mangrove swamps	Mangroves prevent erosion, storm damage	Major benefit to vulnerable, low-lying	Pressures for land use	CP adaptation funding – short-term goals

Notes to Chapter Six

1   Fitzgerald, J., 'Tackling climate change', Irish Co-operative Organisation Society (3 November 2015), http://www.icos.ie/wp-content/uploads/2012/09/ICOSClimateChangeJFitz151103Final.pptx

2   Rusbridger, A., 'Scientists must speak up on fossil-fuel divestment', *Nature*, 520 (7547), p. 265 (16 April 2015), http://www.nature.com/news/scientists-must-speak-up-on-fossil-fuel-divestment-1.17325

3   Lloyd's, the syndicated insurance market, London www.lloyds.com

4   King, E., 'Climate change has dropped off the political radar', *Climate Home* (19 February 2016), http://www.climatechangenews.com/2016/02/19/climate-change-has-dropped-off-the-political-radar/

5   Severns, M., '5 Ways Monsanto Wants to Profit Off Climate Change', *Mother Jones* (9 October 2013), http://www.motherjones.com/environment/2013/10/monsanto-profit-climate-change-corporation

6   Vidal, J., 'Why is the Gates foundation investing in GM giant Monsanto?', *The Guardian* (29 September 2010), http://www.theguardian.com/global-development/poverty-matters/2010/sep/29/gates-foundation-gm-monsanto

7   Allen, M.R., 'The people's planet: Reconnecting climate science, climate policy and reality' (inaugural lecture, 28 November 2011), University of Oxford (2011), http://podcasts.ox.ac.uk/peoples-planet-reconnecting-climate-science-climate-policy-and-reality-0

8   Markusson, N., Shackley, S., Evar, B. (eds.), *The Social Dynamics of Carbon Capture and Storage*, Routledge (2012), https://www.routledge.com/products/9781849713153

9   Allen, M., 'Climate change: let's bury the CO_2 problem', *The Guardian* (5 June 2013), http://www.theguardian.com/commentisfree/2013/jun/05/bury-co2-problem-capture-store-carbon

10 'Utilitarianism', Wikipedia (accessed 17 April 2016), https://en.wikipedia.org/wiki/Utilitarianism

11 Broughton, P.D., 'Book review: *Windfall* by McKenzie Funk', *The Wall Street Journal* (28 January 2014), http://www.wsj.com/articles/SB10001424052702304632204579340560508887126

12 http://pictures.reuters.com/archive/FRANCE--GM1E79I0CV001.html

13   Harvey, F., 'World's energy systems at risk from global warming, say industry group', *The Guardian* (1 October 2015), http://www.theguardian.com/ environment/2015/oct/01/worlds-energy-systems-at-risk-from-global- warming-say-leading-firms

14   Beckman, K., 'Interview Christoph Frei, Secretary General World Energy Council: "The key message from Paris: Be part of the innovation frontier"', *Energy Post* (15 January 2016), http://www.energypost.eu/interview- christoph-frei-secretary-general-world-energy-council-key-message-paris- part-innovation-frontier/

15   'Fukushima Daiichi NPS prompt report 2015: Tepco reports latest findings of technical inquiry into how accident at Fukushima unfolded', Tepco Electric Power Holdings Inc. (20 May 2015), http://www.tepco.co.jp/en/ press/corp-com/release/2015/1250926_6844.html

16   Khan, M., 'These are the four biggest threats to the world right now', *The Telegraph* (15 January 2015), http://www.telegraph.co.uk/finance/ economics/11347752/These-are-the-four-biggest-threats-to-the-world- right-now.html

17   Konrad, K.A., Thum, M., 'What is the role of governments in climate-change adaptation?', Oxford University Press blog (23 July 2014), http://blog.oup. com/2014/07/government-adaptation-climate-change/

18   Sovacool, B.K., Linnér, B-O., Goodsite, M.E., 'The political economy of climate adpatation', *Nature Climate Change*, 5 (7), pp. 616–618 (24 June 2015), http://www.nature.com/nclimate/journal/v5/n7/full/ nclimate2665.html

19   'UK floods: "Complete rethink needed" on flood defences', BBC News (28 December 2015), http://www.bbc.co.uk/news/uk-35188146

20   Vidal, J., 'UK floods and extreme global weather linked to El Niño and climate change', *The Guardian* (27 December 2015), http://www.theguardian. com/environment/2015/dec/27/uk-floods-and-extreme-global-weather- linked-to-el-nino-and-climate-change

21   Pielke Jr, R., *The Climate Fix*, p. 11, Basic Books, New York (2010).

22   'Lewis, M., 'Economic growth is the best climate insurance policy', GlobalWarming.org (3 September 2015), http://www.globalwarming. org/2015/09/03/economic-growth-is-the-best-climate-insurance-policy/. Compare, for example, the two scenarios in Figure 4.3: high growth may temporarily avoid collapse, but is it sustainable in the long run?

23   Jongman, B., et al., 'Declining vulnerability to river floods and the global benefits of adaptation', *PNAS*, 112 (18), pp. E2271–E2280 (5 May 2015).

24   'The end of the Oil Age: Ways to break the tyranny of oil are coming into view. Governments need to promote them', *The Economist* (23 October 2003), http://www.economist.com/node/2155717

25   Editorial, '*The Guardian* view on UK energy policy: The limits of the market', *The Guardian* (4 January 2015), http://www.theguardian.com/commentisfree/2015/jan/04/guardian-view-uk-energy-policy-limits-market

26   'From Bangladesh flood map to the Bank of England, a "carbon bubble" is born', Thompson Reuters Foundation News (6 December 2015), http://news.trust.org//item/20151206230229-bbztk

27   Johnson, K., 'Bill Gates goes for algae, invests in biofuel maker Sapphire Energy', *The Wall Street Journal* (17 Spetember 2008), http://blogs.wsj.com/environmentalcapital/2008/09/17/bill-gates-goes-for-algae-invests-in-biofuel-maker-sapphire-energy/

28   Vaughan, A., 'Scrapping Hinkley for renewable alternatives would save "tens of billions"', *The Guardian* (5 April 2016), http://www.theguardian.com/environment/2016/apr/05/scrapping-hinkley-for-renewable-alternatives-will-save-tens-of-billions

29   'Half-death: Nuclear power emits no greenhouse gases, yet it is struggling in the rich world', *The Economist* (29 October 2015), http://www.economist.com/news/international/21677243-nuclear-power-emits-no-greenhouse-gases-yet-it-struggling-rich-world-half-death/

30   Fountain, H., 'Turning carbon dioxide into rock, and burying it', *The New York Times* (9 February 2015), http://www.nytimes.com/2015/02/10/science/burying-a-mountain-of-co2.html

31   'RGGI benefits', Regional Greenhouse Gas Initiative (accessed 17 April 2016), http://www.rggi.org/rggi_benefits

32   Roberts, M., 'UK air pollution "linked to 40,000 early deaths a year"', BBC News (23 February 2016), http://www.bbc.co.uk/news/health-35629034

33   *Guide to Whole-House Ventilation* (2nd Edition), Vent-Axia (accessed 17 April 2016), http://www.vent-axia.com/files/catdownloads/Guide_to_whole_house_ventilation-2nd_Edition-Web.pdf

34   '*Collapse: How Societies Choose to Fail or Succeed*, by J. Diamond', Wikipedia (accessed 17 April 2016), https://en.wikipedia.org/wiki/Collapse:_How_Societies_Choose_to_Fail_or_Succeed

35   Hirst, K.K., 'The collapse of Angkor', About Education – Archaeology (9 April 2016), http://archaeology.about.com/od/medieval/qt/Collapse-Of-Angkor.htm

36   'Footprint calculator', Global Footprint Network (accessed 17 April 2016), http://www.footprintnetwork.org/en/index.php/GFN/page/calculators/

37   Cooper, J., 'The Inca: Masters of the clouds', BBC 4 (27 February 2016), http://www.bbc.co.uk/programmes/b04xrsx6

38   Shiller, R., 'Buying insurance against climate change', The New York Times (24 May 2014), http://www.nytimes.com/2014/05/25/upshot/buying-insurance-against-climate-change.html

39   Knapton, S., 'We should give up trying to save the world from climate change, says James Lovelock', The Telegraph (8 April 2014), http://www.telegraph.co.uk/news/science/science-news/10752606/We-should-give-up-trying-to-save-the-world-from-climate-change-says-James-Lovelock.html

40   Ip, G., 'Cities built to endure disaster: Resilience is the best answer to future storms like Sandy', The Wall Street Journal (9 October 2015), http://www.wsj.com/articles/cities-built-to-endure-disaster-1444401240

41   Benzak, J., 'NRDC: Congress wrong to try to block federal flood standards, new interactive mapping tool shows', Natural Resources Defense Council (30 November 2015), http://www.nrdc.org/media/2015/151130b.asp

42   Plumer, B., 'Adapting to climate change is going to be a lot messier than we think', Vox Energy & Environment (2 June 2015), http://www.vox.com/2015/6/2/8709913/texas-floods-climate-adaptation

43   Muis, S., Güneralp, B., Jongman, B., Aerts, J.C.J.H., Ward, P.J., 'Flood risk and adaptation strategies under climate change and urban expansion: A probabilistic analysis using global data', Science of the Total Environment, 538, pp. 445–457 (15 December 2015), http://www.sciencedirect.com/science/article/pii/S0048969715305714

44   Moreno, I., 'Colorado considers system to predict fire, flood behavior', CBS Denver (16 February 2016), http://denver.cbslocal.com/2015/02/16/colorado-considers-system-to-predict-fire-flood-behavior/

45   'Flood hazard data', KatRisk (accessed 17 April 2016), http://www.katrisk.com/floodhazarddata/

46   'Earthquake early warning', US Geological Survey (accessed 17 April 2016), http://earthquake.usgs.gov/research/earlywarning/

47   Rowling., M., 'Tweets turned into flood maps that could help save lives', Reuters (14 April 2015), http://www.reuters.com/article/us-disaster-flood-socialmedia-idUSKBN0N51W020150415

48   McVeigh, T., 'The Dutch solution to floods: Live with water, don't fight it', *The Guardian* (16 February 2014), http://www.theguardian.com/environment/2014/feb/16/flooding-netherlands

49   Loney, M., 'Comment: A changing political climate', *Reactions* (5 March 2013), http://www.reactionsnet.com/Article/3164289/Sectors/23074/Comment-A-changing-political-climate.html

50   Helm, B., 'Climate change's bottom line', *The New York Times* (31 January 2015), http://www.nytimes.com/2015/02/01/business/energy-environment/climate-changes-bottom-line.html

51   Doyle, A., 'Curbing climate change will cost $700 billion a year – report', Reuters (22 January 2013), http://in.reuters.com/article/davos-climate-davos-idINDEE90K0GU20130121

52   'NATHAN Risk Suite: Significant natural disasters since 1980', Munich RE (accessed 17 April' http://www.munichre.com/en/reinsurance/business/non-life/natcatservice/significant-natural-catastrophes/index.html

53   Pidcock, R., 'Huge divide in spending on climate-change adaptation across world's megacities', *CarbonBrief* (29 February 2016), http://www.carbonbrief.org/huge-divide-in-spending-on-climate-change-adaptation-across-worlds-megaticities

54   Hsiang, S.M., 'Quantifying the economic cost of climate change', RMS Connection (30 April 2014), https://www.youtube.com/watch?v=yNYZJD_llno

55   Dow, K., Berkhout, F., Preston, B.L., Klein, R.L.T., Midgley, G., Shaw, M.R., 'Limits to adaptation', *Nature Climate Change*, 3 (4), pp. 305–307 (April 2013), http://www.nature.com/nclimate/journal/v3/n4/full/nclimate1847.html

56   Glover, A., et al., 'Oral evidence: Climate-change adaptation, HC453', UK Parliament Environmental Audit Committee (7 January 2015), http://data.parliament.uk/writtenevidence/committeeevidence.svc/evidencedocument/environmental-audit-committee/climate-change-adaptation/oral/17297.html

57   Stabinsky, D., 'Tackling the limits to adaptation', ActionAid/CARE International/WWF (November 2012), http://www.wwf.org.uk/wwf_articles.cfm?unewsid=6348

58 'Turn down the heat: Why a 4°C warmer world must be avoided', Report for the World Bank by the Potsdam Institute for Climate Impact Research and Climate Analytics (November 2012), http://documents.worldbank.org/curated/en/2012/11/17097815/turn-down-heat-4°c-warmer-world-must-avoided

59 'High efficiency low emission coal: Ultrasupercritical technology', World Coal Association (accessed 17 April 2016), https://www.worldcoal.org/reducing-co2-emissions/high-efficiency-low-emission-coal

60 'Pearl GTL (gas to liquids)', Shell Global (accessed 17 April 2016), http://www.shell.com/about-us/major-projects/pearl-gtl.html

61 http://breakingenergy.com/2014/11/14/ccs-breakthrough-sco2-power-cycles-offer-improved-efficiency-and-integrated-carbon-capture/

62 Dodge, E., 'CCS breakthrough: sCO_2 power cycles offer improved efficiency and integrated carbon capture', *Breaking Energy* (14 November 2014), http://www.conserve-energy-future.com/advantages-and-disadvantages-of-biogas.php

63 Hitchon, J., 'Biofuels converting US prairielands at dust bowl rates', Inter Press Service (23 February 2013), http://www.ipsnews.net/2013/02/biofuels-converting-u-s-prairielands-at-dust-bowl-rates/

64 Wilson, R., 'Biomass: The world's biggest provider of renewable energy', Carbon Counter blog (5 June 2015), https://carboncounter.wordpress.com/2015/06/05/biomass-the-worlds-biggest-provider-of-renewable-energy/

65 Siegel, R.P., 'Algae-based biofuel: Pros and cons', Triple Pundit (12 April 2012), http://www.triplepundit.com/special/energy-options-pros-and-cons/algae-based-biofuel-pros-cons/

66 Tamburic, B., Malik, A., 'Sustainable oil from algae: The technology is ready, what about the politics?', *Energy Post* (20 August 2015), http://www.energypost.eu/sustainable-oil-algae-technology-ready-politics/

67 LaMonica, M., 'Bill Gates invests in algae fuel', C|Net (17 September 2008), http://www.cnet.com/uk/news/bill-gates-invests-in-algae-fuel/

68 Porritt, J., 'World's largest concentrated solar power plant', Jonathon Porritt blog (8 October 2012), http://www.jonathonporritt.com/blog/world's-largest-concentrated-solar-power-plant

69 Fecht, S., 'Solar power towers are "vaporizing" birds', *Popular Science* (20 February 2015), http://www.popsci.com/solar-power-towers-are-vaporizing-birds

70 'Welcome to Tokamak Energy: A faster way to fusion', Tokamak Energy (accessed 17 April 2016), http://www.tokamakenergy.co.uk

71 'Pebble bed modular reactor', Wikipedia (accessed 17 April 2016), https://en.wikipedia.org/wiki/Pebble_bed_modular_reactor

72 Rogers, D., 'China set to build world's first fourth-generation nuclear reactor', *Global Construction Review* (24 April 2015), http://www.globalconstructionreview.com/news/china-set-build-worlds-8f0i6r4s8t0-6f4o2u4r6t8h/

73 'LFTR (liquid-fluoride thorium reactor) overview', Energy from Thorium blog (accessed 17 April 2016), http://energyfromthorium.com/lftr-overview/

74 'Accelerator-driven nuclear energy', World Nuclear Association (accessed 17 April 2016), http://www.world-nuclear.org/information-library/current-and-future-generation/accelerator-driven-nuclear-energy.aspx

75 'Asgard's fire: Thorium, an element named after the Norse god of thunder, may soon contribute to the world's electricity supply', *The Economist* (10 April 2014), http://www.economist.com/news/science-and-technology/21600656-thorium-element-named-after-norse-god-thunder-may-soon-contribute

76 Clark, P., 'Carbon capture: Miracle machine or white elephant?', *Financial Times* (9 September 2015), http://www.ft.com/cms/s/2/88c187b4-5619-11e5-a28b-50226830d644.html

77 Levitan, D., 'A vault for carbon dioxide', *Scientific American* (1 December 2013), http://www.scientificamerican.com/article/a-vault-for-carbon-dioxide/

78 'Copper's potential for reducing CO_2 emissions in chemical looping', *Carbon Capture Journal* (19 February 2016), http://www.carboncapturejournal.com/ViewNews.aspx?NewsID=3700

79 'Copper foam turns CO_2 into useful chemicals', *Carbon Capture Journal* (1 October 2014), http://www.carboncapturejournal.com/ViewNews.aspx?NewsID=3510

80 Dr Graciela Chichilnisky (CEO and Co-Founder), Global Thermostat (accessed 17 April 2016), http://globalthermostat.com/who-we-are/gt-team/founders-and-management/#graciela-chichilnisky

81 Doyle, A., 'Many nations wary of extracting carbon from air to fix climate', Reuters (8 April 2014), http://uk.reuters.com/article/climate-un-idUKL6N0N01JX20140408

82   Fox, T., 'CO$_2$ removal from air: Now is the time to invest in research',
      Institution of Mechanical Engineers (12 February 2015), https://www.
      imeche.org/news/news-article/co2-removal-from-air-now-is-the-time-to-
      invest-in-research

83   Pinder, C., 'Moving below zero: Understanding bioenergy with
      carbon capture & storage', The Climate Institute (April 2014), http://
      www.climateinstitute.org.au/verve/_resources/MovingBelowZero_
      SpotlightReport_April2014.pdf

84   'Earth challenge: Removing greenhouse gases from the atmosphere', Virgin
      Earth (accessed 17 April 2016), http://www.virginearth.com

85   'Injection of hydrogen into the German gas distribution grid', ITM Power
      (4 December 2013), http://www.itm-power.com/news-item/injection-of-
      hydrogen-into-the-german-gas-distribution-grid

86   'New Pacific Institute report reveals impacts of Ca. [California] drought
      on hydroelectrcity costs', *Water World* (17 March 2015), http://www.
      waterworld.com/articles/2015/03/pacific-institute-report-highlights-
      costs-of-ca-drought-on-hydroelectricity-generation.html

87   'Energy efficiency: California's highest-priority resource', California Public
      Utilities Commission and California Energy Commission (June 2006),
      http://chinauseealliance.org/wp-content/uploads/2012/02/calif_
      cleanenergy508.pdf

88   'From the ground up: Building our energy future, one turbine at a time',
      MidAmerican Energy Company (22 April 2015), https://www.youtube.
      com/watch?v=84BeVq2Jm88

89   Bullis, K., 'Smart Wind and Solar Power', *MIT Technology Review* (25 April
      2014), https://www.technologyreview.com/s/526541/smart-wind-and-
      solar-power/

90   'Neodymium a bone of contention in wind turbines', *Renewables International*
      (25 May 2011), http://www.renewablesinternational.net/neodymium-a-
      bone-of-contention-in-wind-turbines/150/435/31015/

91   Cookson, C., 'Cambridge chemists make super-battery breakthrough',
      Financial Times (30 October 2015), http://www.ft.com/cms/
      s/0/149ca550-7e30-11e5-a1fe-567b37f80b64.html

92   'A new approach to energy storage', Isentropic (accessed 17 April 2016),
      http://www.isentropic.co.uk

93   'Reliable renewables with cryogenic energy storage', power-technology. com (23 July 2013), http://www.power-technology.com/features/feature-reliable-renewables-cryogenic-energy-storage/

94   'Dearman is a global technology company delivering clean "cold and power"', Dearman (accessed 17 April 2016), http://www.dearman.co.uk

95   LiN (or LN_2) is liquid nitrogen.

96   'The main cause of deforestation in the Bolivian Amazon is poverty. This forces poor farmers to fell prime rainforest to survive. The ArBolivia Project provides a real alternative in a true partnership between investors and farmers.' ArBolvia (accessed 17 April 2016), http://www.arbolivia.org.uk

97   Flannery, T., 'Climate crisis: Seaweed, coffee and cement could save the planet', *The Guardian* (20 November 2015), http://www.theguardian.com/ books/2015/nov/20/climate-crisis-future-brighter-tim-flannery

98   Shepherd, J.G., 'Geoengineering the climate: An overview and update', *Philosophical Transactions of the Royal Society*, 370 (1974), pp. 4166–4175 (6 August 2012), http://rsta.royalsocietypublishing.org/ content/370/1974/4166

99   Meyer, R., 'The best technology for fighting climate change? Trees', *The Atlantic* (9 February 2015), http://www.theatlantic.com/technology/ archive/2015/02/the-best-technology-for-fighting-climate-change-trees/385304/

100   de Pomerai, M., et al., 'The rock cycle: Chemical weathering', The Geological Society (accessed 17 April 2016), https://www.geolsoc.org.uk/ks3/gsl/ education/resources/rockcycle/page3564.html

101   Cole, S., Bastian, G., Vyas, S., Wendel, C., Stein, D., 'The effectiveness of index-based micro-insurance in helping smallholders manage weather-related risks', EPPI-Centre, Social Science Research Unit, Institute of Education, University of London (July 2012), http://r4d.dfid.gov.uk/pdf/ outputs/systematicreviews/MicroinsuranceWeather2012ColeReport.pdf

102   Mahal, A., Krishnaswamy, K., Ruchismita, R., Babu, B.G., 'What is a health card worth? A randomised controlled trial of an outpatient health insurance product in rural India', *The Lancet*, 381 (S87) (17 June 2013), http://www. thelancet.com/journals/lancet/article/PIIS0140-6736(13)61341–0/ abstract

103   'Announces nearly $200 million in new agriculture grants, bringing foundation total to over $2 billion', Bill & Melinda Gates Foundation (23 February 2012), http://www.gatesfoundation.org/Media-Center/Press-

Releases/2012/02/Helping-Poor-Farmers-Changes-Needed-to-Feed-1-Billion-Hungry

104   Woodcock, A., 'Supermarkets urged to scrap buy-one-get-one-free deals due to "morally repugnant" levels of food waste', *Evening Standard*, London (6 April 2014), http://www.standard.co.uk/news/politics/supermarket-urged-to-scrap-buy-one-get-one-free-deals-due-to-morally-repugnant-levels-of-food-waste-9241879.html

105   Angel, E., 'Fog catchers dream big to boost water security', *SciDevNet* (26 August 2014), http://www.scidev.net/global/water/feature/fog-catchers-dream-big-to-boost-water-security.html

106   Monbiot, G., 'Drowning in money: The hidden and remarkable story of why devastating floods keep happening', monbiot.com blog (13 January 2014), http://www.monbiot.com/2014/01/13/drowning-in-money/

107   'What is REDD+?', Forest Carbon Partnership Facility (accessed 17 April 2016), https://www.forestcarbonpartnership.org/what-redd

108   'Palm Oil [Multiple Articles]', *The Guardian* (accessed 17 April 2016), http://www.theguardian.com/environment/palm-oil

109   'An impact analysis of a synthetic palm oil: Outlining a new approach to ethical considerations in the production of high-value chemicals', University of Manchester iGEM Team (2013), http://2013.igem.org/wiki/images/9/9c/MANCHESTERIGEMimpactanalysisofsyntheticpalmoil.pdf

CHAPTER SEVEN

REINSURANCE
EVENT-ATTRIBUTED CARBON TAX

A credible global carbon price based on loss and damage
Clear evidence of climate change in disaster loss data will now enable
the insurance industry to effectively price the excess damage and thus
provide a carbon price signal to businesses and governments worldwide.

Event Attribution

The motivation for having an insurance-led response to climate change came
from Professor Myles Allen's 2011 inaugural lecture, in which he focused on
the emerging science of probabilistic event attribution (PEA).

In event attribution, climate scientists aim to identify how the odds of
a particular (usually major) weather event have altered because of climate
change.[1] In many cases natural variability is the culprit, so the probability
remains the same. With climate change the probability of extreme events is
generally expected to increase but occasionally it will decrease; e.g. if there is
no snow in the mountains the risk of flooding in a valley will reduce.[2]

Event attribution studies are carried out using ensembles (collections)
of sophisticated climate models (computer programs). They are run many
thousands of times with slightly different starting conditions. This 'Monte
Carlo' technique[3] is applied to two primary cases: today's world, and a
'counterfactual' world without man-made (anthropogenic) CO_2 emissions. In
practical terms, the 1960s suffices as the baseline.

Michael Mann, Professor of Meteorology at Pennsylvania State University, has concerns about the design of PEA studies and urges caution if event attribution fails to find evidence of climate change.[4] Additionally, by itself, PEA can be seen as a tool for blaming governments (as some climate scientists have found to their cost).[5]

PEA has been most successful in extreme heat and flood analyses. It gives little insight, as yet, into hurricanes/cyclones or tornadoes (where, in any case, it is hail that usually does the most damage).[6] In 2012 the journal *Nature* suggested in an editorial that PEA may find applications in future but the models need to be better.[7] In taking the science[8] forward, the PEA scientists need to collaborate with potential users – the UN, the insurance industry and legal specialists.

Nevertheless, much progress has been made with PEA and in a few years the science and extraordinary computing power needed may be sufficient to provide near real-time *x* data,[9] which is the extent to which climate change damage can be attributed to man-made CO_2 emissions. In the UK, for example, *x* was found to be 43% for the winter floods of 2014.[10] Here *x* is defined as a ratio of probabilities:

$$x = p_2/p_1 - 1$$

where p_1 = event probability (counterfactual case) and p_2 = event probability (current conditions, CO_2 concentration, etc).

If we focus on disasters and catastrophes, it soon becomes clear that there are many reasons for these major loss events. Finding and predicting these reasons is Predict Ability Ltd's *raison d'être*. It is also evident that climate change is usually not the fundamental reason why weather-related loss events occur: typically *x* <1.

The data Predict Ability Ltd relies on to make these assertions comes from the historical and well-established databases of a reinsurance company (Munich RE)[11] and an initiative aimed at rationalising decision-making for disaster preparedness (CRED EM-DAT).[12] All these databases have flaws, of course, because ultimately what comprises a disaster is a matter of human judgement and circumstances. Opinion varies from country to country.

By examining all the results of Predict Ability Ltd's *PALgamma* disaster loss and prediction model we find that, compared to the early 1960s, the *total number* of weather-related loss events, worldwide, now exceeds the expected number by around 12%, or x ~0.12. In the case of disasters and catastrophes, however, the figure is nearer 20% (x ~0.2).

When averaged across a range of studies, this is consistent with the magnitude of attribution (11–19%) predicted by PEA.[13] It could be a coincidence that the disaster shortfall observed by Predict Ability Ltd is similar, but, as we shall see, it is almost certainly not.

If all other factors held steady, the IPCC expects the number of disasters to rise by about 3% per decade, as the global temperature anomaly (global warming) continues to increase. There is a link between temperature anomaly and disaster numbers.

Probabilistic event attribution science is focused on specific climate-related events, such as the Russian Federation (Moscow) heatwave of 2010[14] or the North of England (Storm Desmond) floods of 2015.[15] Yet there is a pressing need for a *global attribution methodology* today – even if it is inevitably an approximate one. As PEA progresses, it could – and it should – provide the detailed pieces of the jigsaw, enabling an even more exact picture of loss and damage to emerge[16] over time.

Global Attribution

Predict Ability Ltd has investigated and analysed in great depth the question of global attribution. The approach taken was to identify the year-by-year extent of disaster under-prediction in *PALgamma*. Predict Ability Ltd's *PALgamma* model takes into account the key factors needed to accurately predict the detailed form of the disaster events graph published annually by Munich RE.[17] This modelling was able to attain a 96% correlation[18] (the p-value is 10^{-18}).[19] What has been achieved is shown in Figure 7.1. The solid red line includes the effect of climate change, the dotted blue line does not (i.e. it represents the 'counterfactual',[20] the 'what if there were no climate change' model). The fact that counterfactual thinking is a concept of psychology and risk is no accident – one of our core problems is being able to accept climate change.

For reference, a straight-line linear regression of the raw data yields a 93% correlation. The *PALgamma* prediction, however, is completely independent

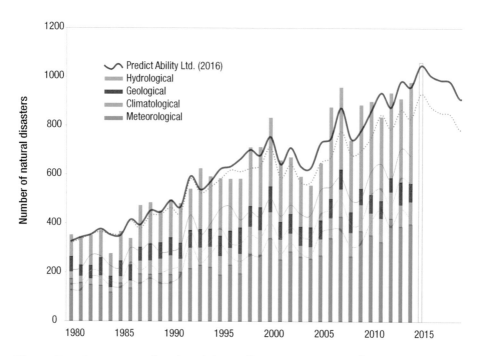

Figure 7.1. *Comparison of Predict Ability Ltd's PALgamma model (with climate change, solid red line; without climate change, dotted blue line) with Munich RE's disaster and catastrophe data. The disaster categories (meteorological, etc) are all-encompassing terms for storms, droughts, earthquakes and floods.[21] PALgamma predicted the number of events in 2015 (1060) within 1%. (© Predict Ability Ltd.)*

of the previous history of disaster numbers and yet it is also significantly more accurate. *PALgamma's* powerful modelling engine has enabled Predict Ability Ltd to identify beyond reasonable doubt the damage attributable to anthropogenic climate change. Uniquely, it also predicts disaster risk density 'hot spots' regionally and globally, both by number of events and disaster type (cyclone, drought, flood, etc) and, in certain cases, when they are likely to occur, all with unprecedented accuracy.

Furthermore, *PALgamma* monetises the consequent dollar losses in advance, enabling much-improved lean loss-provisioning. *PALgamma* is based on a mass of richly textured, public domain data with huge potential for expansion and granularity enhancement across a broad range of applications.

The *PALgamma* model is an algorithm and so does not use multi-parameter curve fitting for predicting extreme weather-related disasters, or 'loss events' as they are known in the insurance industry (see the Predict Ability Ltd website for further information).[22]

A normalisation[23] of the Munich RE and *PALgamma* data provides a key insight. The *PALgamma* algorithm does not, by itself, incorporate the effects of climate change. Thus, if there is any climate effect on the number of disasters, it will be apparent in the normalised disasters and catastrophes ratio, *NDC*, that was calculated for each year i = 1980 to 2014:

$$NDC_i = (disasters_i + catastrophes_i)/PALgamma_i$$

NDC is plotted in Figure 7.2 as a blue line for the period 1980 to 2014 – the 35 years for which there is Munich RE data. The slopes of the straight lines are about 5% per decade, slightly higher than the IPCC's estimate.

Compared to the early 1980s, Figure 7.2 shows there are about 15% more disasters than can be explained by the underlying factors that drive the *PALgamma* model. Although there is residual noise in the *NDC* ratio, there is a clear upward trend. If earthquakes (geological events) are removed, the correlation improves further still.

The red line, *PALca*, is another ratio. It represents the impact of

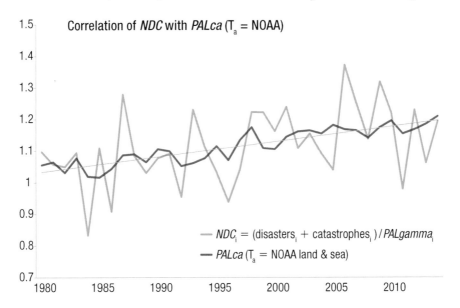

Figure 7.2. *The correlation between normalised disasters and the year-by-year warming trend. (© Predict Ability Ltd.)*

temperature anomaly T_a and thus climate change – more on *PALca*[24] shortly. Through *PALca*, the red trend and blue trend were collapsed in order to reveal something remarkable. There is a significant underlying relationship between the normalised disasters (*NDC*) and the year-by-year warming trend (*PALca*). Comparing the two lines 'by eye' shows a definite correlation. This is the 'smoking gun', confirming that a significant part of the increase in global disaster numbers is related to climate change.

For the statistically minded, there are a number of ways to test such a claim. The *p*-value is 0.0052; *p*-values are used extensively in many sciences to show that the chance of there *not* being a correlation (i.e. the null hypothesis) is acceptably low. A *p*-value of 0.005 suggests there is very good confidence that there is a hypothesis.[25] Finally, if we doubly-normalise the data (i.e. take the blue and red data trends and divide them by their linear trend lines), there is a significant level of correlation. The 'coefficient of determination'[26] R^2 is about 0.13. But if the T_a data (the NOAA temperature anomaly data), and hence *PALca*, are shifted by ± 1 year, any correlation completely disappears ($R^2 \sim 0$). The link between the temperature fluctuations and disaster numbers is not random.

PALca – Predict Ability Ltd (Lightning) Claims Algorithm

In *Science* magazine, one of the leading US research journals, there is a comprehensive overview of the evolving impact of climate change on the insurance industry by Evan Mills,[27] a senior scientist at LBNL (Lawrence Berkeley National Laboratory). Mills is a respected chronicler of the insurance industry's action on climate change. In his study one graph stands out. It shows data obtained by a long-established US insurance firm, the Hartford Steam Boiler Inspection and Insurance Company (HSB).[28] Along the y-axis is temperature (°F) and on the x-axis is the number of claims filed in several northeastern US states for lightning strikes. Several years' data from the mid-1990s follow the general trend, a logarithmic curve. Here, in Figure 7.3, the data has been transposed into a semi-logarithmic plot and temperatures converted to °C. The log-linear plot shows there is an exponential relationship with temperature. It can be used to make an estimation of the relative number of claims there will be as the temperature anomaly increases.

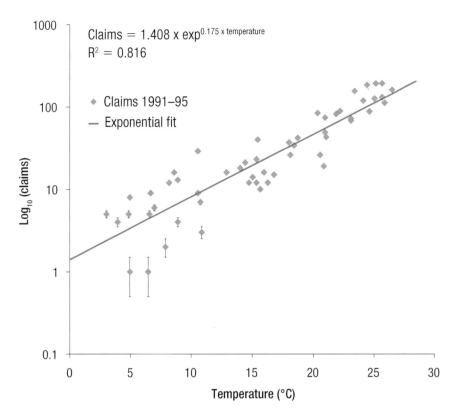

Figure 7.3. *Plot of lightning claims recorded by Hartford Steam Boiler Inspection and Insurance Company.*[29] *(© Predict Ability Ltd from data courtesy of Evan Mills.)*

This is how the *PALca* algorithm works. Suppose the global, pre-industrial temperature, **T**, was 16°C – actually, the precise value does not matter – according to the algorithm, there would have been 23.5 hypothetical claims. If the world is now 0.8°C warmer (i.e. the globally averaged anomaly $T_a = 0.8°C$), there would be 27.1 claims.

Of course, for a simpler correlation a linear equation would suffice, but it might under-predict the effect on claims of an increasing temperature anomaly.

The 2013 IPCC climate change science report[30] defines T_a and the data from the US National Ocean and Atmospheric Administration (NOAA) provides us with an excellent and coherent source of yearly, monthly and daily (imagery) data.[31] NOAA's 'land and sea' temperature has been found to be the most suitable.

In Chapter Five the benefits and drawbacks of using temperature anomaly as a proxy for the effects of climate change were discussed. Whatever the concerns, T_a is recognised worldwide and the '2°C target' (and the 1.5°C ambition)[32] is the goal of the IPCC.[33]

We define the extent to which climate-change damage can be attributed to man-made (anthropogenic) CO_2 emissions using x, a term that can now be defined in terms of $PALca$ as follows:

$x = PALca\{T_{now}\}/PALca\{T_{pre\text{-}industrial}\} - 1$

where

$T_{now} = T_a \text{ (now)} + T_{pre\text{-}industrial}$ and

$T_{pre\text{-}industrial} = T$ before global warming began

and

$PALca\ \{T\} = \exp^{(T + k_a)/k_b}$ where k_a and k_b are given in Table 7.1.

	Table 7.1. Coefficients for *PALca* equation.	
PALca constants	*PALca*$_{body}$ (total losses, fits HSB data)	*PALca*$_{tail}$ (disasters and catastrophes only)
k_a	2	2
k_b	5.72	3.44

This is the *average* fraction of losses that is attributable to man-made (anthropogenic) warming, assuming that natural variations in temperature have been fully taken into account. In the case of 0.8°C of warming $x = 27.1/23.5 - 1 = 0.15$. By extension, 15% of today's weather-related losses need to be attributed to the cause: the producers of CO_2 – all of them, from Newcomen[34] in 1712 right through to the Big Energy, Big Cement, Big Land and Big Everything companies of today. But more of that later.

Returning briefly to the question of lightning, in 2014 there was a major study published in *Science* magazine by earth scientists David M. Romps et al.[35] Their algorithm for lightning-strike prediction links several mechanisms that are likely to be significantly affected by increasing T_a. Using a number of leading climate-prediction models that are well suited to work with their methods, Romps et al. determined that the number of lightning strikes (in the continental US) will increase by 12 ± 5% per °C.

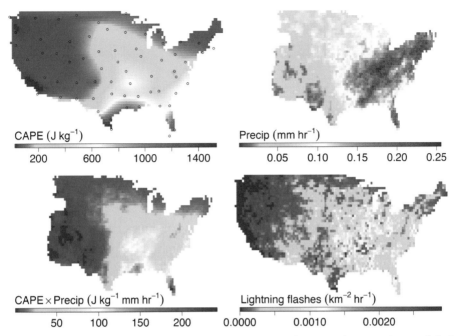

Figure 7.4. *'Projected increase in lightning strikes in the United States due to global warming' (Romps et al.,[36] Science, November 2014), showing predicted flashes (=CAPE × Precip) bottom left and actual flashes bottom right. CAPE = convective available potential energy (J/kg) or, put another way, CAPE is a measure of how explosively clouds can rise. Precip = precipitation rate (mm/hr). (© Science, AAAS.)*

The *PALca* prediction lies within those bounds. The results obtained by Romps et al. are illustrated in Figure 7.4.

Disaster Numbers and Dollar Losses, and Global Total Losses

To determine the actual number of disasters, or the disaster dollar losses, or the global total of dollar losses, the *PALgamma* algorithm first has to be coupled to the appropriate[37] climate-change global attribution factor x:

Total number of events (disasters and catastrophes) = *PALgamma* × $(1 + x)$.

From the total number of events, Predict Ability Ltd has formulated methods to determine the disaster and catastrophe overall dollar losses. They have been compared with data provided by Munich RE as follows:

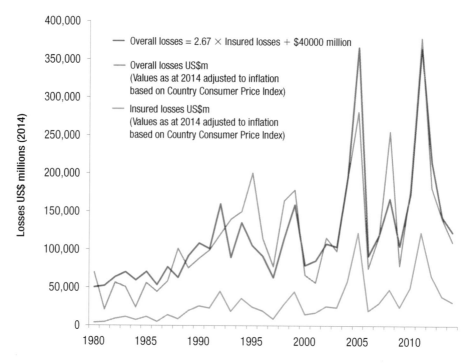

Figure 7.5. *Overall and insured disaster and catastrophe losses. (© Predict Ability Ltd from data courtesy of Munich RE.)*

Disaster and catastrophe overall dollar losses =
$$k_1 \times (\text{insured disaster and catastrophe losses}) + k_2$$

where $k_1 \sim 2.67$, i.e. the ratio of (overall disaster and catastrophe dollar losses)/ (insured disaster + catastrophe dollar losses), and $k_2 \sim \$40$ billion, as shown in the highly (87%) correlated trends in Figure 7.5. US-only data shows a similar picture.[38]

Global, weather-related, total dollar losses =
$$k_3 \times (\text{overall disaster and catastrophe dollar losses}).$$

The constant k_3 is derived as follows. In the paper *An Insurance-Led Response to Climate Change* posted on arXiv.org by Anthony Webster and Richard Clarke,[39] the authors estimate that the insurance industry had a 2012 premium volume of around \$4 trillion per annum (5.63% of global GDP) and that one-third of that is connected with weather-related losses.[40] In 2014 global GDP was \$77.8 trillion. From this we can estimate the loss ratio k_3:

$$k_3 \sim (\tfrac{1}{3} \times 5.63\% \times \$77.8 \text{ trillion} \times k_1)/$$
$$(\text{overall disaster and catastrophe losses} - k_2)$$

thus $k_3 \sim 26.7$ for 2014.

In the above expression for k_3, two of the key terms are known, i.e. the size of the insurance industry (premium volume) and global GDP. The disaster and catastrophe losses have been determined using *PALgamma*, but what is the reach and magnitude of weather losses in the insurance industry and elsewhere? A conventional analysis suggests that perhaps 50% of the Fire and Property market is weather-affected, with other sectors such as Life, Motor (Auto) and Accident much less so. All in all, such an approach would indicate that perhaps 10% to 15% of insurance premiums are weather-related. However, at Predict Ability Ltd, we are interested in the global picture. This includes unclaimed losses and the widely ignored uninsured losses in developing countries and emerging markets. Weather-related losses come in many forms and magnitudes and some have been cited elsewhere in the book: the perils of thin ice; an inter-state pile-up during a hailstorm; homes damaged by extreme rainfall and flooding; crop failure from heatwaves, etc. A 2012 study[41] by DARA's Climate Vulnerability Forum estimated climate-change-related losses to be 1.6% of global GDP. By 2030, these could be over 3%. If the global attribution factor $x \sim 0.15$, then the 1.6% figure indicates that GDP is impacted by $\sim 10\%$ from the whole spectrum of weather-related losses. Even if we take note of the insurance claims/premiums ratio $\sim \tfrac{2}{3}$, the $\tfrac{1}{3}$ factor in the equation for k_3 needs, if anything, to be doubled. Consequently, the *PALcarbon* system is conservatively priced. By using k_3, we can calculate the weather-related, global total dollar losses.

(If d_i = disaster insured losses and d_o = disaster overall losses, then the proportion of insured disaster losses/overall disaster losses $d_i/d_o = d_i/(k_1 \times d_i + k_2) \sim 30\%$ in 2015 and it is increasing by $\sim 0.4\%$ per year. The message for the insurance industry is that, if there is a global carbon tax, nearly one-third of the tax revenue arguably should be allocated to reinsurance companies – the insurers' insurers – to compensate for climate-change-related losses!)

Reinsurance Event-Attributed Carbon Taxation (REACT)

Now we are very close to determining the price of carbon. There is one more term required: the basic carbon pricing formula

y = attributable losses/carbon emissions

$= 1/C \times \Sigma\, (L_i \times x_i)$

where

y = carbon price ($/tonne CO_2),
C = global carbon emissions (tonnes/year),
L_i = weather-related loss events during year and
x_i = the per event attribution ratio
(note that the subscript i applies to each loss event).

If the global attribution method discussed in this chapter is applied, then y can be approximated by:

$y = L \times x / C$

In 2014, $L = k_3 \times d_0 \sim 26.7 \times \$185.8 \sim \$5$ trillion. If $x \sim 0.15$ and $C \sim 37$ billion tonnes CO_2 then $y \sim \$20$ per tonne CO_2.[42] This is a credible carbon price and, if imposed broadly, it would impact on consumer prices by less than 0.7%, a 2016 LSE study indicates.[43]

Predict Ability Ltd's methodology creates a much higher-resolution picture about both risk and pricing. This we term 'fine gamma'. The resulting spot carbon price is shown on Predict Ability Ltd's website and it is updated as new insights and information become available.

Our Carbon Legacy Must Be Paid For

So there it is, finally, the price of carbon. It is meaningful and realistic and, if needs be, an instantaneous or spot carbon price can be calculated. Alternatively, an integrated or cumulative carbon price can readily be generated to capture both the long-term nature of emissions and the damage they cause. This is considered further in Chapter Eight. The variation in prices (Figure 7.6) is partly related to variations in T_a but *PALgamma* values also change from year to year, as the underlying risks evolve.

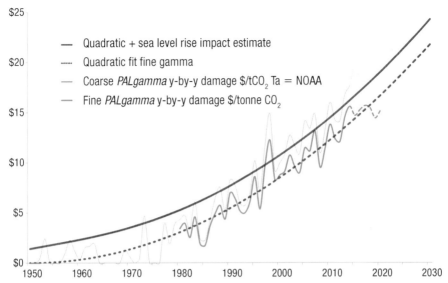

Figure 7.6. *Predict Ability Ltd's historic, current and future carbon-price projections.*[44] *Sea-level rise (SLR) impact was estimated using Hinkel et al.*[45] *(low SLR scenario, two-thirds adapted). (© Predict Ability Ltd.)*

In essence, Predict Ability Ltd's carbon-pricing system captures a fundamental aspect of mankind's interaction with nature and the growing civilisations within it. Two major questions arise:

▸ Until recently there has been no attempt to put a price on carbon – on CO_2 and other GHG emissions – although belatedly a number of 'cap and trade' carbon markets have evolved.[46] But because we, collectively, have failed to address what those in authority are alleged to have known[47] since the 1980s – that CO_2 emissions cause climate change – there is now a gigantic debt. That will be our *carbon legacy* for future generations. Should we – could we – pay that debt? Or has it been written off?

▸ Let us make no mistake, carbon fuels and hydrocarbons have enabled a huge human transformation in the late 20th and early 21st centuries. This is our *carbon inheritance*.[48] But putting a price on carbon without considering the long term is unwise. If carbon markets proceed as they are today, then a really good idea for tackling climate change is in danger of being squandered. This is what Chapter Ten ('Carbon

Intensity Weighting') seeks to address. We must tax energy of all kinds in a fair and progressive way, not just fossil fuels. Why? Because the damage being caused by the CO_2 we have emitted (and will yet emit) will persist in the atmosphere for a very long time – until the biosphere, the oceans and rocks[49] can absorb our greenhouse gas legacy, which will be long after the last giga-tonne of CO_2 is emitted.

The Persistence of CO_2 in the Atmosphere

How long will anthropogenic (man-made) CO_2 remain in the atmosphere? It is an easy question to ask. There is no simple answer, although 'half of it for ever' is a good and somewhat terrifying approximation. However, it partly depends on how fast we emit the CO_2 and at what concentration we stop emitting CO_2. 'Equilibration among the various carbon reservoirs of the atmosphere, the ocean and the terrestrial biosphere occurs on timescales of a few centuries', say geophysical scientists David Archer et al. at the University of Chicago.[50]

There is considerable variation amongst the mathematical models available. Archer et al. note that 'a sizeable fraction [20–35%] of the CO_2 remains in the atmosphere, awaiting a return to the solid Earth by much slower weathering processes and deposition of $CaCO_3$ [calcium carbonate]'.[51] Or, to put it another way, a recent paper in *Nature*[52] suggests that mankind has effectively cancelled the next one and maybe two ice ages. Our carbon footprint already extends hundreds of thousands of years ahead of us.

Simulation of the effect of a 1 trillion tonne pulse of CO_2 (which, on a geological timescale, is exactly what we are doing today) yields a form of decay that illustrates the two mechanisms Archer et al. describe. The predictions are shown in Figure 7.7.

These decay curves were approximated by Predict Ability Ltd to produce a function of CO_2 with time, following the sudden (artificial) cessation of emissions. The calculated CO_2 concentrations were then converted into estimated temperature anomalies[53] to see how long the loss and damage caused by the emissions would last. The answer, in practical terms, is for thousands of years. Possibly one-third to one-half of the CO_2 that was produced by Newcomen's engine in 1712 is effectively still up there somewhere in the atmosphere.

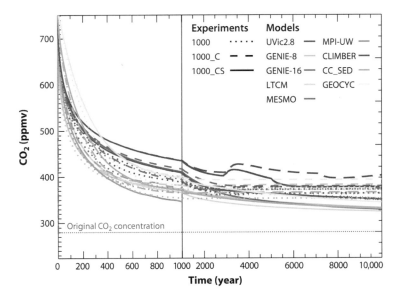

Figure 7.7. *Simulating our 1 trillion tonne pulse of CO_2 into the atmosphere. (From 'Atmospheric lifetime of fossil fuel carbon dioxide', Annu. Rev. Earth Planet Sci, 2009, 37, pp. 117–134, courtesy of David Archer and Michael Eby.)*

REACT in a Nutshell

The main ideas introduced in this chapter were gathered together into a spreadsheet model called 'REACT in a nutshell'. It shows the impact of temperature anomaly on losses for (a) the total losses ($PALca_{body}$) and (b) the disaster and catastrophe losses ($PALca_{tail}$). The concept of 'body' and 'tail' was introduced in Chapter Three. Disasters and catastrophes are governed by the statistics of the probability curve's tail, whereas the whole body of the curve dictates the likely influence of climate change on the total losses and hence carbon prices.

Losses will continue for centuries even if emissions were to abruptly stop. Moreover, the painfully slow decline of temperature anomaly is expected to be more than offset by the growth in *PALgamma*. Losses are expected to continue to increase throughout most of the 21st century. The trends calculated in the 'REACT in a nutshell' spreadsheet for the tail (disasters and catastrophes) and body (total losses) are shown in Figure 7.8. It illustrates a 2°C global-warming scenario.

We now have the basis for a realistic carbon price. It is directly linked to loss and damage and that is increasing all the time. Even after the last giga-tonne of

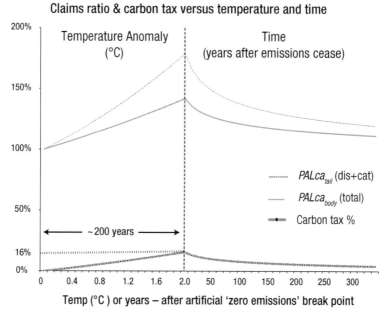

Figure 7.8. *Loss and damage pathways for two classes of loss: total losses and disasters and catastrophes (dis+cat) for a 2°C (550 ppm CO_2) global-warming target. Even 300 years after emissions stop, much of the emitted CO_2 remains in the atmosphere causing loss and damage. (Note: in these calculations PALgamma was kept constant.) (© Predict Ability Ltd.)*

CO_2 is emitted, whether there is an abrupt cessation of emissions or not, the CO_2 lingers in the atmosphere for a very long time. This means there must be a mechanism for fairly transferring the costs of these emissions to current and future generations, even if the damage already done is written off, as seems to be inevitable. We cannot go on ignoring this damage. If we do, then, as Chapter Four suggests, we may be 'written off' by nature!

Notes to Chapter Seven

1   Pall, P., et al., 'Anthropogenic greenhouse gas contribution to flood risk in England and Wales in autumn 2000', *Nature*, 470 (7334), pp. 382–385 (17 February 2011), http://www.nature.com/nature/journal/v470/n7334/abs/nature09762.html

2   'Explaining extreme events of 2014 from a climate perspective', *Bulletin of the American Meteorological Society*, 96 (12), Supplement (December 2015), https://www.ametsoc.org/ams/index.cfm/publications/bulletin-of-the-american-meteorological-society-bams/explaining-extreme-events-from-a-climate-perspective/

3   Baez, J.C., Tweed, D., 'Monte Carlo methods in climate science', *Math Horizons* (19 September 2013), http://math.ucr.edu/home/baez/horizons.pdf

4   'If a tree falls in the forest, but no scientist says so . . .', Earth Techling (3 October 2014), http://earthtechling.com/2014/10/if-a-tree-falls-in-the-forest-but-no-scientist-says-so/

5   Yeo, S., 'Who's to blame for climate change?', *Climate Home* (17 November 2014), http://www.climatechangenews.com/2014/11/17/whos-to-blame-for-climate-change/

6   'Hail', Insurance Information Institute (accessed 17 April 2016), http://www.iii.org/fact-statistic/hail

7   Editorial, 'Extreme Weather', *Nature*, 489 (7416), pp. 335–336 (20 September 2012), http://www.nature.com/news/extreme-weather-1.11428

8   Pidcock, R., 'In-depth: The scientific challenge of extreme weather attribution', *CarbonBrief* (11 March 2016), http://www.carbonbrief.org/in-depth-the-scientific-challenge-of-extreme-weather-attribution

9   McSweeney, R., 'Q&A: How scientists link extreme weather to climate change', *CarbonBrief* (14 January 2016), http://www.carbonbrief.org/qa-how-scientists-link-extreme-weather-to-climate-change

10   Schaller, N., et al., 'Human influence on climate in the 2014 southern England winter floods and their impacts', *Nature Climate Change* (1 February 2016 online), http://www.nature.com/nclimate/journal/vaop/ncurrent/full/nclimate2927.html

11   'NatCatSERVICE', Munich RE (accessed 17 February 2016), https://www.munichre.com/touch/naturalhazards/en/homepage/index.html

12   'EM-DAT database', EM-DAT (accessed 17 February 2016), http://www. emdat.be/database

13   Bindoff, N.L., Stott, P.A., AchutaRao, K.M., Allen, M.R., Gillett, N., Gutzler, D., Hansingo, K., Hegerl, G., Hu, Y., Jain, S., Mokhov, I.I., Overland, J., Perlwitz, J., Sebbari, R., Zhang, X., 'Detection and attribution of climate change: From global to regional', in Stocker, T.F., Qin, D., Plattner, G.-K., Tignor, M., Allen, S.K., Boschung, J., Nauels, A., Xia, Y., Bex, V., Midgley, P.M. (eds.), *Climate Change 2013: The Physical Science Basis*. Contribution of Working Group I to the Fifth Assessment Report of the Intergovernmental Panel on Climate Change. Cambridge University Press (2013), http://www. climatechange2013.org/images/report/WG1AR5_Chapter10_FINAL. pdf

14   Otto, F.E.L., Massey, N., van Oldenborgh, G.J., Jones, R.G., Allen, M.R., 'Reconciling two approaches to attribution of the 2010 Russian heatwave', *Geophysical Research Letters*, 39, L04702 (2012), http://onlinelibrary.wiley. com/doi/10.1029/2011GL050422/abstract

15   Clark, P., 'Scientists link Storm Desmond floods to man-made global warming', *Financial Times* (10 December 2015), http://www.ft.com/ cms/s/0/e1466920-9f81-11e5-8613-08e211ea5317.html

16   Otto, F., James, R., Allen, M., 'The science of attributing extreme weather events and its potential contribution to assessing loss and damage associated with climate change impacts', University of Oxford Environmental Change Institute (2015), https://unfccc.int/files/adaptation/workstreams/loss_ and_damage/application/pdf/attributingextremeevents.pdf

17   'Natural catastrophes 2013: Analyses, assessments, positions', *Munich RE Topics Geo* (2014 issue), http://www.munichre.com/site/corporate/get/ documents_E1043212252/mr/assetpool.shared/Documents/5_Touch/_ Publications/302-08121_en.pdf

18   'Pearson function', Microsoft Office (accessed 17 April 2016), https:// support.office.com/en-us/article/PEARSON-function-0c3e30fc-e5af-49c4-808a-3ef66e034c18

19   '*p*-value', Wikipedia (accessed 17 April 2016), https://en.wikipedia.org/ wiki/P-value

20   'Counterfactual thinking', Wikipedia (accessed 17 April 2016), https:// en.wikipedia.org/wiki/Counterfactual_thinking

21   'NatCatSERVICE peril categories', Munich RE (accessed 17 April 2016), https://www.munichre.com/us/weather-resilience-and-protection/rise-weather/natcat-service/index.html

22   'Predict Ability Limited (PAL) independently benchmarks the price of carbon: past, present and future', Predict Ability Limited (accessed 15 June 2016), http://predictability.ltd.uk/

23   Normalisation involves creating a set of ratios of raw data divided by what the model predicts. In a perfect model all members of the set should have a value of 1.

24   *PALca* = Predict Ability Ltd's (Lightning) Claims Algorithm uses insurance claims data from the Hartford (Insurance Company).

25   '*p*-value', Wikipedia (accessed 17 April 2016), https://en.wikipedia.org/wiki/P-value

26   'Coefficient of determination R²', Wikipedia (accessed 17 April 2016), https://en.wikipedia.org/wiki/Coefficient_of_determination

27   Mills, E., 'Insurance in a climate of change', *Science*, 309, pp. 1040–1044 (12 August 2005), http://evanmills.lbl.gov/pubs/pdf/insurance_and_climate.pdf

28   'Welcome to Hartford Steam Boiler', Munich RE (accessed 17 April 2016), https://www.munichre.com/HSB/home/index.html

29   Mills, E., 'Insurance in a Climate of Change', *Science*, 309, pp. 1040–1044 (12 August 2005), http://evanmills.lbl.gov/pubs/pdf/insurance_and_climate.pdf

30   Bindoff, N.L., et al., 'Detection and attribution of climate change'.

31   'Global surface temperature anomalies FAQ', National Oceanic and Atmospheric Administration (accessed 17 April 2016), https://www.ncdc.noaa.gov/monitoring-references/faq/anomalies.php

32   Pidcock, R., 'Scientists compare climate change impacts at 1.5C and 2C', *CarbonBrief* (21 April 2016), http://www.carbonbrief.org/scientists-compare-climate-change-impacts-at-1-5c-and-2c

33   'Understanding the IPCC reports: Infographics', World Resources Institute (accessed 17 April 2016), http://www.wri.org/ipcc-infographics

34   'Newcomen atmospheric engine (animated)', Wikipedia (accessed 17 April 2016), https://en.wikipedia.org/wiki/Newcomen_atmospheric_engine

35   Romps, D.M., Seeley, J.T., Vollaro, D., Molinari, J., 'Projected increase in lightning strikes in the United States due to global warming', *Science*, 346

(6211), pp. 851–854 (14 November 2014), http://www.sciencemag.org/content/346/6211/851

36   A composite of the figures obtained from endnote 35.

37   For disaster losses $x = x_{tail}$ and for total losses $x = x_{body}$ (see 'REACT in a Nutshell', p. 139).

38   Biello, D., 'Who's paying the price for global warming?', *Scientific American* (19 May 2013), http://www.scientificamerican.com/podcast/episode/whos-paying-the-price-for-global-wa-13-05-19/

39   Webster, A.J., Clarke, R.H., 'An insurance-led response to climate change', arXiv:1509.01157v2 (7 October 2015), http://arxiv.org/abs/1509.01157

40   'Value of gross premiums written by non-life insurance companies in the United States from 2009 to 2025, by type (in billion \$US)', Statista (accessed 17 April 2016), http://www.statista.com/statistics/408335/non-life-insurance-sector-usa-by-type/

41   Harvey, F., 'Climate change is already damaging global economy, report finds' (26 September 2012), http://www.theguardian.com/environment/2012/sep/26/climate-change-damaging-global-economy

42   A value of \$15 per tonne CO_2 is used for illustrative purposes in subsequent chapters because it was found that the more exact calculations used in *PALgamma* result in lower $L \times x$ values (as Figure 7.6 illustrates, fine *PALgamma* < coarse *PALgamma*).

43   Murray, J., 'UK-wide carbon tax would have "little impact" on consumers, study finds', *The Guardian* (11 January 2016), http://www.theguardian.com/environment/2016/jan/11/uk-wide-carbon-tax-would-have-little-impact-on-consumers-study-finds

44   Quadratic equation of price (dotted line) = $0.0034 \times (year-1950)^2$.

45   Hinkel, J., et al., 'Coastal flood damage and adaptation costs under 21st century sea-level rise', *PNAS*, 111 (9), pp. 3292–3297 (4 March 2014), http://www.pnas.org/content/111/9/3292.full.pdf

46   Cap and trade schemes have a specific job: to reduce carbon emissions. They are not designed to put a price on carbon.

47   Nuccitelli, D., 'Two-faced Exxon: The misinformation campaign against its own scientists', *The Guardian* (25 November 2015), http://www.theguardian.com/environment/climate-consensus-97-per-cent/2015/nov/25/two-faced-exxon-the-misinformation-campaign-against-its-own-scientists

48   Webster, A.J., Clarke, R.H., 'An insurance-led response to climate change'.

49 Fountain, H., 'Turning carbon dioxide into rock, and burying it', *The New York Times* (9 February 2015), http://www.nytimes.com/2015/02/10/science/burying-a-mountain-of-co2.html

50 Archer, D., Eby, M., Brovkin, V., Ridgwell, A., Cao, L., Mikolajewicz, U., Caldeira, K., Matsumoto, K., Munhoven, G., Montenegro, A., Tokos, K., 'Atmospheric lifetime of fossil fuel carbon dioxide', *Annual Review of Earth and Planetary Science*, 37, pp. 117–134 (26 January 2009), http://climatemodels.uchicago.edu/geocarb/archer.2009.ann_rev_tail.pdf

51 'Calcium carbonate', Wikipedia (17 April 2016), https://en.wikipedia.org/wiki/Calcium_carbonate

52 Ganopolski, A., Winkelmann, R., Schellnhuber, H.J., 'Critical insolation–CO_2 relation for diagnosing past and future glacial inception', *Nature*, 529 (7585), pp. 200–203 (14 January 2016), http://www.nature.com/nature/journal/v529/n7585/full/nature16494.html

53 CO_2 concentration/ppm $\sim k_t \times \exp^{(Ta/3.61)}$ where k_t = 316 ppm (NOAA land&sea T_a), 290 ppm (NOAA land T_a).

CHAPTER EIGHT

CARBON REVENUE
AND ITS SIGNIFICANCE TO INSURERS

Can the insurance industry weather climate change?
Two models demonstrate why cumulative carbon emissions matter,
why carbon revenue trumps the impact of carbon price and why 30%
of the revenue belongs to the insurance industry.

Back to Basics

What is the price of carbon? Can the impact of emitting one tonne of CO_2 be
determined from first principles? Would it be possible to simply model the
impact of carbon taxation on the global economy and determine if this form
of decarbonisation strategy works? Does carbon pricing provide a reliable and
sufficient form of feedback to compensate for the effects of CO_2 emissions?

Without the combined feedback that carbon taxation, carbon revenue and
carbon strategies provide there may come a point, a tipping point, where the
global economy falters, severely affecting the vast majority of human societies
that depend on it.

Central to this discussion is the global insurance industry, the thousands
of national insurance companies and, in particular, the global reinsurance
companies – the insurers' insurers. And yet this industry is peculiarly, some
might say obstinately, passive about what lies ahead;[1] in surveys, immediate
concerns such as cyber-risk (hacking) rank higher than climate change.[2] There
are an enlightened few, encouragingly, but most companies think they have

climate change, whatever its cause, priced into their products. Typically, many insurers see climate change as a future concern, not the emergent threat that is today lapping at their feet.

We have seen how governments, too, can also get mired in this mind-set. With flooding, for example, 'the refusal to address the problem because of conflicts of interests',[3] as Jared Diamond recalls, may lead to backward-looking policies that fail to acknowledge changed realities. If the odds of flooding have worsened, then *de facto* flood management strategies need to be reassessed.

Governments have the option to raise taxes or divert revenue to address flood problems. Alternatively, they face the backlash of negative media coverage in flooded towns and cities. For the insurance industry there is less flexibility – either claims thresholds and premiums have to increase, or insurance companies withdraw their insurance coverage.[4] In the short term[5] 'insurance retreating' may be pragmatic. In the long term it erodes the industry's business model. And if premiums increase, the insured may decide to do without insurance altogether. That is not a good outcome for anyone. It is the wrong direction of travel. Insurance must not become a sideshow, affordable only to the rich. At its best, insurance is an economic and social good.

This climate-induced adverse trajectory for the insurance industry could be avoided if major companies start to realise they could harness a major source of funding – carbon revenue from carbon taxation schemes. The insurance industry needs to make its pitch for a proportion of the revenue, and do it soon.

A Cumulative Carbon-Price Model

Using the global attribution factor x, introduced in Chapter Seven, it is possible to build from first principles a simple model that predicts the integral or cumulative price of carbon. The starting point is the CO_2 emissions, C, entering the atmosphere from fossil fuels, cement-making and changed land use. Examining the emissions data, it appears that 1945, perhaps 1950, was the starting point of what is sometimes known as the 'great acceleration'.[6] Economic policies introduced after WW2 (the Second World War) kick-started the modern age of development, with its mass communications (TV), the mass-production of motorcars, consumerism and a huge increase in the global population. All this is highly significant in terms of carbon pricing.

What is of interest here is the cumulative emissions **D** (the integral of **C**). In Chapter Two the idea of carbon 'stocks' and 'flows' was introduced. It is the accumulated 'stock' **D** of CO_2 that matters in climate change, not the rate at which it enters the atmosphere. Even if we were to consider earlier emissions, perhaps back to 1750, it seems that only the post-WW2 emissions are pertinent in a carbon-pricing model. Although 1945 was chosen as a starting point, any year from 1935 up until the early 1960s yields a similar result (event attribution scientists typically use the 1960s as a baseline).[7]

Figure 2.8 shows there is a huge flux of carbon in the ecosphere, and the Earth's system was in near-equilibrium until our emissions upset the balance. The reason **D** is important is that a tonne of CO_2 effectively stays in the atmosphere for a long, long time (as shown in Chapter Seven). Discounting the relatively short-lived effects of three large volcanic eruptions (1964, 1982 and Pinatubo in 1992), the rate of increase in atmospheric CO_2 concentration is almost invariably proportional to emissions.[8] The concentration increases 1 ppm (part per million) for every 14.138 giga-tonnes of CO_2 emitted.

In March 2015, $[CO_2]$ – the chemist's annotation[9] for the concentration of CO_2 in the atmosphere – passed 400 ppm. It has not been that high for many millions of years.[10] Approximately 1,500 giga-tonnes (1½ million million tonnes) of CO_2 has been emitted since the end of WW2. Alas, also in 2015, the global temperature anomaly T_a passed 1°C (NOAA land temperature records) for the first time since meteorological records began.[11] There is a logarithmic relationship between T_a and $[CO_2]$ which is convenient, because, in Chapter Seven, the global attribution factor, *x*, was defined in terms of T_a using an exponential function.

Combining the logarithmic T_a and the exponential *x* yields relationships that are essentially linear, as plotted in Figure 8.1. For reference, the temperature (°C) versus concentration $[CO_2]$ curve is shown. If some climate scientists call into question[12] the year-to-year temperature records, it should be noted that $[CO_2]$ provides a reliable indicator of where T_a is heading. For policy purposes, a steadily rising temperature trend may be more useful than actual temperature records, provided that the decade-long trends continue to concur.

Over a decade or two[13] it appears that GDP (gross domestic product, corrected for PPP – purchasing power parity)[14] is proportional to both **C**

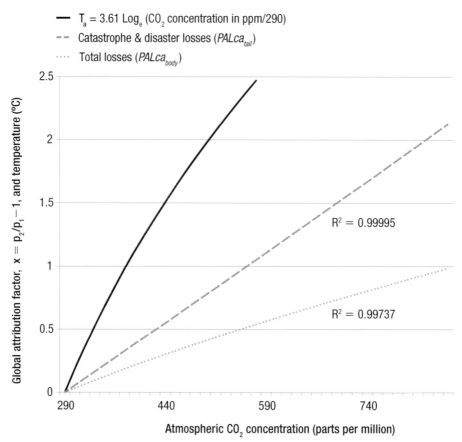

Figure 8.1. *The essentially linear relationship between global attribution factor, x, and the atmospheric CO_2 concentration (the R^2 values show the high degree of linearity). (© Predict Ability Ltd.)*

and **D** but, in the long run, it is clear that cumulative emissions have been growing more slowly than the economy. A reasonably accurate relationship is $GDP_{year} = GDP_{1962} \times ((D_{year} + 1350)/(D_{1962} + 1350))^{2.5}$. This equation works both with actual GDP growth and with a constant 3% growth assumption. As globalisation took hold in the noughties[15] there was a period of technology re-learning and excess emissions as global manufacturing shifted to Asia, but over an extended period the equation is suitable for use with the carbon-price model. It is of great concern that **D** is still so strongly coupled with the global economy,[16] because, in the 21st century, we have to turn that around and learn how to grow sustainably with much reduced emissions.

Key to determining a theoretical carbon price is knowledge of total global weather-related losses, **L**. This was discussed in Chapter Seven, where Predict Ability Ltd's *PALgamma* model was used. Roger Pielke Jr has examined this loss data extensively and it is clear that disaster losses **L** do not increase proportionally[17] to **GDP**, more likely $(\text{GDP})^{0.5}$. Thus, if **GDP** doubles, **L** increases about 1.4 times but the disaster loss data is quite erratic. Pielke Jr rejects the possibility that any climate-change signal can be discerned in the disaster loss data, but Predict Ability Ltd claims otherwise. If the effect of climate change, as discussed in Chapter Seven, is removed, then it appears **L** is proportional to $(\text{GDP})^{0.4}$ and that, in 2015, the total of global, weather-related losses was about \$4.4 trillion (= \$4 trillion[18] adjusted for inflation). Without the effects of climate change this reduces to \$3.7 trillion for 2015.

Now we have the information needed to create a simple carbon-price model. The cumulative carbon price **y** = summation of attributable losses **L** × **x** /cumulative CO_2 emissions **D** or, expressed mathematically, $\mathbf{y} = \int (\mathbf{L} \times \boldsymbol{x})\, dt / \int (\mathbf{C}\, dt)$ over time t.

L is a function of $(\text{GDP})^{0.4}$ and **GDP** is a function of cumulative emissions $(\mathbf{D}+1350)^{2.5}$. Thus, $\mathbf{L} = \mathbf{k}'(\mathbf{D}+1350)$ where k' = \$1.29/tonne CO_2 in 2015. In other words, global gross domestic product is the fruit of the cumulative emissions, but until recently the downside, the economic externality[19] of climate change, has been completely ignored. Therefore there is an accumulated 'carbon debt'.

The global attribution factor $\boldsymbol{x}$ is given by *PALca* (see Chapter Seven), an almost linear function of $[CO_2]$ which, in turn, is a nearly linear function of cumulative emissions **D**. Thus $\boldsymbol{x} = (\mathbf{k}''\mathbf{D} + \mathbf{k}^0)$ where k'' = 0.000125 per giga-tonne.[20] The offset $\mathbf{k}^0 = 0.01$ corrects for the slight non-linearity of $\boldsymbol{x}$ versus $[CO_2]$.

Overall, the cumulative carbon price is

$$\mathbf{y} = \int (\mathbf{L} \times \boldsymbol{x})\, dt / \int \mathbf{C}\, dt =$$
$$\int 1.29 \times (0.000125 \times \mathbf{D}(t) + 0.01) \times (\mathbf{D}(t) + 1350) / \int \mathbf{C}\, dt$$

where **D**(t) expresses **D** as a function of t (year). When numerically or analytically integrated **y** can be approximated by the exponential equation

$$\mathbf{y} = \exp^{0.02 \times (t - 1896)}$$

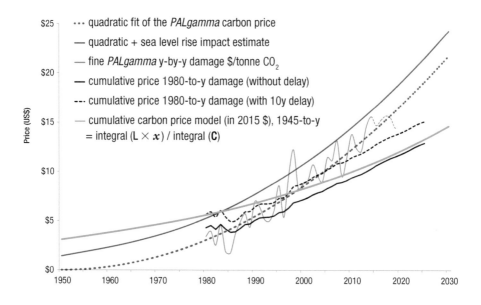

Figure 8.2. *Predict Ability Ltd's yearly price predictions can be approximated by quadratic equations (red lines). The two cumulative prices described below are compared with the predictions of the cumulative carbon model based on* **D,** *from 1945 onwards. (© Predict Ability Ltd.)*

which shows that the inflation-adjusted price (cost) of carbon was $1/tonne CO_2 in 1896 and $11 in 2016.

The exact solution is shown in Figure 8.2 (blue line) along with the yearly carbon prices generated from *PALgamma* and *x*, again as described in Chapter Seven. Additionally, two cumulative carbon prices based on *PALgamma* and *x* are shown. In one, the attributable losses from 1980 onwards are divided by cumulative emissions from 1980 onwards. In the other, the same losses are divided by cumulative emissions delayed by 10 years (i.e. 1970 onwards). The '10y delay' curve has been added because there is some indication that the effects of emissions take several years or even a decade to come into effect because of the immense heat capacity of the oceans.[21] Note how the cumulative carbon price (1980-to-year) is converging with the cumulative carbon price predicted by the model.

The cumulative carbon-price model tells us that

▸   the magnitude of the carbon price needed to offset the climate-related losses will accelerate until carbon emissions are reduced,

▸   the CO_2 emissions since 1945 need to be included in the model,

▸   the 'carbon debt' accrued since 1945 could be paid down by 2050 by introducing a fixed global carbon price of $25 per tonne CO_2 – it might become less if global carbon emissions are reduced in line with the COP21 Paris agreement,

▸   carbon emissions can be directly interpreted into a temperature anomaly T_a and hence the global attribution factor x,

▸   the global attribution factor x is increasing by about 0.46% per year (as was found in Chapter Seven),

▸   climate-related losses appear to be proportional to $GDP^{0.4}$,

▸   the cumulative carbon-price model can be approximated by an exponential equation; it indicates the following carbon price mileposts 1896 ($1), 1930 ($2), 1951($3), 1965 ($4), 1977 ($5)…2016 ($11) (and, in terms of carbon-pricing progress, we are responding[22] like it is still 1896!),

▸   the integral or cumulative carbon price will continue to increase, as climate-related losses increase, even after the last giga-tonne of CO_2 is emitted,

▸   and, unlike 'cap and trade' markets, the cumulative carbon price is not at risk of becoming unstable as 2050 decarbonisation targets approach (more on this in Chapter Ten).

Carbon Price and the Global Economy

Modelling the global economy is intractable unless the problem is broken down into manageable segments. System Dynamics (SD) is a computer-modelling methodology that has been used successfully to model complex systems, such as the global helium market[23] or the effect of climate change on the global economy.[24] One of the key insights from SD climate modelling is that considerable skill is needed to avoid both the impacts of climate change and the negative impacts of climate policy itself on the economy. Industrial physicist Dr Simon Roberts and colleagues at Arup,[25] a global engineering consultancy, have pursued this kind of systems thinking for some time.

Dieter Helm warns that economic models tend to be dependent on so-called exogenous inputs (external assumptions), rational utility (people making economically rational economic choices) and market equilibrium prevailing.[26] There have been many attempts, for example, to determine the social price of carbon. That question will be explored further in Chapter Nine.

With all this in mind, and with the limited objective of seeing what might be the impact of carbon pricing and investing the revenue raised, another model has been created. This time it is a lumped model of the global economy.

The starting point is GDP and the potential impact of three scenarios (Figure 8.3):

▸   no carbon tax and no specific funding of renewable/low-carbon energy
▸   having a carbon tax with revenue returned to the general taxation pool
▸   having a carbon tax with some proportion of the revenue being diverted to renewable/low-carbon energy

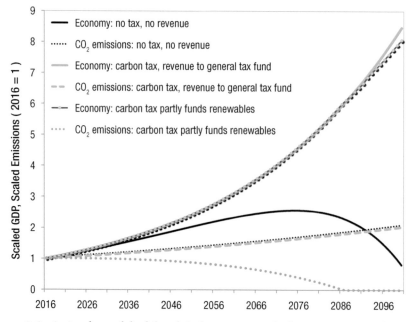

Figure 8.3. *A simple model of the global economy with three taxation and revenue scenarios. (© Predict Ability Ltd.)*

For each case the following assumptions were made: nominal GDP growth 2.6%; total weather-related losses (insured + non-insured) 6% of GDP; interest rate on losses 3%; the energy market makes up 15% of GDP; fossil-fuel price elasticity[27] −0.6; fossil-fuel scarcity factor 3% (makes fuel prices rise over time due to the depletion of hydrocarbon resources). The results are shown below as normalised plots of GDP and emissions (2016 = 1).

In the first case (no tax, no funding), no specific action is taken to reduce emissions, but the impacts of unabated loss and damage (T_a ~2.3°C) have a significant impact on the global economy and, possibly, might cause it to stagnate and then collapse. Indeed, the carbon emissions are only held in check by the increasing scarcity effect on fuel prices. This finding is similar to that shown in Chapter Four, where the cumulative carbon price (losses) was sufficient to tip over a weakening global economy.

In the second case the carbon-tax revenue based on loss and damage is returned to the general taxation pool. The carbon tax makes little difference to emissions (fuel prices are high and rising) but the economy is not burdened with climate-change losses (T_a ~2.25°C).

In the third case 12% of the carbon-tax revenue is diverted into renewables and low-carbon energy. The carbon revenue makes a big difference to emissions – indeed they essentially cease by 2100, leading to a lower T_a of ~1.4°C. There is a slight impact on the economy when carbon emissions cease.

This simple example illustrates what many economists have long been saying. Firstly, there needs to be a carbon price. This provides feedback. However, the price elasticity (demand sensitivity to price) means the impact of a tax on fossil-fuel consumption will be limited – particularly if there are no viable alternatives to petrol and diesel fuels.[28] Nevertheless, the economists continue, it is the revenue that really matters. The tax is what they call a Pigovian fee[29] – it corrects a market for an unaccounted-for externality, in this case climate change. The problem with taxes is that they meet with public and political resistance, so, unless the public sees a benefit from the tax (as so-called 'fee and dividend' schemes might achieve), the correct level of taxation will not be achieved. A global alliance of carbon taxes should be less prone to political interference of this kind. For carbon taxation to work at its best there has to be global reach through a single price or a network of prices if global trade deals are problematic.

The Allocation of Revenue

In Chapter Six much of the discussion concerned the problem of under-funding of adaptation schemes – the measures needed to build resilience to climate change, whatever the cause is deemed to be. In Chapter Seven, Predict Ability Ltd's *PALgamma* model was described. It is based on loss and damage data derived from Munich RE's *Nathan* database. By extension, today around 30% of global losses may occur within the auspices of the global insurance industry (in the Munich RE data $d_o \sim 2.67 \times d_i + \$40$ billion where d_o = disaster overall losses and d_i = disaster insured losses). d_i/d_o is currently 30% and rising ~0.4% per year. This reality is acknowledged in the pie diagram below (Figure 8.4).

If a \$15 per tonne CO_2 tax raises \$600 billion, it is suggested that there might be four outlets for the carbon revenue: adaptation \$240 billion (40%), insurance \$180 billion (30%), mitigation \$150 billion (25%) and a social fund \$30 billion (5%) – AIMS for short (Figure 8.4). The social fund, a means to offset the negative impact of carbon pricing on low-income households, might be best administered by the global insurance industry in conjunction with the UN and World Bank Group. Some suggested activities were outlined in Chapter Six in the 'Adaptation' section.

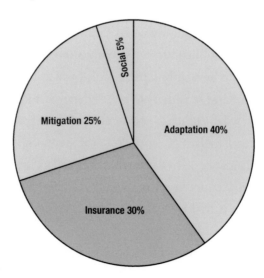

Figure 8.4. *AIMS – adaptation, insurance, mitigation and social fund – a possible protocol for allocating carbon-tax revenues.*(© *Predict Ability Ltd.*)

Referring back to the cumulative carbon-price model, the funding proportions of AIMS reflect the damage involved: from 1945 to 2050 for adaptation (40%), and from 2016 to 2050 for mitigation (25%). This is a suggested funding strategy. There are bound to be other ideas.

Can the Insurance Industry Weather Climate Change?

From the very outset of this investigation into the price of carbon, the opportunities and issues raised by the insurance industry have loomed large. Can the industry adapt to 2°C or 4°C of global warming? What actions are being taken to protect the interests of insurers and the insured? What more could be done?

Can the insurance industry survive climate change, asked Reuter's Francesca Rheannon[30] in 2012, after a spate of devastating river floods, forest fires and – in New England – tornadoes. Whilst some insurers admitted a probable link to climate change, their first response was to announce soaring increases in premiums to homeowners and businesses. Other companies started pulling out of 'climate-challenged' markets altogether. 'Insurance may well become unaffordable for millions in the US and elsewhere in the developed world as premiums skyrocket', Rheannon explains. The industry has also been increasing deductables,[31] reducing insurance limits and introducing novel exclusions. After '[Hurricane] Katrina, some homeowners were denied coverage when their house flooded, because it was claimed the damage came from the hurricane-force winds', observed Rheannon. Meanwhile the pressure is on businesses to identify and declare their climate risks, including those in the insurance industry itself.

Not all the market players are running for the hills. Major reinsurers such as Swiss Re have been implementing novel 'parametric insurance models' that transfer risk away from public or city authorities into the commercial insurance markets. Others have devised better procedures to get funds into the hands of disaster victims in a more timely manner than has historically been the case.

It is clear that the insurance industry will not solve climate change, although there may be metrics that can help it better rationalise their risk portfolio. Obviously insurance companies must protect their businesses. The 328-year-old London reinsurance market Lloyd's has called on the industry to take climate change into account in their risk pricing, in particular in the computer models used to assess catastrophe risks such as hurricanes.[32] That changing risk may be implicit in models that use masses of historical data. For example, the losses from the 2012 Superstorm Sandy in New York were 30% higher because of sea-level rise. Had all the tide gauge information been factored-in on New York insurance pricing?

'Insurance companies will make money on climate change either way', claims the online science forum Science 2.0. With $4.6 trillion in premiums, insurers know their way around the risk business.[33] According to the insurance expert Evan Mills at the Lawrence Berkeley National Laboratory, thousands of climate-change adaptation and mitigation activities have been implemented in over 50 countries worldwide. These represent $2 trillion in revenue and range from energy-efficient homes, investment in renewable energy, and pay-as-you-drive motor insurance that encourages lower mileages. Carbon-neutrality is a goal being targeted by many insurers themselves. The Science 2.0 article goes on:

> A creative example [of carbon neutrality] is the mangrove restoration by Tokio Marine and Nichido Insurance Company taking place in India and south-east Asian countries. Begun in 1999, this project is close to reaching its goal of restoring 8,200 hectares (more than 20,000 acres) of mangrove forests in coastal areas of seven countries. Mangrove reforestation reduces exposure of coasts to storm damage, and helps sequester carbon.

Then there is the 'Sage of Omaha', Warren Buffett.[34] In his latest annual letter to Berkshire Hathaway shareholders,[35] the renowned business billionaire claims that climate change is not 'a major worry' for his insurance businesses. He says he is not denying climate change is likely to be a problem, but he is just not one hundred per cent certain it will be. However, 'if there is only a 1% chance the planet is heading toward a truly major disaster and delay means passing a point of no return, inaction now is foolhardy'. But here's the rub: 'insurance policies are customarily written for one year or re-priced annually to reflect changing exposures. Increased possibilities of loss translate promptly into increased premiums'. Buffett adds 'that Berkshire Hathaway's insurance business stands to *benefit* from an increase in property damage caused by the effects of climate change'.

While the effects of climate change may only increase most premiums a fraction of 1% per year, there surely comes a point at which a client decides to take their business elsewhere. In the long run these small increments add up to a game-changing debt, as the cumulative carbon-price model and economic model illustrated. Additionally, every few cents on the dollar lost to climate change impacts on profits. Certainly, talking up climate change has a healthy impact on premiums, as Warren Buffett has observed elsewhere.[36] Perhaps in a world of Net Present Values the long term is too far out, but isn't the possibility of tipping over the world's economy enough to make us question if 'inaction now is foolhardy'?

Climate finance think-tank expert Kate Mackenzie[37] expresses concerns about Buffett's arguments in a *Financial Times* Alphaville column. Mackenzie cites a Standard and Poor's (S&P) study that found 'Reinsurers . . . they're still capitalised like it's 2004; as if Hurricane Katrina, Superstorm Sandy and the [2011] Thai Floods were aberrations'. It is not just premiums that need to be raised. Reinsurers' capital holdings too are weak. There is not enough in the pot for a rainy mega-flood. And climate-related risks spill over into other areas as well: health, pensions investment and liability obligations all hang like a sword of Damocles.

Many insurance industry commentators, such as Eli Lehrer[38] at *Right Street Blog*, reiterate the idea that any risk from climate change is priced into the product. If it were not, the insurer would soon be out of business. Perhaps, but climate risk does not come in small lumps like motor or life risks. Big storm events seem to come in clusters. Will the industry be ready if and when the US hurricane drought[39] ever ends? The US National Flood Insurance Program would have declared Chapter 11 bankruptcy if it had been a corporation. US flood history has had 'fat tails', Biblical floods that came out of nowhere. This really is a case of the tail wagging the dog.[40] To make matters worse, the boundary between state and commercial insurance is blurred, as the UK's Flood Re[41] scheme illustrates. It is an alliance of insurers and government aimed at protecting at-risk homeowners through a fixed levy on all properties, as is explained very well by Mary Dhonau, a flooding risk expert.[42]

How Proactive Should the Insurance Industry Be?

There are conflicting views about whether the industry should weather climate change as and when it happens or, alternatively, adapt. John Nelson, formerly Chairman at Lloyd's in London, argued that after the shock of Hurricane Katrina and Superstorm Sandy the industry must adapt by improving its catastrophe modelling. He points to the increases in disaster losses, from $50 billion in 1980 to close on $200 billion in 2014 (at Predict Ability Ltd we maintain, however, that most of that increase is *not* due to climate change). For an insurer, understanding risk is fundamental.

On the other hand, Joel Makower, Chairman and Executive Editor at GreenBiz Group, argues on his LinkedIn blog:

> There's risk in inaction, of course, but also in proaction: if you spend too much, too soon to adapt to or mitigate climate risks, you could put your company at a competitive disadvantage. For insurers and their clients alike, things simply aren't yet bad enough to push climate and extreme weather to the forefront of concerns.

Change itself is a problem for organisations and individuals alike, and insurers are no exception. In an online comment at *Reactions*, the insurance industry monthly magazine, Gordan Gardašanić, a senior specialist at Croatia Insurance Ltd,[43] wrote:

> The biggest problem in insurance and reinsurance are actuaries because they [cannot] accept the new methods. They must have a background in something that happened and based on the past events they calculate insurance premiums. Actuaries do not realize that scientists have created new tools today and these tools could say what will happen tomorrow. It's just too much for them.

There is a widely held view in the insurance industry that the underwriting market follows a multi-year cycle,[44] each phase of which was denoted as an hour on a clock by reinsurance company chairman and CEO Paul Ingrey (as updated in Figure 8.5). Does this 1985 idea still hold in the new insurance world order?

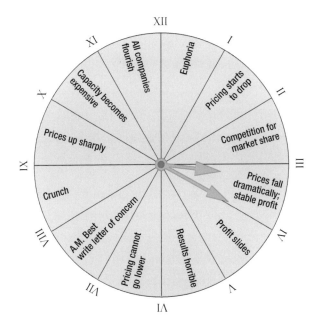

Figure 8.5. *Many in the reinsurance industry assert that there is a reinsurance cycle with phases, like a clock, that drive patterns of insurance pricing. (© Predict Ability Ltd, after Paul Ingrey).*[45]

With outside capital flooding the market in search of a safe home and the erosive effects of climate change, the windows of opportunity for innovation may be restricted. In this cycle A.M. Best, the insurance ratings agency, may have written their letter of concern,[46] but perhaps the clock has jammed?

Collectively, the insurance industry has been putting its house in order. In the industry's ClimateWise programme[47] companies are 'doing as they would be done by'.[48] Writing in the *Guardian*, Trevor Maynard, Head of Exposure Management and Reinsurance at Lloyd's, explains:

> ClimateWise, a partnership of insurers, brokers and risk modellers, includes more than 40 insurance companies and organisations globally that are working together to reduce the risks of climate change. The ClimateWise mission is to promote best practice, and to date this has already resulted in significant advances in modelling the risks of climate change impact, increasing the incorporation of climate change into member investment decisions, developing an approach for considering

climate change as a systematic risk in asset management strategies affecting capital allocation, and moving towards top-level responsibility for company sustainability.[49]

One of the key challenges to all this is the inherent short-termism of business decision-making; the insurance industry is no exception. Maynard concludes:

> None of this should overshadow attempts to halt climate change altogether, the reduction of carbon dioxide emissions is a global priority. But extreme weather is already a reality, and unless we can find a way to adapt to the effects of the changes which have already taken place and those unavoidable changes to come, people, businesses and governments will continue to feel the impact of this growing level of risk.

Adaptation comes in many guises, but for most people it is the risk to their home that worries them most, wherever they live. Shown in Figures 8.6 to 8.9 are a selection of modern and traditional designs that embody the principles of adaptation and mitigation. Would these qualify for preferential insurance premiums?

On the whole, insurers are reluctant to take the lead on climate change. They look to governments, and in particular to international climate-change agreements such as that negotiated in Paris. Sociologist at the Sorbonne, Paris, Razmig Keucheyan wrote in a *Guardian*[50] column that climate change cannot be left to the 'wild west of the markets' even though extreme weather events put further strain on debt-laden states. Keucheyan is concerned about the trend towards the use of Catastrophe Bonds[51] and Micro-insurance[52] 'to lighten the burden on the state in the face of a changing climate. Where the state does not have the resources to act, financial markets should take charge.' Apart from the possible democratic risk, there is another risk with these instruments. They are financed by the capital markets that are, as the sub-prime mortgage crisis illustrated, prone to risks themselves. After a cyclone, a city mayor does not want to be left stranded with worthless paper. This is perhaps where carbon revenue could play a role.

In terms of leadership, a straw poll conducted in *Insurance Journal*

Figure 8.6. *Carbon-negative house on a budget: Pyle, near Bridgend, Wales. (© Welsh School of Architecture at Cardiff University.)*[53]

Figure 8.7. *Flood-protected floating house: Phra Nakhon Si Ayutthaya, Thailand. (© Chutayaves Sinthuphan, Site-Specific.)*[54]

Figure 8.8. *Flood-resilient, intrinsically low CO_2 limestone house: Pakistan.* *(© Magnus Wolfe Murray/DFID.)*[55]

Figure 8.9. *A house on stilts: on Inle Lake, Myanmar. (© Wikipedia, Creative Commons.)*[56]

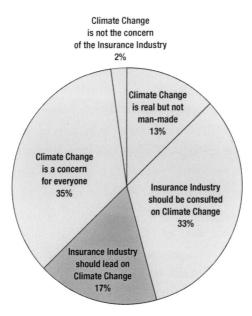

Figure 8.10. Insurance Journal's *poll of May 2015 asked 'who should take responsibility for climate change?' (© Predict Ability Ltd.)*

following Florida Governor Jeb Bush's comments[57] on insurance and climate change in May 2015 suggests that only 18 out of 104 insurance executives think their industry should take a leading role in climate-change policy (Figure 8.10).

There it is in essence. At the outset of this study it was anticipated that the insurance industry would want to take the lead on the use of an attribution-based carbon tax. It seems the industry is interested in a carbon tax, as long as governments worldwide administer it. This will be discussed in Chapter Nine.

Notes to Chapter Eight

1   'The reinsurance market – a new structural reality: A.M. Best', *Artemis* (2 September 2015), http://www.artemis.bm/blog/2015/09/02/the-reinsurance-market-a-new-structural-reality-a-m-best/

2   'Insurers must work with governments to reduce loss exposure: Lloyd's', *The Insurance Insider* (3 September 2015), http://www.insuranceinsider.com/insurers-must-work-with-governments-to-reduce-loss-exposure-lloyd-s

3   '*Collapse: How Societies Choose to Fail or Succeed* by J. Diamond', Wikipedia (accessed 17 April 2016), https://en.wikipedia.org/wiki/Collapse:_How_Societies_Choose_to_Fail_or_Succeed

4   Murray, S., 'Risk management industry must adjust to climate change loss', *Financial Times* (26 April 2015), http://www.ft.com/cms/s/0/ec2e7e30-ccc9-11e4-b5a5-00144feab7de.html

5   Neslen, A., 'Costa's last stand: Climate change could see tourists swap the Med for the Baltics', *The Guardian* (13 August 2015), http://www.theguardian.com/environment/2015/aug/13/climate-change-tourists-swap-med-for-baltics

6   Skunce, A., 'The history of emissions and the Great Acceleration', Skeptical Science blog (7 April 2015), http://www.skepticalscience.com/EmmissionsAcceleration.html

7   Stott, P.A., et al., 'Attribution of weather and climate-related extreme events', World Climate Research Programme Conference, Denver (October 2011), http://www.wcrp-climate.org/conference2011/documents/Stott.pdf

8   'What you can('t) do about global warming', World Climate Report blog (30 April 2009), http://www.worldclimatereport.com/index.php/2009/04/30/what-you-cant-do-about-global-warming/

9   'Bjerrum plot – pH, species concentrations', Wikipedia (accessed 17 April 2016), https://en.wikipedia.org/wiki/Bjerrum_plot

10   Palmer, B., 'One million, two million, three million years ago', Natural Resources Defense Council (8 May 2015), http://www.onearth.org/earthwire/carbon-dioxide-400ppm

11   'Global climate in context as the world approaches 1°C above pre-industrial for the first time', UK Meteorological Office (November 2015), http://www.metoffice.gov.uk/research/news/2015/global-average-temperature-2015

12   Tollefson, J., 'Global warming "hiatus" debate flares up again', *Nature News* (24 February 2016), http://www.nature.com/news/global-warming-hiatus-debate-flares-up-again-1.19414

13   'Carbon dioxide and the global economy', The Breakthrough Institute (12 January 2009), http://thebreakthrough.org/archive/carbon_dioxide_and_the_global

14   'Purchasing power parity', Wikipedia (accessed 17 April 2016), https://en.wikipedia.org/wiki/Purchasing_power_parity

15   'Noughties: Definition', Cambridge Dictionaries Online (accessed 17 April 2016), http://dictionary.cambridge.org/dictionary/english/noughties

16    $GDP_{2015}/GDP_{1962} \sim 5$ but cumulative emissions ratio $\mathbf{D}_{1750\text{-}2015}/\mathbf{D}_{1750\text{-}1962} \sim 3$.

17   Morano, M., 'Professor Roger Pielke Jr "Have global weather disasters become worse? As a proportion of global GDP since 1990, the answer is No" ', Climate Depot blog (6 March 2013), http://www.climatedepot.com/2013/03/06/prof-roger-pielke-jr-have-global-weather-disasters-become-worse-as-a-proportion-of-global-gdp-since-1990-the-answer-is-no/

18   Webster, A.J., Clarke, R.H., 'An Insurance-Led Response to Climate Change', arXiv:1509.01157v2 (7 October 2015), http://arxiv.org/abs/1509.01157

19   Greenstone, M., 'Paying the cost of climate change', Brookings Institution (19 September 2014), http://www.brookings.edu/blogs/planetpolicy/posts/2014/09/19-paying-cost-of-climate-change-greenstone

20   For our annual CO_2 emissions of 37 billion tonnes, the slope $dx/dt = 0.46\%$ per year.

21   'Climate forcings and global warming', NASA The Earth Observatory (accessed 17 April 2016), http://earthobservatory.nasa.gov/Features/EnergyBalance/page7.php

22   Around 20% of the world's emissions are priced, on average, at $5/tonne$CO_2$ = $1 in effect.

23   Cai, Z., Clarke, R.H., Glowacki, B.A., Nuttall, W.J., Ward, N., 'Ongoing ascent to the helium production plateau: Insights from system dynamics', *Resources Policy*, 35 (2), pp. 77–89 (June 2010), 'http://www.sciencedirect.com/science/article/pii/S0301420709000518

24   Roberts, S.H., Axon, C.J., Goddard, N.H., Foran, B.D., Warr, B.S., 'A robust data-driven macro-socioeconomic-energy model', *Sustainable Production and Consumption*, 7, pp. 16–36 (28 January 2016 online), http://www.spc.ichemejournals.com/article/S2352-5509(16)00004-X/pdf

25　'We shape a better world', Arup (accessed 17 April 2016), http://www.arup.com

26　Helm, D., *The Carbon Crunch*', p. 177.

27　'Price elasticity of demand', Economics Online (accessed 17 April 2016), http://www.economicsonline.co.uk/Competitive_markets/Price_elasticity_of_demand.html

28　Helm, D., *The Carbon Crunch*, p. 177.

29　Jenkins, J., 'Why does politics keep getting in the way of pricing carbon? – Part 1 of 2', *Energy Collective* (21 July 2014), http://theenergycollective.com/jessejenkins/434246/why-does-politics-keep-getting-way-carbon-pricing-policies-part-1

30　Rheannon, F., 'Can the insurance industry survive climate change?', Reuters (13 June 2011), http://www.reuters.com/article/idUS238251745220110613

31　Deductible: the part of an insurance claim to be paid by the insured; an excess.

32　'Lloyd's urges [catastrophe] modellers on climate change', *Reactions* (9 May 2014), http://www.reactionsnet.com/Article/3340048/Sectors/23074/Lloyds-urges-cat-modellers-on-climate-change.html

33　'Insurance companies will make money on climate change either way', Science 2.0 blog (17 December 2012), http://www.science20.com/news_articles/insurance_companies_will_make_money_climate_change_either_way-99035

34　Johnson, S., 'The Sage of Omaha has very few disciples', *Financial Times* (16 March 2014), http://www.ft.com/cms/s/0/dd386a86-a870-11e3-b50f-00144feab7de.html

35　Oyedele, A., 'Warren Buffett on global warming: "This issue bears a similarity to Pascal's Wager on the Existence of God"', Business Insider UK (27 February 2016), http://uk.businessinsider.com/warren-buffett-on-climate-change-2016–2

36　Long, S., 'Warren Buffett: Supposed increase in extreme weather "hasn't been true so far"', CBS News (3 March 2014), http://cnsnews.com/mrctv-blog/sean-long/warren-buffett-supposed-increase-extreme-weather-hasnt-been-true-so-far

37　Mackenzie, K., 'Guest post: Buffett's climate certainty', FT Alphaville, *Financial Times* (7 March 2016), http://ftalphaville.ft.com/2016/03/07/2155503/guest-post-buffetts-climate-certainty/

38 Lehrer, E., 'Insurers and climate change: The truth is more complicated than the sound bytes', *Insurance Journal* (24 May 2013), http://www.insurancejournal.com/blogs/right-street/2013/05/24/293288.htm

39 Geggel, L., 'US in longest "hurricane drought" in recorded history', Live Science (4 May 2015), http://www.livescience.com/50704-hurricane-drought.html

40 Kousky, C., Cooke, R.M., 'The unholy trinity: Fat tails, tail dependence, and micro-correlations', Resources for the Future (November 2009), http://www.rff.org/files/sharepoint/WorkImages/Download/RFF-DP-09-36-REV.pdf

41 'Flood Re-explained', Association of British Insurers (accessed 17 April 2016), https://www.abi.org.uk/Insurance-and-savings/Topics-and-issues/Flood-Re/Flood-Re-explained

42 'MDA community flood consultants', Mary Dhonau Associates (accessed 17 April 2016), http://www.marydhonau.co.uk

43 'Gordan Gardašanić – Director – Croatia Insurance Company Plc', LinkedIn (accessed 17 April 2016), https://www.linkedin.com/title/director-at-croatia-insurance-company-plc.

44 'Convergence capital triggers behavioural change among reinsurers', *Artemis* (9 September 2014), http://www.artemis.bm/blog/2014/09/09/convergence-capital-triggers-behavioural-change-among-reinsurers/

45 Winston, P.D., '"Time" for new horizon or just well-worn trail?', *Business Insurance* (27 April 2008), http://www.businessinsurance.com/article/20080427/ISSUE04/100024738/time-for-new-horizon-or-just-well-worn-trail

46 'Reinsurance may be "uglier" than expected in 2016, negative outlook: A.M. Best' (21 December 2015), http://www.artemis.bm/blog/2015/12/21/reinsurance-may-be-uglier-than-expected-in-2016-negative-outlook-a-m-best/

47 'ClimateWise', University of Cambridge Institute for Sustainability Leadership (accessed 17 April 2016), http://www.climatewise.org.uk

48 Wakefield, M., 'What "The Water Babies" can teach us about personal morality', *Independent* (26 December 2009), http://www.independent.co.uk/voices/commentators/mary-wakefield-what-the-water-babies-can-teach-us-about-personal-morality-1850416.html

49   Maynard, T., 'Extreme weather is a reality – the insurance industry must adapt', *The Guardian* (31 January 2014), http://www.theguardian.com/sustainable-business/extreme-weather-insurance-industry-climate-change

50   Keucheyan, R., 'Adapting to climate change can't be left to the wild west of the markets', *The Guardian* (10 September 2014), http://www.theguardian.com/commentisfree/2014/sep/10/adapting-climate-change-markets-extreme-weather-events-expensive

51   'What is a catastrophe bond (or cat bond)?', *Artemis* (accessed 17 April 2016), http://www.artemis.bm/library/what-is-a-catastrophe-bond.html

52   'Microinsurance', Wikipedia (accessed 17 April 2016), https://en.wikipedia.org/wiki/Microinsurance

53   http://www.cardiff.ac.uk/__data/assets/image/0019/122077/Solcer-House.jpg

54   http://www.eco-business.com/media/uploads/ebmedia/fileuploads/thaiamphibioushouse_news_featured.jpg

55   http://www.slideshare.net/MagnusMurray/update-of-dfid-funded-shelters-oct-2012

56   https://en.wikipedia.org/wiki/Stilt_house#/media/File:Inle-Yawnghwe.jpg

57   Huertas, A., 'Jeb Bush on climate change: What do we really want politicians to debate?', Union of Concerned Scientists (21 May 2015), http://blog.ucsusa.org/aaron-huertas/jeb-bush-on-climate-change-743

CHAPTER NINE

GLOBAL CARBON PRICING
IS A PRACTICAL REALITY

A partnership of national carbon price schemes underpinned by a credible carbon price floor

Should there be a global carbon tax? Could it be administered properly? Underpinning the evolving 'cap and trade' markets with a carbon price based on loss and damage would combine market efficiency with carbon-price credibility.

Wide Agreement

Beneath the headlines surrounding the COP21 Paris climate agreement of December 2015 there was intense debate about carbon pricing. Should such a market mechanism be included in the agreement? In the end it was deemed to be too complex,[1] but it was a testament to the many organisations that lobbied for it that the critical two words 'carbon pricing' reached the final narrative. Carbon pricing has come a long way in just a year thanks to IETA (International Emissions Trading Association)[2] and others. Now, a consensus is building and is being led through a forum called the Carbon Pricing Leadership Coalition,[3] an IMF and World Bank-driven global alliance of leaders, business and civic society that promotes the use of carbon pricing. If we are to have carbon pricing, then let us do it properly and create, somehow, a global carbon price or at least a global federation of markets. After all, a tonne of CO_2 emissions acts on the whole planet, not just on the country that emitted it.

A global carbon price is not a panacea[4] or a silver bullet that will solve climate change. For a start, there is a headwind of contradictory policies – $5.3 trillion of subsidies, one quarter of which create perverse incentives to emit more CO_2.[5] Moreover, a price of less than $15 per tonne of CO_2 (as determined in Chapter Seven) will not by itself greatly change behaviour. That problem, and the need to future-proof carbon taxation, are discussed in Chapter Ten, in the context of 'carbon intensity weighting'.

Carbon pricing must be part of a suite of solutions.[6] Without additional policy tools we will not reach the 2050 emissions targets that have been set in the EU and elsewhere.[7] Pricing is, nevertheless, a great enabler that allows significant sums of money to be diverted to less polluting, fairer energy solutions and the adaptation measures needed to offset the damage already done. Too often the immense fundraising side of carbon pricing is forgotten.[8]

The cost of carbon emissions must be 'internalised'[9] into the world's energy markets. As new views and information emerge about the cost of GHG emissions, such as those Predict Ability Ltd proposes, our carbon-pricing tools and mechanisms need to be refined. The markets we have today may achieve some CO_2 emissions reductions, but they do not – they cannot – set a strong, clear and meaningful carbon price. Even at $20 per tonne, Reuter's Alister Doyle reports, there may only be 'a roughly 60% chance'[10] of achieving the 2°C upper limit global-warming target agreed in Paris.

Big Business Wants a Price on Carbon

Alongside the clear decarbonisation message that the Paris deal signalled, there is another significant development. Major companies, including the electricity giants, have been calling for carbon pricing for quite a while.[11] For example, reinsurance leader Swiss Re and one hundred other business majors signed the Carbon Price Communiqué[12] in 2012. Even Exxon expects a $10 carbon price before long, despite the negative impact that this will have on oil revenues. In 2016, carbon pricing is both a hedge and for many, but not all,[13] a statement of commitment on climate change. Nevertheless, the reinsurance companies should worry if they are not in the driving seat on carbon pricing – as discussed in Chapter Eight, more than 30% of the carbon revenue should be heading in the direction of the insurance industry!

For years large companies have been evaluating business scenarios that include the reality of carbon pricing. They call it 'internal carbon pricing'. Many businesses, such as Microsoft, not only 'get it', they embraced the idea and Microsoft wrote a 'how to' guide on their 'Carbon Fee' system.[14] It informs users how to become carbon neutral – which is a place they will have to be within in a few decades anyway. So far, perhaps surprisingly, the Carbon Fee strategy has saved Microsoft millions of dollars by scrutinising the entire company's use of energy. Carbon-heavy departments or divisions have to justify their emissions or their inability to switch to low-carbon energy sources or manufacturing processes. Some may scoff at the idea of 'internal carbon pricing', but it is happening. One of the drivers here is that carbon disclosure programmes are being pushed up the corporate agenda by governments, and reinsurers too. More needs to be done in Asia, where there is significant under-reporting on emissions. The other worry is corporate air travel, doggedly increasing at 6.5% per year. It is a side-effect of globalisation. Apparently, bridging cultural divides on Skype does not work very well.[15] And let us not forget that the so-called 'eco-tourism' industry is worth $1.5 trillion worldwide.[16]

The general public, it should be said, is less enamoured with carbon pricing. To many it smacks of bigger government or bigger profits. Roger Pielke Jr[17] calls it the 'Iron law': a small measure of taxation is acceptable in the US, say $80 per adult per year, but at $300 much resistance would kick in. If there is to be a form of global carbon pricing, it has to be seen to be fair. When it is a trade-off between the economy and tackling climate change, the former always wins.

Of course, there are intrinsic things that cannot be priced. George Monbiot fears we are losing perspective when the term 'nature' is replaced by 'natural capital'.[18] The survival of coral reefs, rare species and even the great ice formations are all under threat. Perhaps forestry is the most challenging of these. A mature hardwood tree is priceless and wonderful, as Oxford University's Dr George McGavin explained: when you know how it all works 'you will never look at an oak tree quite the same way again'.[19] How many saplings does it take to replace an ancient hardwood tree? The UK Forestry Commission has produced a valuable guide on the complex interaction between forestry and climate change.[20] It concludes: 'overall, tree planting can only ever play a very small part in climate change mitigation'.

Nevertheless, if we make progress on carbon emissions through targets and carbon pricing, that will indeed be a great start. Some of the revenue from carbon pricing could be used to protect ancient forests and coastal eco-systems.[21] A carbon price coupled with a good legal framework for disaster risk reduction (DRR) would be better still.[22] In order for the forests to be protected, their value has to be fully determined. That is being done in the UN's REDD+ programme (REDD means reducing emissions from deforestation and forest degradation). The message is simple: REDD+ 'seeks to put a greater economic value on keeping trees alive, rather than chopping them down'.[23]

The Road from Rio: Cap and Trade

It worked well in the 1970s when high levels of sulphur and nitrogen oxides polluted North America's cities.[24] Permits to pollute were rationed and priced by a market in order to bring the pollution to within acceptable limits. The problem was relatively localised and the solution was rational. Can the 'cap and trade' system, adapted for use with greenhouse gases (GHGs) at the Rio Earth Summit in 1992, be made to work well for pollutants like CO_2?

Since the Kyoto agreement (outlined in Chapter Five) the concept of International Emissions Trading (IET) has been quite widely adopted – principally in Europe, Quebec and California. Yet many other schemes are under construction or consideration, not least China, where several small schemes have been prototyped in selected provinces. These markets have had a painful history and have been much analysed: A. Denny Ellerman et al.'s book examines the EU Emissions Trading Scheme,[25] and the World Bank Group periodically publishes a report on the state and trends in carbon pricing.[26]

As the map in Figure 9.1 shows, there are two principal mechanisms used to determine carbon prices at a country or regional level: (a) a fixed or scaled carbon tax set by governments and (b) a 'cap and trade' price.

We shall return to carbon taxation later. The second method, 'cap and trade', has proven to be very challenging. Although several markets are now – finally – operating in a reasonably functional form, they still need continual interventions to prevent unwanted excursions. For example, in early 2016, oil prices continued to fall and so did the price of carbon[27] – slackening growth has reduced energy demand and that means there are too many emissions permits

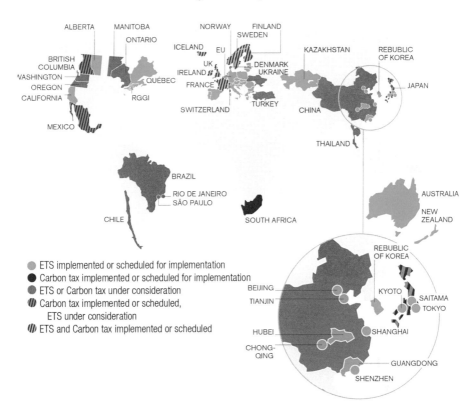

Figure 9.1. *Around the world, countries are developing ways to put a price on carbon to fight climate change. The World Bank Group has been working on mechanisms to network these initiatives and facilitate an integrated international carbon market.*[28] *(© World Bank. 2014. State and Trends of Carbon Pricing 2014. Washington, DC: World Bank.)*

available. On 9 February 2016, this came in from the on-line carbon news service, *Carbon Pulse*: 'EU carbon prices dropped below €5 ($6) on Tuesday to its lowest for 22 months as analysts slashed their forecasts and some observers urged lawmakers to step in with tougher reforms.'[29]

The problem is 'leakage'. It is a leakage not of CO_2 into the atmosphere, but of permits to emit CO_2 (a 1 tonne CO_2 permit is called an EUA in EU parlance). The central idea of 'cap and trade' is that a (global) climate-change target effectively imposes the need to reduce carbon emissions and that dictates how many tonnes of CO_2 can be emitted each year in a given jurisdiction, as part of a global goal. In practice, only about 40% of Europe's emissions come under the aegis of the European Trading System (ETS). Nevertheless, those emissions come from over 11,000 large plants or power stations that have been registered and vetted.[30] It is a very bureaucratic process.

The permit leakage problem comes about because of economic cycles, fraud, misreporting and political horse-trading. The net effect is that since the banking crisis of 2008 there have been too many permits. There is a permit glut. We are still, more or less, on target, in terms of emissions reduction, but the politicians, traders and renewable energy companies are bothered about the low and volatile prices.[31] Why not cancel the excess permits? On this no one can agree, so another layer of complexity has been added. From 2021 there will be MSR – the market stability reserve – effectively a floor price. Many argue that this is far too long to wait for a solution.[32]

Whilst the volatile prices have been deeply disconcerting for industry, the energy traders are quite pleased.[33] London expects to do very well from carbon trading. In a 2007 *New York Times* report[34] James Kanter quotes Louis Redshaw,[35] formerly head of environmental markets at Barclays Capital: 'Carbon will be the world's biggest commodity market, and it could become the world's biggest market overall.'

Energy-related businesses want to know where they stand and what to plan for. Instead the prices have been wildly erratic. At its worst, a tonne of CO_2 was trading in Europe at about $3 per tonne in 2008 (€2.81)[36] as the global recession took hold. No renewable energy project can be justified if the carbon price is that low.

Although the EU introduced mechanisms – ETS Phase 3 (2013–2020) – for imposing floor prices, the market continues to throw up issues regularly.[37] The ETS alone is unlikely to become the driver of low-carbon electricity supply. In Germany's grid, after the lamentable withdrawal of nuclear power,[38] flexible but dirty lignite-fired (brown coal) power stations are being built to offset the Energiewende wind generators and solar panels when there is no wind or daylight. Meanwhile new, efficient and cleaner gas-fired plants lie idle. For political reasons, it seems to be easier for Germany to provide aid for solar plants in India than to fix the energy mess at home.[39]

What happens to the revenue from EU ETS? According to Anja Esch at Germanwatch, a not-for-profit advancing sustainable development, 'It is up to each EU Member State to decide "in accordance with their respective constitutional and budgetary requirements" (EU council 2008) on the use of its EU ETS revenues. However, it can be assumed that within the EU Member States earmarking of the EU ETS revenues [e.g. for climate action] causes resistance.' Does this unallocated EU revenue reduce or increase emissions overall, or do they just get moved overseas?

Why not divert some of the EU ETS revenue to the European Central Bank, so that it can be used to underwrite renewable energy projects? A huge variation in the cost of capital in the EU means wind farms are not being built where there is most wind.[40]

All this has not gone unnoticed by moral and spiritual leaders, at the Vatican for example. The 2015 encyclical, Laudato-si',[41] addressed global environmental deterioration and climate change. In paragraph 171 it states, 'The strategy of buying and selling "carbon credits" can lead to a new form of speculation which would not help reduce the emission of polluting gases worldwide.'

Evidently, there are several problems with 'cap and trade':

► If the permit supply is simplistically controlled, then carbon price *per se* cannot be controlled.
► Volatile carbon prices arise but industry wants a stable, predictable price, so that it can plan ahead.
► Revenue from carbon trading is often pooled with general tax revenue.
► Speculative carbon (permit) trading creates moral hazards.

Let us consider the first point further. The 'cap and trade' community, in popular parlance, 'want their cake and eat it too'. In other words, two incompatible outcomes are desired: (1) to constrain carbon emissions and (2) to constrain carbon prices so they are neither too high nor too low. The first desire has its roots firmly in the Kyoto Protocol,[42] where the imperative to reduce emissions translated into emissions trading schemes. The second one, the carbon equivalent of the Goldilocks Principle (neither too hot, nor too cold, but just right),[43] is not easily realised, as Figure 9.2 illustrates.

Faced with such systems, control engineers would recognise that the 'carbon price' loop is stable – the carbon price more or less adjusts the

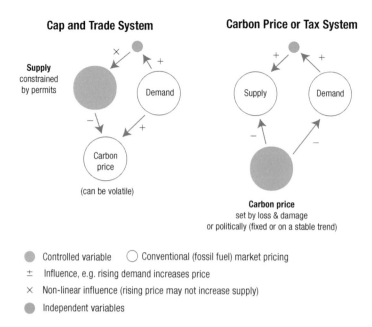

Figure 9.2. *With 'cap and trade' there is a conflict between two pricing mechanisms: if conventional pricing fails to generate more supply there will be market instabilities. With 'carbon pricing' both supply and demand are advised, but are not constrained, by information about the damage fossil-fuel burning causes. (© Predict Ability Ltd.)*

demand downwards – but the system on the left is at best metastable, or more likely unstable. One approach to such a problem would be to have a model-based supply strategy, i.e. the release of permits is the result of a multi-variable algorithm or mathematical model of the energy and carbon markets. This sort of calculation is euphemistically called 'non-trivial'. Researchers at the Massachusetts Institute of Technology (MIT) claim[44] that it takes a supercomputer to find the price of carbon! And even then, the answer depends heavily on the starting assumptions.

The Future of 'Cap and Trade'

Of all the 'cap and trade' markets, perhaps California's is the most mature and functional. Maybe that is because it is a one-state solution or, more likely, they have learned from Europe. It has certainly been successful in attracting $12 billion of green energy venture capital into the state.[45] It is an open question whether anything similar will be established in the Southern energy states in the US, although the US Supreme Court ruling in February 2016 to block President Obama's 'Clean Power Plan' is a setback that might work in favour of 'cap and trade' proponents.[46]

In the US Mid-Atlantic and Northeast states there is another scheme, the Regional Greenhouse Gas Initiative (RGGI),[47] which started operating in 2008. A particular feature of RGGI is the way in which the revenue is allocated: on average, 52% to energy efficiency; 11% to renewable energy; 14% to low-income ratepayer energy bill assistance; and 1% to various greenhouse gas reduction schemes. This means that 63% is used for mitigation, yet adaptation receives nothing (does climate change necessitate no extra infrastructure?).

The next big development is taking place in China, where a national 'cap and trade' project is being put through final testing ready for its rollout in 2017.[48] The priorities have been to avoid the mistakes made overseas and learn from the experience gained in regional trials. China's system will be the biggest 'cap and trade' scheme in the world.

There has been much time squandered in UN negotiations – Copenhagen 2009[49] was the low point – trying to allocate charges and responsibility for past emissions. In April 2008, US President George W. Bush had sought only to introduce 'carbon intensity' targets, for fear of promoting a Sino-US trade war.[50] Since then China has changed the agenda, with President Xi Jinping offering $3.1 billion in aid for clean development prior to the UN's Paris talks in 2015. The direction of flow has changed. History, it seems, is a sunk cost.

David Hone, Chief Climate Adviser at Shell and Board Member at IETA,[51] wants to see an 'internet of carbon pricing',[52] i.e. a global carbon price achieved through regional markets. In 2015 that remained a talking point, but perhaps the arbitrage mechanisms of foreign exchange markets might provide a way forward. If such an idea gained traction, probably without carbon taxation schemes included, there would need to be a global benchmark price to which the 'internet of prices' can be referenced.

Examining California's Carbon Allowance Futures price (Figure 9.3), it appears that Predict Ability Ltd's suite of carbon prices could provide such a baseline. Reliable predictions can be made for five or even ten years ahead. Canada is mulling a C$15 ($11) price floor,[53] which is close to the 2016 cumulative carbon price described in Chapter Eight.

Carbon Taxes and Carbon Pricing

Would carbon taxation schemes fare better than 'cap and trade', or will the die have been cast if China leads the way with its giant new permit market? Looking back at the World Bank's carbon map, we see that carbon taxation has a few footholds but their history has been erratic too. Australia's carbon tax came and went after a change of government,[54] and emissions have jumped 5.5% since.[55] In Europe there are parallel systems in the UK, France and several Nordic countries – but that may simply reflect the historical inadequacy of the EU ETS. In the UK, a hefty £18 ($24) carbon price floor policy came under intense scrutiny[56] (perhaps it should; Predict Ability Ltd's cumulative carbon price will not reach that level until the mid-2030s).

Like 'cap and trade', any form of carbon taxation is designed to compensate for the unaccounted for damage that CO_2 (or GHG) emissions cause.[57] Both

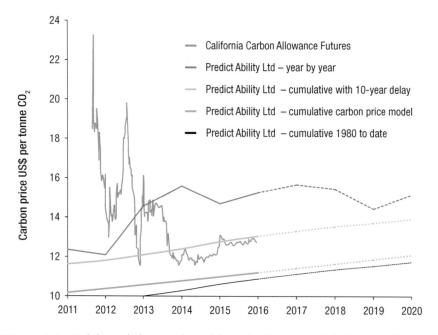

Figure 9.3. *California's 'cap and trade' market*[58] *has settled down well over the last two years.*[59] *Predict Ability Ltd's carbon prices, based on loss-and-damage, are comparable. The 'integral' prices are the ratio of attributable losses (in constant US$) and total CO_2 emissions ('cumulative 1980 to date' = 1980–2015 CO_2 data, '10-year delay case' = 1970–2005 CO_2 data). The cumulative carbon-price model was described in Chapter Eight. (© Predict Ability Ltd.)*

systems put a price on carbon and use the power of markets to effect change. Both generate revenue, but diverting all the revenue either into the general taxation pool or low-carbon infrastructure[60] are both deeply problematic. Without safeguards, both create adverse impacts (e.g. on energy-intense industry and the low-waged). Both require monitoring and verification.

When it works, 'cap and trade' can deliver a decarbonisation trajectory, but the unwanted side-effect has been price volatility. With carbon taxation there is no prescribed path to a low-carbon economy; it is up to the market to determine the equilibrium point between benefits and damage. Even if rigorously designed and enforced, carbon taxation alone will not protect vulnerable people and countries.

Responsibility for carbon pricing – the generic term for 'cap and trade' and carbon taxation schemes – is widely considered to be the job of government. Political pressure may result in price adjustments or even the rescinding of carbon tax laws. It is tempting to think that a carbon taxation scheme would be simpler to administer, but as yet there is not enough evidence to support that view. Would carbon taxes still look as good after the energy lobbyists have pummelled them? Probably not,[61] suggests Bradford Plumer in his succinct *New Republic* essay.

Plumer also comments on carbon 'offsets', a 'particularly gruesome aspect of "cap and trade" ... Many "cap and trade" proposals would allow polluters to get "credit" by, say, planting some trees or bankrolling methane capture at a landfill. In many cases, these projects would [have] happened anyway, which means they do [not] *really* offset the extra pollution emitted by the company getting the credit.' Offsetting is not always that bad,[62] but great care is needed to avoid stimulating future carbon emissions. Small village offset schemes may start 'green' but sooner or later motor vehicles tend to appear.

Is there a 'unique selling proposition' that carbon pricing has to offer? Robert Shapiro, chair and cofounder of the US Climate Task Force and former Undersecretary of Commerce for Economic Affairs, makes the case that 'the costs and lessons of the [2009] financial crisis may effectively swamp the prospects for "cap and trade". If "cap and trade" has become a dead policy walking, those who care deeply about climate change will find that a carbon tax system has become the last, reasonable policy standing.'[63]

The CTC (Carbon Tax Center, a US lobby group) regards carbon taxes as superior to 'cap and trade' for a number of reasons in addition to those already identified:

▸ Carbon taxes can be implemented more efficiently and quickly than complex 'cap and trade' schemes, and with climate change time is of the essence.

▸ Carbon taxes are transparent and easier to understand.

▸ Carbon taxes are less prone to manipulation.

▸ Carbon taxes address emissions from every sector, not just the 40% that comes from power stations, etc.

▸ It is likely that carbon-tax revenue would be returned to the public through dividends or other, progressive tax shifting.

Such a 'revenue neutral' or 'fee and dividend' scheme is, finally, gaining traction in the US Congress.[64] There is evidence that it will increase employment and the approach appeals to political conservatives, because it is a free market solution that does not increase the size of government. A partial-rebate scheme is operating in British Columbia. Around two-thirds of the revenue is used to reduce business taxes and much of the remainder is targeted at low-income households. Since the tax was introduced, fuel use has dropped 16%.[65] In Switzerland, a non-fiscal 'cap and trade' scheme provides participant companies with lower health-care insurance premiums.[66]

But what should be the tax rate? Perhaps it should be Predict Ability Ltd's carbon paydown[67] price[68] of $25 per tonne CO_2, or the EU ETS price[69] of $6–7 or California's[70] $12? If retiring coal-fired power stations were the objective, then a carbon price of $10 would not be enough.

The Bottom Line

We have examined 'cap and trade' and some actual and notional carbon-tax systems. There is no perfect solution but the world's 'cap and trade' systems have developed the most momentum. The arguments against 'cap and trade' highlight flaws that are well known in the carbon-trading community. Price volatility, permit 'leakage' and speculation reduce the efficiency of the market and – most of all – the reliable carbon price signal that the clean energy investment community really needs to do the $1 trillion-a-year job that has been identified.[71]

So, what needs to be done? The IMF[72] and World Bank Group[73] see carbon pricing in some shape or form as being central to the climate-change challenge. All the necessary preparations are being made. Poor nations, however, are concerned, fearing that existing market mechanisms are insufficient to reach the world's poorest that are suffering disproportionately from climate-change impacts.[74] In addition, why is it so hard for rich nations to stop sending aid to now quite well-developed nations? As always, government programmes are relatively easy to establish and devilishly difficult to stop – the holy grail is to have 'no regrets' development, adaptation and mitigation policies.[75]

Professor Dieter Helm suggests in *The Carbon Crunch*[76] that we should adopt a learning-by-taxing process. Others worry about the problem of untaxed emissions that are embodied in imported goods.[77] (The solution, if it does not create a trade dispute, is 'YCOWC', which Roger Arnold, a systems architect, defines as 'you collect or we collect'. It means that if an exporting nation does not adopt an appropriate carbon tax, then [the importer] will collect the tax in the form of import duties based on its assessment of the embodied carbon content of the products.)

Here are some ideas on carbon tax rates. A starting point might be to consider the 'social cost of carbon', as calculated in studies that estimate the damage done by each tonne of CO_2 emitted.[78] This, of course, is what Predict Ability Ltd claims to do. How do the prices compare? The Interagency Working Group on the Social Cost of Carbon (US Government) published a table in 2007 US$.[79] This has been updated for the effect of inflation (Table 9.1).

The cost depends strongly on the assumed discount rate.[80] For most power plants the discount rate is well above 5%; the highest rate, 6%, is for CCGT gas plants. Using this approach indicates that Predict Ability Ltd's discount rate is effectively 5% (using the current cumulative carbon price).

Finding the right discount rate is important. If the answer is near zero, as Lord Stern's review 'The economics of climate change'[81] determined, then the cost could be as high as $1000 per tonne CO_2. This has been widely rejected by

Table 9.1. Social cost of CO_2 (in estd. 2015 US$/tonne CO_2).			
Discount rate	5.0%	3.0%	2.5%
2010	12	36	57
2015	12	42	64
2020	14	48	72
2025	16	53	78
2030	18	59	84
2035	21	63	90
2040	24	69	97
2045	27	74	104
2050	29	80	109
Adapted from US Interagency Working Group on Social Cost of Carbon.			

economists as unrealistic, so it is significant that in the US Government study the range is limited to 2.5–5%, with $42 ($37 in 2007) being the central estimate.

There has to be a balance between the burden placed on current and future generations. Increasing inequality worldwide – as economist Professor Thomas Piketty explains in his bestseller *Capital in the Twenty-First Century*[82] – means that it is dangerous to assume that people's ability to adsorb the impacts of climate change will increase with time.

For When There Is No Carbon Price, or if the Market Fails

Dieter Helm suggests that any carbon price is better than no price, provided it is not woefully low, or driven by politicians (they tend to change their minds).[83] Predict Ability Ltd's prices provide a science-based, predictable and credible benchmark for the world's 'cap and trade' markets. They also can provide a shadow carbon price for states, countries or regions (SCR) where there is not yet a carbon price. Figure 9.4 illustrates what can be done when there is no carbon price, or when the market fails.

The diagram shows that Predict Ability Ltd's price data can be used to underpin existing market prices, in particular the EU ETS, which is still dysfunctional.[84] For SCRs without carbon price we must take account of the differing GDP and cost of energy around the world. What is needed is a carbon price that is effective, not punitive.

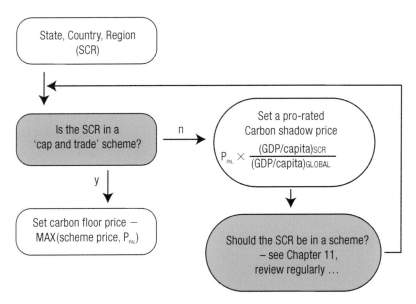

P_{PAL} Predict Ability Ltd's (cumulative) carbon price based on loss and damage

Figure 9.4. *For states, countries and regions (SCR) without a 'cap and trade' or carbon-tax scheme in place, there are straightforward steps that can be taken to prepare. In early 2016 Predict Ability Ltd's cumulative carbon price was about $11 per tonne CO_2. It may not be necessary for every SCR to participate in carbon trading; this is considered in Chapter Eleven. (© Predict Ability Ltd.)*

India has a 200 Rupee ($3–5) carbon tax on coal, as David Hone reports[85] (although in 2017 the coal tax will double).[86] India's GDP per capita[87] is $5,808 and the global figure is $14,900. Taking the Predict Ability Ltd cumulative carbon price (early 2016) of $10.88, the carbon tax in India is about right, i.e. $10.88 \times 5808/14900 = \$4.24$.

In the UK there is a GDP/capita of $39,826, which gives a shadow carbon price of about $29, slightly higher than UK Chancellor George Osborne's £18.08 ($24) carbon price floor.[88] For the US (GDP/capita $54,370) the price is about $40, very close to the published social cost of carbon. For China ($13,224 per capita) the shadow carbon price would be about $10.

These prices show that Predict Ability Ltd's method is credible. Perhaps this will facilitate the move towards a globally connected system of carbon prices, which proved a step too far at COP21 in Paris.[89]

Chapter Ten, 'Carbon Intensity Weighting', shows why it is now necessary to future-proof existing and emerging carbon markets and to incentivise fuel transitions using an energy-based, rather than fossil-fuel-based, pricing system.

Notes to Chapter Nine

1   Reuters, 'Paris climate deal will not include global carbon price, say UN climate chief', *The Guardian* (27 October 2015), http://www.theguardian. com/environment/2015/oct/27/paris-climate-deal-global-carbon-price-christiana-figueres-un

2   'Market solutions for climate change', International Emissions Trading Association (accessed 17 April 2016), http://www.ieta.org

3   'What if the cost of carbon emissions was instead paid at the source, where choices about fuel use are made?' Carbon Pricing Leadership (accessed 17 April 2016), http://www.carbonpricingleadership.org

4   Leach, A., 'Carbon pricing is not a panacea', Rescuing the frog – Andrew Leach's energy, climate and oil sands blog (11 October 2013), http://andrewleach.ca/oilsands/carbon-pricing-is-not-a-panacea/

5   Gaspar, V., Keen, M., Parry, I., 'How to ensure the right price for carbon', *The Weekend Australian* (16 January 2016), http://www.businessspectator.com. au/article/2016/1/15/climate/how-ensure-right-price-carbon

6   Whitmore, A., 'A new framework for climate policy: Why carbon pricing is not enough', *Energy Post* (26 March 2015), http://www.energypost.eu/new-framework-climate-policy-carbon-pricing-enough/

7   'New EU CCS policy: "The most important document that the European Commission has produced on CCS for the last two years" ', says Frederic Hauge', Bellona (13 January 2013), http://bellona.org/news/ccs/2013–01-new-eu-ccs-policy-the-most-important-document-that-the-european-commission-has-produced-on-ccs-for-the-last-two-years-says-frederic-hauge

8   Allen, M., 'Green levies may well be "crap". The way to deal with carbon is to bury it', *The Guardian* (26 November 2013), http://www.theguardian.com/environment/2013/nov/26/green-levies-crap-carbon-burial-fossil-fuels

9   'Cost internalisation – definition', Glossary of Statistical Terms (accessed 17 April 2016), https://stats.oecd.org/glossary/detail.asp?ID=458

10 Doyle, A., 'Cost of combating climate change surges as world delays – study', Reuters (2 January 2016), http://www.reuters.com/article/climate-costs-idUSL5E9C295520130102

11   Schofield, M., 'Appetite for change: Global business perspectives on tax and regulation for a low-carbon economy', Price Waterhouse Coopers (2010), https://www.pwc.co.uk/assets/pdf/appetite-for-change.pdf

12   'Swiss Re joins global call for a price on carbon emissions', Swiss Re (29 November 2012), http://www.swissre.com/rethinking/sustainable_ energy/Swiss_Re_joins_global_call_for_a_price_on_carbon_emissions. html

13   Zwick, S., 'In Davos, big business send mixed signals on climate, clear call for carbon price', Ecosystem Marketplace (22 January 2016), http://www. ecosystemmarketplace.com/articles/in-davos-big-business-sends-mixed-signals-on-climate-will-a-carbon-price-sort-them-out/

14   'Footprint of our products – we track the environmental impact of our products from start to finish', Microsoft (accessed 17 April 2016), https:// www.microsoft.com/environment/our-commitment/our-footprint.aspx

15   Hausmann, R., 'Should business travel be obsolete?', Project Syndicate (20 January 2016), https://www.project-syndicate.org/commentary/why-travel-for-business-by-ricardo-hausmann-2016–01/

16   Bricker, K.S., 'Shared planet: Eco-tourism', BBC Radio 4 (16 December 2013), http://www.bbc.co.uk/programmes/b03kqf02

17   Pielke Jr, R., *The Climate Fix*, pp. 46–50.

18   Monbiot, G., 'The price of everything: The natural capital agenda looks like an answer to the environmental crisis. But it's a delusion', monbiot.com (24 July 2014), http://www.monbiot.com/2014/07/24/the-pricing-of-everything/

19   McGavin, G., 'Oak tree: Nature's greatest survivor', BBC 4 (7 October 2015), http://www.bbc.co.uk/programmes/b06fq03t

20   'Trees and climate change', Forestry Commission England (accessed 17 April 2016), http://www.forestry.gov.uk/pdf/eng-trees-and-climate-change.pdf/$FILE/eng-trees-and-climate-change.pdf

21   Flannery, T., *Atmosphere of Hope*, Chapter 3, Penguin Books (2015).

22   Kelly, T., 'Reducing disaster risks through law', OneWorld South Asia (26 October 2012), http://southasia.oneworld.net/peoplespeak/reducing-disaster-risks-through-law

23   Funnell, A., 'The REDD scheme: Putting a price on forests in order to save them', Australian Broascasting Corporation (19 August 2015), http:// www.abc.net.au/radionational/programs/futuretense/putting-a-price-on-forests-in-order-to-save-them/6707916

24 'Emissions trading: History', Wikipedia (accessed 17 April 2016), https://en.wikipedia.org/wiki/Emissions_trading#History

25 Ellerman, D.A., *Pricing Carbon: The European Union Emissions Trading Scheme*, Cambridge University Press (January 2010), http://www.cambridge.org/asia/catalogue/catalogue.asp?isbn=9780521196475

26 'State and trends of carbon pricing 2014 (English)', The World Bank (13 May 2014), http://documents.worldbank.org/curated/en/2014/05/19572833/state-trends-carbon-pricing-2014

27 Ali, Z., 'EU carbon price falls more than 6 per cent', *Business Recorder* (25 January 2016), http://www.brecorder.com/markets/commodities/europe/275135-eu-carbon-price-falls-more-than-6pc.html

28 Widge, V., 'Networking climate actions for stronger, international carbon markets', The World Bank (28 January 2015), http://blogs.worldbank.org/climatechange/networking-climate-actions-stronger-international-carbon-markets

29 Garside, B., 'EU market: EUAs break below €5 as market looks to lawmakers for support', *Carbon Pulse* (9 February 2016), http://carbon-pulse.com/15384/

30 'The EU Emissions Trading System (EU ETS)', European Commission Climate Action (accessed 17 April 2016), http://ec.europa.eu/clima/policies/ets/index_en.htm

31 Helm, D., *The Carbon Crunch*, p. 183.

32 Oliver, C., Clark, P., 'EU plans to revive lifeless carbon market', *Financial Times* (13 October 2014), http://www.ft.com/cms/s/0/23d2b622-4fce-11e4-a0a4-00144feab7de.html

33 Helm, D., *The Carbon Crunch*, p. 184.

34 Kanter, J., 'Carbon trading: Where greed is green', *The New York Times* (20 June 2007), http://www.nytimes.com/2007/06/20/business/worldbusiness/20iht-money.4.6234700.html

35 'Louis Redshaw', Redshaw Advisors Ltd (accessed 17 April 2016), http://www.redshawadvisors.com/louis-redshaw/

36 Haszeldine, S., 'Keeping the momentum with carbon capture and storage', *Carbon Capture Journal* London Conference (19 November 2013), http://events.r20.constantcontact.com/register/event?llr=z6ibj5bab&oeidk=a07e7dptzfl9a795146

37   'News and intelligence on carbon markets, greenhouse gas pricing and climate policy', *Carbon Pulse* (accessed 17 April 2016), http://carbon-pulse.com

38   'Nuclear power in Germany', Wikipedia (accessed 17 April 2016), https://en.wikipedia.org/wiki/Nuclear_power_in_Germany

39   Busvine, D., Daniel, F.J., 'Germany offers India $2.25 billion for solar, clean energy', Reuters (5 October 2015), http://uk.reuters.com/article/us-india-germany-environment-idUKKCN0RZ0S920151005

40   van Renssen, S., 'Cost of capital for renewables varies hugely across EU', *Energy Post* (10 February 2016), http://www.energypost.eu/cost-capital-renewables-varies-hugely-across-eu/

41   'Full text: Laudato Si'', *Catholic Herald* (18 June 2015), http://www.catholicherald.co.uk/news/2015/06/18/full-text-laudato-si/

42   'International emissions trading', UN Framework Convention on Climate Change (accessed 17 April 2016), http://unfccc.int/kyoto_protocol/mechanisms/emissions_trading/items/2731.php

43   'The Goldilocks Principle: A model of atmospheric gases', University Corporation for Atmospheric Research Introduction to the Atmosphere (accessed 17 April 2016), https://www.ucar.edu/learn/1_1_2_1t.htm

44   Gross, D.A., 'Pricing carbon is a very complex challenge, and not just politically', ICSU Road to Paris (18 May 2015), http://roadtoparis.info/2015/05/18/pricing-carbon-is-a-very-complex-challenge-and-not-just-politically/

45   Dismore, L., 'Cap and trade', Price on Carbon (accessed 17 April 2016), http://priceoncarbon.org/pricing-mechanisms/cap-trade/

46   Szabo, M., 'US Supreme Court stays EPA's Clean Power Plan in blow to Obama climate strategy', *Carbon Pulse* (10 February 2016), http://carbon-pulse.com/15398/

47   'RGGI, Inc.', Regional Greenhouse Gas Initiative (accessed 17 April 2016), http://www.rggi.org/rggi

48   Cunningham, E.A., 'China's new plans for a cap and trade system just might work', *Foreign Policy* (6 October 2015), http://foreignpolicy.com/2015/10/06/china-carbon-emissions-climate-change-cap-trade-us/

49   'Copenhagen Accord', UN Framework Convention on Climate Change (accessed 17 April 2016), http://unfccc.int/meetings/copenhagen_dec_2009/items/5262.php

50 Bush, G.W., 'President Bush's speech on greenhouse gas emissions and climate change, April 2008', Council on Foreign Relations (16 April 2008), http://www.cfr.org/climate-change/president-bushs-speech-greenhouse-gas-emissions-climate-change-april-2008/p16043

51 'Governance', International Emissions Trading Association (accessed 17 April 2016), http://www.ieta.org/governance

52 Hone, D., 'Reaching net-zero emissions', LinkedIn (1 May 2015), https://www.linkedin.com/pulse/reaching-net-zero-emissions-david-hone

53 Szabo, M., 'Canadian government mulling national carbon price floor – paper', *Carbon Pulse* (18 February 2016), http://carbon-pulse.com/15822/

54 'Repealing the carbon tax', Australian Government Department of the Environment (1 July 2014), https://www.environment.gov.au/climate-change/repealing-carbon-tax

55 Parkinson, G., 'Australia's electricity emissions jump 5.5% since Coalition dumps carbon price', *RE New Economy* (6 April 2015), http://reneweconomy.com.au/2016/australias-electricity-emissions-jump-5–5-since-coalition-dumps-carbon-price-61546

56 Szabo, M., 'UK Treasury mulling next move for divisive carbon price floor – paper', *Carbon Pulse* (25 January 2016), http://carbon-pulse.com/14664/

57 'Climate policy memo #1: Cap and trade vs. taxes', Center for Climate and Energy Solutions (accessed 17 April 2016), http://www.c2es.org/publications/cap-trade-vs-taxes

58 'California carbon dashboard – $12.57', CalCarbonDash.org (accessed 21 April 2016), http://calcarbondash.org

59 Hiltzik, M., 'Emissions cap-and-trade program is working well in California', *Los Angeles Times* (12 June 2015), http://www.latimes.com/business/hiltzik/la-fi-hiltzik-20150613-column.html

60 Pickens, T.B., 'T. Boone Pickens on Obama oil tax plan: "Dumbest idea ever"', *Newsmax Finance* (5 February 2016), http://www.newsmax.com/Finance/StreetTalk/obama-oil-tax-crude/2016/02/05/id/712927/

61 Plumer, B., 'Are carbon taxes really simpler', *New Republic* (24 February 2009), https://newrepublic.com/article/47961/are-carbon-taxes-really-simpler

62 'Climate-friendly air travel (carbon offsetting)', Atmosfair (accessed 17 April 2016), https://www.atmosfair.de/en/

63 'Cap and trade', Carbon Tax Center (accessed 17 April 2016), http://www.carbontax.org/dead-ends/cap-and-trade/

64   Nuccitelli, D., 'In charts: How a revenue neutral carbon tax creates jobs, grows the economy', *The Guardian* (13 June 2014), http://www.theguardian.com/environment/climate-consensus-97-per-cent/2014/jun/13/how-revenue-neutral-carbon-tax-creates-jobs-grows-economy

65   Jessen, M., 'Greening up: What can I do?', *Castlegar The Source* (13 August 2014), http://castlegarsource.com/news/putting-carbon-tax-better-use-32465

66   Rittenhouse, K., et al., 'Switzerland: An emissions trading case study', Environmental Defense Fund (2015), https://www.edf.org/sites/default/files/switzerland-case-study-may2015.pdf

67   Predict Ability Ltd's estimate of the price needed to pay down the cost of past and future emissions (Chapter Eight).

68   'PALcarbon: UK electricity carbon dashboard', Predict Ability Ltd (accessed 21 April 2016), http://palcarbon.predictability.ltd.uk/

69   'Carbon emissions futures €5.97 – Dec 16 (CFI2Z6)', Investing.com (accessed 21 April 2016), http://uk.investing.com/commodities/carbon-emissions-streaming-chart

70   'California carbon dashboard – $12.57', CalCarbonDash.org (accessed 21 April 2016), http://calcarbondash.org

71   Bank, D., 'The $1 trillion challenge: Can clean energy investors fulfill global climate deal?', *Impact Alpha* (30 November 2015), http://impactalpha.com/the-1-trillion-challenge-can-clean-energy-investors-fulfill-global-climate-deal/

72   Rumney, E., 'IMF: Carbon pricing central to climate-change challenge', Public Finance International (12 January 2016), http://www.publicfinanceinternational.org/news/2016/01/imf-carbon-pricing-central-climate-change-challenge

73   'Preparing for carbon pricing: Case studies from company experience – Royal Dutch Shell, Rio Tinto, and Pacific Gas and Electric Company', PMR Technical Note No. 9, The World Bank (2015), https://openknowledge.worldbank.org/handle/10986/21358

74   Carr, M., 'World Bank carbon-market push facing poorer-nation suspicion', Bloomberg (4 June 2015), http://www.bloomberg.com/news/articles/2015–06-04/world-bank-carbon-market-push-facing-developing-nation-suspicion

75   Siegel, P.B., '"No regrets" approach to decision-making in a changing climate: Toward adaptive social protection and spatially enabled governance', World Resources Institute (2015?), http://www.wri.org/our-work/project/

world-resources-report/no-regrets-approach-decision-making-changing-climate-toward

76 Helm, D., *The Carbon Crunch*, p. 179.

77 Lane, L., 'Would a carbon tax effectively combat climate change?', Our Energy Policy (24 July 2014), http://www.ourenergypolicy.org/would-a-carbon-tax-effectively-combat-climate-change/

78 Minh Ha Duong, 'What is the price of carbon? Five definitions', *Sapiens*, 2 (1), 2009, https://sapiens.revues.org/793 (accessed 17 April 2016).

79 'Technical support document: Technical update of the social cost of carbon for regulatory impact analysis – under Executive Order 12866', Interagency Working Group on Social Cost of Carbon, United States Government (November 2013), https://www.whitehouse.gov/sites/default/files/omb/assets/inforeg/technical-update-social-cost-of-carbon-for-regulator-impact-analysis.pdf

80 'Discount rates and net present value', Centre for Social Impact Bonds UK Cabinet Office (accessed 17 April 2016), https://data.gov.uk/sib_knowledge_box/discount-rates-and-net-present-value

81 Stern, N., et al., 'Stern review: The economics of climate change', Grantham Research Institute on Climate Change and the Environment at the London School of Economics (30 October 2006), http://www.wwf.se/source.php/1169157/Stern%20Report_Exec%20Summary.pdf

82 Piketty, T., *Capital in the Twenty-First Century*, The Belknap Press of Harvard University Press (French August 2013, English April 2014), https://en.wikipedia.org/wiki/Capital_in_the_Twenty-First_Century

83 Helm, D., *The Carbon Crunch*, p. 72.

84 Garside, B., ' "Cannot be right" that the EU ETS is long while falling short of GHG goals – think-tank', *Carbon Pulse* (22 February 2016), http://carbon-pulse.com/15995/

85 Hone, D., 'Carbon pricing in 2015', Blogs.shell.com/climatechange (7 January 2016), http://blogs.shell.com/climatechange/category/cap-and-trade/

86 King, E., 'India to double coal tax under 2016–17 budget', Climate Home (29 February 2016), http://www.climatechangenews.com/2016/02/29/india-to-double-coal-tax-under-2016–17-budget/

87 'List of countries by GDP (PPP) per capita', Wikipedia (accessed 17 April 2016), https://en.wikipedia.org/wiki/List_of_countries_by_GDP_(PPP)_per_capita

88   'The UK carbon price floor', Sandbag (accessed 17 April 2016), https://
     sandbag.org.uk/site_media/pdfs/reports/Sandbag_Carbon_Floor_
     Price_2013_final.pdf

89   Chestney, N., Doyle, A., 'Global CO_2 pricing seen unlikely to be big part of
     Paris climate deal', GMA News Online Philippines (3 June 2015), http://
     www.gmanetwork.com/news/story/497454/scitech/science/global-co2-
     pricing-seen-unlikely-to-be-big-part-of-paris-climate-deal

CHAPTER TEN

CARBON INTENSITY WEIGHTING

Behavioural change and rational investment

A particular problem in carbon pricing is that a one-size-fits-all carbon price is a blunt instrument for encouraging behavioural change. A spectrum of prices based on impact (carbon intensity) would be more effective as well as future-proof.

A Change of Course

The UN, the World Bank and many other bodies are now calling for carbon pricing, either as a means of implementing carbon emissions caps or in recognition of the power of markets to effect change. It is this second aspect that is explored here.

> The transition to a cleaner future will require both government action and the right incentives for the private sector. At the centre should be a strong public policy that puts a price on carbon pollution. Placing a higher price on carbon-based fuels, electricity and industrial activities, will create incentives for the use of cleaner fuels, save energy, and promote a shift to greener investments. Measures such as carbon taxes and fees, emissions-trading programs and other pricing mechanisms, and removal of inefficient subsidies, can give businesses and households the certainty and predictability they need to make long-term investments in climate-smart development. (Christine Lagarde, MD, IMF, and Jim Yong Kim, President, World Bank)[1]

Whatever the framework or carbon-pricing methodology, a primary or secondary outcome of a carbon price is a signal, as Lagarde and Kim describe, that incentivises the use of cleaner fuels, etc. The logic is the logic of the market: that market players are dissuaded – to varying degrees – by an increase in the price of a commodity. This only works if there are alternatives to coal, for example, to generate electricity competitively. Yet if an investment decision is about to be made in a coal-fired power station, then a small or erratic price movement will not be enough to prevent it.[2] For a carbon price to be credible it has to provide a sustained signal of significant magnitude, one that is both verifiable and to some extent predictable. This, we believe, is where Predict Ability Ltd's loss- and damage-based carbon price has an advantage over 'cap and trade'. The latter will only work if there is sustained credibility that the system will be supported and that it cannot be manipulated by political or other factors. Their history is not encouraging here. Nevertheless, both the 'damage-based' and 'cap and trade' mechanisms will require careful auditing.

Suppose a stable carbon price could be generated, for example $15 per tonne of CO_2. Would that be enough to curtail emissions sufficiently to achieve internationally discussed or agreed targets? Probably not. In the UK, one of the world's most fuel-taxed nations,[3] a $15 per tonne tax (~£10) equates to about 3.5¢ (2.3p) per litre for petrol and 4¢ (2.7p) per litre for diesel.[4] Unless imposed overnight, the carbon-price effect would be dwarfed by existing duties and, indeed, international energy price movements.

A one-size-fits-all carbon price is a blunt instrument for encouraging behavioural change. More importantly, as the world decarbonises, carbon markets will become literally *incredible* and could collapse.

In the case of 'cap and trade' systems, as we head towards the 2050 goal, fewer and fewer emissions permits must be issued. The carbon price may escalate, exceeding the cost of coal itself, at which point politicians will come under pressure to relent and issue more permits. Alternatively, market players will have found low-carbon alternatives. Even though some decarbonisation will have been achieved, the revenue stream may either be tainted by market manipulation or evaporate. The whole process is predicated on the idea that 2°C of global warming is acceptable. It is not. Great damage has been done already (as the secondary target of 1.5°C agreed at the Paris 2015 conference tacitly acknowledges).

With all forms of carbon pricing that are based solely on fossil-fuel CO_2 emissions, the price will increase over time and eventually become absurd. Yet carbon-tax revenues are vitally important in completing the loop, to provide incentives for low-carbon alternatives, adaptation or compensatory measures. So what should be done? There has to be an ongoing, long-term revenue stream to ensure that the increasingly compounding effects of already-released emissions (legacy CO_2) are counteracted.

Energy Not Fossil Fuels

Two things now become apparent. Firstly, to incentivise the movement from 'dirty' carbon-intensive fuels to 'clean' low-carbon fuels or energy, there has to be a stronger price signal, whatever pricing system is implemented. Secondly, it will be necessary *from the very start* to link the carbon prices to all energy types and not just fossil fuels.

That may sound bizarre, but consider this. If the IPCC is successful in obtaining global agreement on emissions, the demise of fossil fuels could be quite rapid, particularly in the electricity sector. If all the revenue required to deal with the effects of climate change is sourced from fossil fuels alone, there will be escalating prices and price volatility and the revenue stream will become erratic. Today, despite all the efforts on renewable energy, most energy is still derived from fossil fuels. But renewables are emerging fast, so we should plan for their eventual market dominance.

The idea of using energy units in environmental policy is not new. In 1993 US President Bill Clinton proposed an energy tax, dubbed the 'BTU tax',[5] as a way to reduce energy imports and cut the federal deficit. Although widely applauded by economists and environmentalists, the tax implications met strong political resistance. All manner of special pleadings began. It is a cautionary tale, as economist Dawn Erlandson explains: 'the [President] was unable to invoke public understanding that energy taxes are more beneficial to the country than other taxes ... because they discourage pollution'.[6]

Life Cycle Emissions

At the February 2014 Oxford Climate Forum[7] one of the expert panellists asked a young trader 'You're a bright Oxford graduate. If you want to effect change, why are you trading lignite?' The answer, of course, is that there is money to be made. The profit margin on lignite, a soft brown easily mined coal with high CO_2 emissions per unit of energy, is three times higher than conventional hard coal. A basic carbon tax, for now, is unlikely to reduce the use of lignite.

Coal consumption hit a 44-year high[8] not so long ago, so talk of its demise is premature, not least in energy-hungry economies like China, India and Indonesia.

If King Coal is to be retired, there are four possible strategies:

▸ Campaign, as the US Sierra Club does (Figure 10.1), to impede or prevent coal-fired power plants from operating or being built, through the use of existing environmental laws.[9]
▸ Ban unabated (non-CCS) coal plants from being built, as proposed in the EU.[10]
▸ Provide cheaper alternatives, such as shale gas or wind energy.
▸ Impose an increasingly potent carbon tax.

If business carries on as usual, coal looks set to remain very much a part of the energy mix worldwide. In Asia, the main issues facing coal are the public's growing concerns about the impacts of climate change (extreme weather-related disasters and damage) and, most of all, the devastating air pollution. However, air-quality regulations are increasingly being implemented in China.[11] Perhaps the tide really is turning on coal when the American coal giant Peabody files for bankruptcy.[12] The map (Figure 10.1) shows what has been happening to coal-fired power stations in the US.

Why is coal singled out as the bad actor? For every fuel there is a ratio **e**, the amount of CO_2 emitted divided by the useful energy the fuel produces. Often this is called 'carbon intensity'. The emissions are expressed as kg-CO_2/tonne and the energy is expressed as kWh/tonne, so the ratio becomes kg-CO_2/kWh (kilograms of CO_2 per kilowatt-hour). Typically for coal, the ratio is 0.979 kg-CO_2/kWh. On an industrial scale the units are

Figure 10.1. *In the US, one coal-fired power plant shuts every ten days.*[13] *Red markers indicate active or upcoming plants, yellow are progressing plants and green defeated plants. (© Sierra Club.)*

scaled up to become tonneCO_2/GWh (gigawatt-hour), as shown in Figure 10.2.[14] The chart shows a range of fossil-fuel, low-carbon and renewable-energy sources. Expressed as 'life cycle' values, even wind turbines and solar panels have some CO_2 footprint. This is called embedded carbon. Until steel-production processes become fully electrified (e.g. electric-arc steel production)[15] and sustainable there is, inevitably, some fossil-fuel energy embodied in the processes that make up renewable-energy equipment.

There are some subtleties when it comes to certain fuels (not shown in Figure 10.2) such as JET-A (jet engine kerosene) and natural gas derived from fracking processes. It appears that a tonne of CO_2 emitted by a jet aircraft flying in the stratosphere is up to four times more potent than the equivalent amount of CO_2 emitted at ground level.[16]

With fracking (the hydraulic fracturing of rock to release natural gas), there is the vexed question of so-called fugitive emissions, i.e. natural gas that leaks out of the high-pressure processing equipment. Some reports put the leakage rate at about 3% and, given the GHG-potency of methane, that would make fracked gas as bad as coal. In the long term this is a side issue. If fracking were stopped tomorrow, the atmosphere would assimilate the escaped methane. Compared to CO_2, the lifetime of a methane molecule in the atmosphere is quite short.

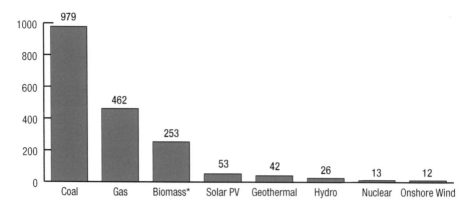

Figure 10.2. *Life-cycle emissions account for all the CO_2, in every way possible, associated with the total output of an energy source. Nuclear power and wind score well because the equipment assets produce much power per kg-steel. (*There is some debate about the value for biomass).*[17] *(© Predict Ability Ltd, with thanks to NEI.)*

Accordingly, provided the leakage is within permitted limits, fracked gas should be considered to be equivalent to conventional natural gas. There are other issues with fracking, such as the despoliation of landscapes, chemical pollution and noise, but scientists and governments spend too much time fretting about fugitive and minor GHG emissions.[18] Address this further if air pollution falls.

The Energy Transition Equation – EzefyN

To address, fully, the consequences of CO_2 emissions, a carbon-pricing system is needed that accounts for the long-term impact of fossil-fuel emissions. As things stand today, 'cap and trade' schemes do not and, by definition, cannot go far enough. They only trade fossil fuels, so when fossil-fuel usage abates will they die out?

With an energy-based pricing scheme a similar problem could arise, so from the outset it is essential that embedded carbon, as well as carbon emissions, be used in the accounting process. Embedded carbon accounts for the CO_2 emissions that occur, for example, during the manufacture of steel used in a wind turbine's tower and blades.

Two weighting factors that we call **f** and **z** must be introduced to appropriately position the carbon prices of each form of energy, whether a fossil fuel or not. Note that the reciprocal of **f** gives us the weighted average 'carbon intensity' (today, $1/f$ is roughly 0.345 kg-CO_2/kWh in the United States). The term z, the 'revenue weighting' factor, ensures that the revenue from a 'carbon intensity weighted' carbon-pricing scheme is the same as the revenue from a simple 'uniform price' carbon-pricing scheme (Appendix 10.1, p. 216, shows how z is derived).

The rationale here is that in the future, when fossil-fuel usage has abated but the consequences of their use are all too obvious (and probably growing), somebody has to pay for the damages. Partly that will be our generation, if we finally accept carbon pricing, and partly it will be future generations. So, when it comes to damage payments, it should be those who now and in the future emit relatively the most CO_2 who should pay the most. In 100 years' time, even the profligate use of solar power should attract a lot of tax. A prince with a solar-powered, air-conditioned palace should pay much more than one of his subjects running a couple of solar-powered light bulbs. The loss and damage from climate change will still be very much in evidence a century from now and it must be paid for.

In order to achieve a seamless transition from carbon-intense energy to low-carbon energy, the 'carbon intensity' weighting factor f is defined as follows:

$$f = \Sigma E_i / \Sigma (E_i \times e_i)$$

where[19] the subscript 'i' denotes each energy type: coal, gas[20] and so on. There can be as many fuel or energy types as required, and the list can be updated at any time. E_i is the amount of fuel/energy type i used globally (expressed in GWh so the total numbers are comprehensible).

It should be noted that a problem would arise if the world completely decarbonised and all the e_i numbers became zero. In practice this is unlikely to happen, but to avoid the chance of, shall we say, the 'spurious decarbonisation' of wind turbines, for example, it is suggested that e_i = maximum of e_i or 0.05 (the e-value for today's solar panels). This approach is echoed by Bryony Worthington,[21] Director of Sandbag, UK, who commented:

> The CO_2 intensity of our electricity supply is not getting the attention it deserves. By 2030, we need the total power supply to be around 50g/kWh, whilst the current average hovers around 400g/kWh. Quick gains can be made by preventing

the UK's old, inefficient and unabated coal stations providing anything other than a short-term back-up role.

If the global carbon price, and it should be global, is denoted as **y** (US$/tonneCO$_2$), then we have all the terms except two in the *energy transition equation* **EzefyN**. Firstly, $E = \Sigma\ E_i$. Secondly, the term **N** applies if there are multiple energy suppliers, as there normally would be, of the same fuel/energy type i – each supplier would pay a proportionate part of the overall tax required and pass the costs on to the consumer.

Let us consider an example: suppose we have one low-carbon energy source (wind, with an **e** = 0.01 for simplicity), one carbon intense fuel (coal, **e** ~ 1) and one intermediate fuel, natural gas (**e** ~ 0.5). Furthermore, to keep things simple, let us assume that there are just three suppliers: the Wind Turbine Company, the Coal Company and the Gas Company, so **N** = 1 in each case.

To begin with, let us assume that there is no gas and no wind power, so all the energy E is coal energy, thus **f** = 1 and **z** = 1. The tax to be paid by the Coal Company will be **EzefyN** = Ey, thus their end-use customers will experience a tax of **y** $/tonne (with a measure of mark-up, no doubt).

As Chapter 9 shows, coal dominates today's carbon markets. Of the 11,000 large plants and power stations registered under the EU's Emission Trading Scheme most are coal-fired power stations. Thus, in the EU ETS, **f** ~ 1 but in Europe 1/**f** ~ 0.35 if all energy sectors (including transport) are included. The **EzefyN** methodology would facilitate and accelerate carbon market transitions beyond today's coal-dominated pricing schemes.

Returning to the example, let us imagine, some years later, that the size of the energy market E is the same as before, but the Gas Company has gained a 10% market share, thus

$$E = E_{coal} + E_{gas}$$
$$= 0.9 \times E + 0.1 \times E$$

The revenue weighting factor is **z** = 0.9757 (Appendix 10.1) and the carbon-intensity weighting factor

$$f = E/(0.90 \times E \times 1 + 0.1 \times E \times 0.5)$$
$$= 1/(0.9 \times 1 + 0.1 \times 0.5)$$
$$= 1.053$$

The Coal Company customers would pay $1 \times 1.053 \times 0.9757 \times y = 1.027 \times y$ \$/tonne, while the Gas Company customers would pay $0.5 \times 1.053 \times 0.9757 \times y = 0.5135 \times y$ \$/tonne.

Let us continue. If the market E remains the same but the Gas Company now has a 40% market share and the Wind Turbine Company has a 20% share, then

$$E = E_{coal} + E_{gas} + E_{wind}$$
$$= 0.40 \times E + 0.40 \times E + 0.20 \times E$$

and the 'carbon intensity' weighting factor becomes

$$f = E/(0.40 \times E \times 1 + 0.40 \times E \times 0.5 + 0.20 \times E \times 0.01)$$
$$= 1/(0.40 \times 1 + 0.40 \times 0.5 + 0.20 \times 0.01)$$
$$= 1.661 \text{ (and } z = 0.7248)$$

The Coal Company customers would pay $1 \times 1.661 \times 0.7248 \times y = 1.204 \times y$ \$/tonne and the Gas Company customers would pay $0.5 \times 1.661 \times 0.7248 \times y = 0.602 \times y$ \$/tonne. The Wind Turbine Company customers, however, would pay just $0.010 \times 1.661 \times 0.7248 \times y = 0.01204 \times y$ \$/tonne. Both coal and gas carbon prices have increased proportionately. In absolute terms, the coal carbon price has increased the most, but, because of coal's falling market share, the carbon revenue from coal has *decreased*.

Depending on the actual mix of fuels in the market, two features of the 'carbon intensity' weighted prices emerge. A low-carbon energy source will attract less tax than it would otherwise; equally, coal attracts more. However, when the higher-emission fuels disappear, the lower carbon energy sources have to be taxed more, to ensure the required revenue is achieved.

Note the absence of a wind turbine subsidy. The heavier tax on coal and gas should eliminate the need for subsidies. However, it may be that even with a carbon tax the Wind Turbine Company would struggle to compete. Under these circumstances, governments (within existing subsidy rules) might wish to intervene. This could be done by temporarily introducing *negative* e_i values until wind turbine prices had fallen sufficiently. However, there is some danger here that the subsidy could be held in for too long or phased out too quickly – like political careers, many government subsidy schemes end badly! Have we already reached the point where solar PV subsidies, for example, are no longer needed? Apparently so: in the UK, solar subsidies are being phased out (badly)[22] and in Germany Chancellor Angela Merkel introduced a tax on solar energy to help rein in power costs.[23]

Finally, when there are no coal or gas emissions, then

$$E = E_{wind} = 1.00 \times E$$

and the weighting factor becomes

$$f = E/(0 + 0 + 1.0 \times E \times 0.01)$$
$$= 1/(0 + 0 + 1.0 \times 0.01)$$
$$= 100 \text{ (and } z = 1 \text{ again)}$$

Thus the Wind Turbine Company customers would pay *all* the tax required: $0.01 \times 100 \times 1 \times y$ \$/tonne = y \$/tonne. As already outlined, the more energy a wind turbine or solar user demands, the more tax they pay. Yes, of course, the carbon emissions will have largely stopped, but, for the foreseeable future, the loss and damage and hence the need for a carbon tax will continue.

Table 10.1 shows how the **EzefyN** strategy would work in practice. The data is based on the US electricity market with an approximation of the US transport sector.

Although in 2012 coal was only 13.9% of the total US energy market, it was still a big component of the US electricity market and, because of its high e-value, the tax on coal would have been one of the highest; 68% of the carbon revenue would have come from coal. The tax on renewables and the revenue from them would have been quite small. Natural gas and road transport fuels would make up most of the non-coal revenue.

If a lower limit of **e** = 0.05 were imposed on renewables, as suggested earlier, the picture today would change only slightly and yet that small change would make the energy transition equation **EzefyN** completely future-proof. The result is shown in Table 10.2.

In compiling Tables 10.1 and 10.2 from various data sources, it was clear that there is a need for a globally agreed, self-consistent source of **e**-values and fuel-usage data. Perhaps if the data is used for carbon pricing, that will focus people's attention. 'Life cycle assessments' are required.

Table 10.1. United States based on fuel or energy carbon prices with estimated E- and e-values.

US fuel/energy type	Carbon Intensity e_i (tonneCO$_2$/ GWh)	Energy E_i (GWh/y)	Emissions C_i (emissions)	Carbon Price $y_i =$ e.f.y.z	Carbon Tax Revenue $R(\$) = C_i \times e_i$
PAL US EG Coal	979	1,585,697	1,552,396,984	$25.82	40,088,708,986
PAL US EG Natural Gas	462	1,121,928	518,330,516	$12.19	6,316,628,590
PAL US EG Nuclear	13	797,067	10,361,877	$0.34	3,553,190
PAL US EG Hydropower	26	258,749	6,727,473	$0.69	4,613,833
PAL US EG Biomass	253	43,050	10,891,615	$6.67	72,685,770
PAL US EG Geothermal	42	16,628	698,394	$1.11	773,725
PAL US EG Solar	53	18,321	971,037	$1.40	1,357,526
PAL US EG Wind	12	181,791	2,181,497	$0.32	690,514
PAL US EG Petroleum	241	30,489	7,347,817	$6.36	46,710,227
PAL US EG Industrial Waste	1,200	21,269	25,522,878	$31.65	807,881,157
PAL ×11 RT Petrol	240	1,927,945	462,706,832	$6.33	2,929,231,815
PAL ×11 RT Diesel	244	3,118,174	760,834,570	$6.44	4,896,848,323
PAL ×11 RT LPG	215	14,872	3,197,533	$5.67	18,133,854
PAL ×11 Rail Gas Oil	271	94,728	25,671,171	$7.15	183,506,544
PAL ×11 Shipping Gas Oil	271	265,949	72,072,206	$7.15	515,197,441
PAL ×11 Shipping Fuel Oils	268	229,285	61,448,492	$7.07	434,392,790
PAL ×11 Aviation Turbine	238	1,686,287	401,336,373	$6.28	2,519,544,695
Totals	2012 data	11,412,231	3,922,697,265	$15.00	58,840,458,979

Notes: US = UK data ×11, RT = road transport, EG = electricity plants. **y** = $15/tonne CO$_2$ (see endnote 42 on p. 144). Data sources: US EIA,[24] US RITA,[25] UK DECC).[26] This data and the form of calculation is the basis of *PALcarbon*, Predict Ability Ltd's real-time carbon-pricing phone 'app'.

Table 10.2. United States based on fuel or energy carbon prices with e-values = maximum {e-value, 0.05} shown in grey cells.

US fuel/energy type	Carbon Intensity e_i (tonneCO$_2$/ GWh)	Energy E_i (GWh/y)	Emissions C_i (emissions)	Carbon Price $y_i =$ e.f.y.z	Carbon Tax Revenue $R(\$) = C_i \times y_i$
PAL US EG Coal	979	1,585,697	1,552,396,984	$26.07	40,474,796,708
PAL US EG Natural Gas	462	1,121,928	518,330,516	$12.30	6,377,462,994
PAL US EG Nuclear	50	797,067	39,853,373	$1.33	53,068,191
PAL US EG Hydropower	50	258,749	12,937,447	$1.33	17,227,323
PAL US EG Biomass	253	43,050	10,891,615	$6.74	73,385,794
PAL US EG Geothermal	50	16,628	831,422	$1.33	1,107,110
PAL US EG Solar	50	18,321	916,073	$1.33	1,219,830
PAL US EG Wind	50	181,791	9,089,569	$1.33	12,103,543
PAL US EG Petroleum	241	30,489	7,347,817	$6.42	47,160,085
PAL US EG Industrial Waste	1,200	21,269	25,522,878	$31.96	815,661,727
PAL x11 RT Petrol	240	1,927,945	462,706,832	$6.39	2,957,442,762
PAL x11 RT Diesel	244	3,118,174	760,834,570	$6.50	4,944,009,058
PAL x11 RT LPG	215	14,872	3,197,533	$5.73	18,308,498
PAL x11 Rail Gas Oil	271	94,728	25,671,171	$7.22	185,273,866
PAL x11 Shipping Gas Oil	271	265,949	72,072,206	$7.22	520,159,222
PAL x11 Shipping Fuel Oils	268	229,285	61,448,492	$7.14	438,576,355
PAL x11 Aviation Turbine	238	1,686,287	401,336,373	$6.34	2,543,810,013
Totals	2012 data	11,412,231	3,965,384,872	$15.00	59,480,773,078

Notes: US = UK data ×11, RT = road transport, EG = electricity plants. **y** = $15/tonne CO$_2$ (see endnote 42 on p. 144).

Divestment

There has been much discussion and, indeed, action on divestment since 2013, when the environmental activist Bill McKibben released the film *Do the Math*,[27] an explosive documentary that triggered the global divestment movement. Wikipedia states: 'Fossil fuel divestment is the removal of investment assets including stocks, bonds, and investment funds from companies involved in extracting fossil fuels,[28] in an attempt to reduce climate change.'[29] Many universities and similar organisations have moved their pension funds out of fossil-fuel-related investments. Not all universities agree. Some believe they are better off investing in oil and gas, notwithstanding the 'moral dimension'. Overall, there is most agreement about divesting from the most carbon-intense fuels, such as tar sands and lignite, etc. **EzefyN**, the energy transition equation, directly conveys the priorities here and the direction of travel that is needed in our energy-use behaviour.

Tomatoes

British Sugar operates a large sugar beet processing plant at Wissington in eastern England. It is a model of sustainability, and yet one of its activities creates a carbon conundrum (Figure 10.3). Firstly, farmers deliver sugar beet from across the region, the soil and aggregates are recovered, the sugar is processed. Then the sugar refinery waste (molasses) is converted into bio-ethanol for petrol-driven motorcars. A small power plant provides the energy, steam and electricity. The flue gases are sent to some huge greenhouses where a whole range of tomatoes is grown hydroponically. Yet if we follow the tomatoes' carbon molecules, where have they come from and where do they end up?

To say the tomatoes are 'green' is only partially correct. The CO_2 from the power plant is used twice – once by way of raising steam and once for growing tomatoes. Yet the carbon (in the form of carbohydrates) is *fossilised* carbon and, when the tomato is eaten and digested, the waste ends up in sewage where the CO_2 is released into the atmosphere via a methane step. A conundrum arises if there are carbon taxes. Should the power plant pay the whole amount due, or should the cost be shared with the tomato grower? If it were the latter, why would he want to use flue gases at all? Possibly the extra growth rate (the greenhouse air contains ~1200 ppm CO_2) would compensate. Under the controlled conditions of the greenhouse, the extra CO_2 has beneficial effects.

Figure 10.3. *A tomato conundrum: is it true there are no emissions? (© Wikipedia, Creative Commons.)*

EOR – Enhanced Oil Recovery

Another area where there needs to be carbon-pricing clarity is in the field of enhanced oil recovery (EOR). This is a technique used by the oil industry to extend the life of oil fields. High-pressure nitrogen or CO_2 is injected at several locations to boost the field pressure and create a movement of oil molecules towards the wellhead. CO_2 is particularly good for EOR because at high pressure the gas acts as a superb solvent, teasing out every last drop of oil.

It might be argued that EOR is simply prolonging the oil era and that oil industry efforts, and money, should be redirected to more sustainable activities. That may be so, yet the EOR process is in fact a form of carbon capture and storage. CCS has had a tough time gaining traction, partly because the CO_2 is buried without any benefits and partly because communities fear the CO_2 might leak out suddenly and dangerously, or ground movement might damage their homes. With EOR, the concerns about CCS do not generally apply – the oil fields are already in operation, their structural integrity is well known and above all the CO_2 will be creating value. Is EOR sustainable? The general consensus is that, at best, it is carbon neutral,[30] i.e. for every CO_2 molecule injected, another one is released from burning the oil. At about $15/tonne$CO_2$, EOR becomes cost-effective. That makes EOR a potentially attractive transitional technology.

Those that inject CO_2 captured from a coal-fired power plant could be credited at coal carbon tax rates. On the other hand, the oil producer would be paying an oil-based carbon tax. It comes down to this: if CO_2 is captured (or sequestered), then some carbon credit will be due. Tomatoes do not do that, so the burden will have to be shared between the growers and whoever supplies the CO_2 or flue gases.

Drax power station in Yorkshire was the UK's biggest coal-fired power plant. The owners invested heavily in recent years in a new plant to burn wood chips from southern states in the US. Until 2015 Drax had been studying other options to further reduce their emissions. Although unconnected with EOR and the UK North Sea oil sector, the White Rose carbon capture project[31] was being promoted by some UK politicians as an opportunity to demonstrate the possibility of carbon-negative[32] power generation. But that was never the intention. Situated next to Drax, the White Rose plant was designed to be Europe's first commercial-demonstration, super-efficient, coal-fired CCS power plant. If it ever goes ahead, it is expected to remove 90% of the CO_2 in its flue gas and compress the CO_2 for injection in saline aquifers under the North Sea. In September 2015 Drax pulled out of the project, citing the uncertainty caused by the UK Government's removal of industrial Feed-In Tariffs.[33]

Let us suppose the White Rose CO_2 gas were to be used for EOR. It is true, a substantial amount of CO_2 would be prevented from going into the atmosphere, but would it make sense to grow trees, chip and ship them 5,000 miles[34] to a power station in the UK and then use the resultant CO_2 for EOR? The answer is no. Let us suppose, optimistically, that the e-value of wood chips is 50 tonneCO_2/GWh on average,[35] similar to that of solar panels. Using the intensity weighting strategy discussed in this chapter, there would be no financial incentive – unless distorted by subsidies – to use wood-chip-derived CO_2 for EOR, but there would be every incentive to use coal-derived CO_2.

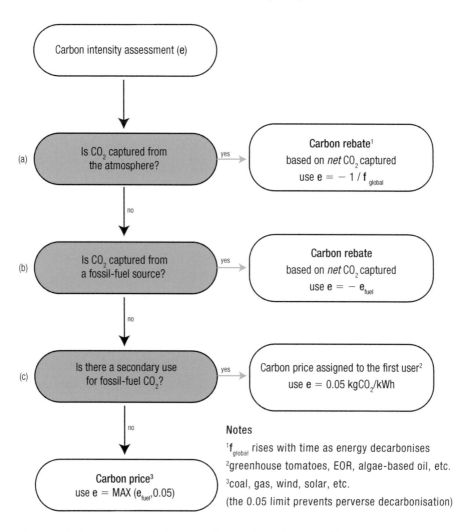

Figure 10.4 contents:

Carbon intensity assessment (e)

(a) Is CO_2 captured from the atmosphere? — yes → Carbon rebate[1] based on *net* CO_2 captured use $e = -1/f_{global}$

no ↓

(b) Is CO_2 captured from a fossil-fuel source? — yes → Carbon rebate based on *net* CO_2 captured use $e = -e_{fuel}$

no ↓

(c) Is there a secondary use for fossil-fuel CO_2? — yes → Carbon price assigned to the first user[2] use $e = 0.05\ kgCO_2/kWh$

no ↓

Carbon price[3] use $e = MAX(e_{fuel}, 0.05)$

Notes
[1] f_{global} rises with time as energy decarbonises
[2] greenhouse tomatoes, EOR, algae-based oil, etc.
[3] coal, gas, wind, solar, etc.
(the 0.05 limit prevents perverse decarbonisation)

Figure 10.4. *The carbon labyrinth. (© Predict Ability Ltd.)*

The Carbon Labyrinth

Figure 10.4 brings together the themes discussed in this chapter, particularly secondary CO_2 uses and the possibility of 'air capture', where CO_2 is captured directly from the atmosphere using chemical engineering processes.

This three-step strategy would incentivise transitional technologies, such as EOR, but we should not be deflected from the primary goal – to phase out unabated coal-fired power stations worldwide.

Arguably there should be a transition from dirty coal to oil via carbon capture and storage technology, but definitely not from wood chips to oil! That illustrates the power of the carbon intensity weighting strategy. It encourages energy transitions, from dirty to clean, and it guides energy investment policy and ethical concerns such as divestment.

Finally, Tables 10.3 to 10.6 show a more detailed example of how the 'carbon intensity weighted' carbon-pricing scheme might be implemented. Here the system has been applied to a country, notionally the United Kingdom. There are five stages of transition from a coal-dominated electricity supply to a low-carbon supply. A nominal carbon price of $15/tonne$CO_2$ has been used (note the price increases as the emissions decrease to ensure that the revenue remains stable, i.e. $y' = y \times f_{future} / f_{now}$ where f_{future} = 1/carbon intensity in future and f_{now} = 1/carbon intensity now).

Compare, in particular, the revenue breakdown for the 'carbon intensity' weighted system (Table 10.5) with that of the normal, uniform carbon price approach (Table 10.6). Certainly, we have to 'follow the money',[36] to know how big energy influences politics and investment decisions, taxes and tariffs. But we also have to 'follow the molecules' (the CO_2 molecules)! As the famous American physicist Richard Feynman once said, in another context, 'For a successful technology, reality must take precedence over public relations, for nature cannot be fooled.'[37] The atmosphere will find us out.

Table 10.3. Energy mix scenarios.					
Energy Mix Scenarios (%)	1990-like mainly coal	2016-like transitional	2025-low coal, coal phased out	2050-lower gas, gas phases out	2100-low carbon [and storage]
	0	1	2	3	4
Bioenergy	2%	6%	10%	5%	0%
Coal	53%	23%	3%	0%	0%
Oil	0%	0%	0%	0%	0%
Gas	23%	46%	56%	29%	0%
Solar	0%	0%	0%	0%	0%
Nuclear	21%	21%	21%	33%	40%
Wind	1%	4%	10%	33%	60%
Total (E)	100%	100%	100%	100%	100%

Calculated Values					
SUM(Ee)	0.633	0.456	0.317	0.155	0.012
SUM(Eee)	0.558	0.323	0.155	0.065	0.000
f (MWh/ tonneCO$_2$)	1.58	2.19	3.15	6.46	80.65
$1/f$ (tonneCO$_2$/ MWh)	0.63	0.46	0.32	0.15	0.01
z	0.72	0.64	0.65	0.37	1.00

Scenario Emissions (Million tonneCO$_2$/y)	1990-like mainly coal 0	2016-like transitional 1	2025-low coal, coal phased out 2	2050-lower gas, gas phases out 3	2100-low carbon [and storage] 4
Table 10.4. Emissions arising from energy mix scenarios.					
Bioenergy	1.55	4.66	7.76	3.88	—
Coal	159.19	69.08	9.01	—	—
Oil	—	—	—	—	—
Gas	32.60	65.20	79.38	41.11	—
Solar	—	—	—	—	—
Nuclear	0.84	0.84	0.84	1.32	1.60
Wind	0.04	0.15	0.37	1.21	2.21
Total	194	140	97	48	4

Calculated Values					
Price ($/tonneCO$_2$)	15	20.82	29.92	61.31	765.77
Damages ($m)	2,913	2,913	2,913	2,913	2,913
Energy Usage (MWh/y)	306,810,000	306,810,000	306,810,000	306,810,000	306,810,000
Energy Usage (MW)	35,000	35,000	35,000	35,000	35,000
Price ($/ MWh)	9.50	9.50	9.50	9.50	9.50

Table 10.5. Carbon prices and revenue arising from energy mix scenarios, EzefyN.

Carbon Prices $y_i = e.f.y.z$ ($\$/tonneCO_2$)	1990-like mainly coal	2016-like transitional	2025-low coal, coal phased out	2050-lower gas, gas phases out	2100-low carbon [and storage]
	0	1	2	3	4
Bioenergy	4.30	7.45	15.53	36.85	15,599.91
Coal	16.65	28.82	60.08	142.57	60,364.89
Oil	13.60	23.55	49.09	116.51	49,327.79
Gas	7.86	13.60	28.35	67.28	28,486.80
Solar	0.90	1.56	3.25	7.72	3,267.97
Nuclear	0.22	0.38	0.80	1.89	801.58
Wind	0.20	0.35	0.74	1.75	739.92

Scenario Revenue ($\$m/y$)	1990-like mainly coal	2016-like transitional	2025-low coal, coal phased out	2050-lower gas, gas phases out	2100-low carbon [and storage]
	0	1	2	3	4
Bioenergy	7	35	121	143	—
Coal	2,650	1,991	541	—	—
Oil	—	—	—	—	—
Gas	256	887	2,251	2,766	—
Solar	—	—	—	—	—
Nuclear	0	0	1	2	1,279
Wind	0	0	0	2	1,635
Total	2,913	2,913	2,913	2,913	2,913

Carbon Prices $y_i = y$ ($/tonneCO_2$)	1990-like mainly coal	2016-like transitional	2025-low coal, coal phased out	2050-lower gas, gas phases out	2100-low carbon [and storage]
	0	1	2	3	4
Bioenergy	15.00	20.82	29.92	61.31	765.77
Coal	15.00	20.82	29.92	61.31	765.77
Oil	15.00	20.82	29.92	61.31	765.77
Gas	15.00	20.82	29.92	61.31	765.77
Solar	15.00	20.82	29.92	61.31	765.77
Nuclear	15.00	20.82	29.92	61.31	765.77
Wind	15.00	20.82	29.92	61.31	765.77

Table 10.6. Carbon prices and revenue arising from a normal, uniform pricing scheme.

Scenario Revenue ($m/y)	1990-like mainly coal	2016-like transitional	2025-low coal, coal phased out	2050-lower gas, gas phases out	2100-low carbon [and storage]
	0	1	2	3	4
Bioenergy	23	97	232	238	—
Coal	2,388	1,438	270	—	—
Oil	—	—	—	—	—
Gas	489	1,358	2,375	2,520	—
Solar	—	—	—	—	—
Nuclear	13	17	25	81	1,222
Wind	1	3	11	74	1,692
Total	2,913	2,913	2,913	2,913	2,913

Appendix 10.1. Revenue weighting factor (z)

The carbon-tax revenue R_i for fuel type i is given by

$$R_i = E_i \times e_i \times y_i$$

The carbon price y for fuel type i is given by

$$y_i = e_i \times z \times y \times f$$

The carbon intensity weighting factor f is defined as

$$f = \Sigma E_i / \Sigma (E_i \times e_i)$$

The revenue weighting factor z is defined as the weighting to ensure that the total premium from individual fuel prices y_i is consistent with premium using a global carbon price y. Thus, both $R = \Sigma R_i$ and $R = y \times \Sigma (E_i \times e_i)$ are satisfied and

$$z = \frac{(\Sigma(E_i \times e_i))^2}{\Sigma E_i \times \Sigma(E_i \times e_i^2)}$$

where

E_i = amount of fuel type i used globally (GWh)
e_i = emission factor for fuel type i (tonne CO_2/GWh)
y_i = carbon price for a given fuel type i ($/tonne CO_2)
y = global carbon price ($/tonne CO_2).

Notes to Chapter Ten

1   Lagarde, C., Kim, J.Y., 'The path to carbon pricing', *Project Syndicate* (19 October 2015), https://www.project-syndicate.org/commentary/carbon-pricing-fiscal-policy-by-christine-lagarde-and-jim-yong-kim-2015–10

2   Carrington, D., '$1 trillion could be wasted on "unneeded" new coal plants, report warns', *The Guardian* (30 March 2016), http://www.theguardian.com/environment/2016/mar/30/1tn-could-be-wasted-on-unneeded-new-coal-plants-report-warns

3   'Fuel taxes by country', US Department of Energy (accessed 17 April 2016), http://www.afdc.energy.gov/data/10327

4   Bowen, A., 'The case for carbon pricing', Policy Brief London School of Economics (December 2011), http://www.lse.ac.uk/GranthamInstitute/wp-content/uploads/2014/02/PB_case-carbon-pricing_Bowen.pdf

5   BTU = British Thermal Unit (1055 Joules).

6   Erlandson, D., 'The BTU tax experience: What happened and why it happened', *PACE Environmental Law Review*, 12 (1), Article 9, pp. 173–184 (September 1994), http://digitalcommons.pace.edu/cgi/viewcontent.cgi?article=1528&context=pelr

7   'Climate change: An opportunity', Oxford Climate Forum Spring 2014 (Saïd Business School Oxford, 7–8 February 2014), http://www.oxfordclimateforum.org/oxford-climate-forum-spring-2014.html

8   'King coal: Consumption hits 44 year high', *Russia Today* (16 June 2014), https://www.rt.com/business/166232-coal-consumption-1970-high/

9   'We're over half way there! Check out our progress with our coal plant tracker', Sierra Club (accessed 17 April 2016), http://content.sierraclub.org/coal/

10   Evans, S., 'UK and Germany balk at coal exit plea', *CarbonBrief* (19 September 2014), http://www.carbonbrief.org/uk-and-germany-balk-at-coal-exit-plea/

11   'Beijing to shut all major coal power plants to cut pollution', Bloomberg (24 March 2015), http://www.bloomberg.com/news/articles/2015–03-24/beijing-to-close-all-major-coal-power-plants-to-curb-pollution

12   Wilson, J., 'Peabody Energy warns of bankruptcy risk', *Financial Times* (16 March 2016), http://www.ft.com/cms/s/0/3e78b3fe-eb73-11e5-888e-2eadd5fbc4a4.html

13   Grunwald, M., 'Inside the war on coal: How Mike Bloomberg, red-state businesses, and a lot of Midwestern lawyers are changing American energy faster than you think', Agenda Politico (26 May 2015), http://www.politico.com/agenda/story/2015/05/inside-war-on-coal-000002

14   'Comparison of lifecycle emissions of energy technologies', Nuclear Energy Institute Washington DC (accessed 17 April 2016), http://www.nei.org/Issues-Policy/Protecting-the-Environment/Life-Cycle-Emissions-Analyses/Comparison-of-Lifecycle-Emissions-of-Selected-Ener

15   'Electric steel production', Siemens (accessed 17 April 2016), http://www.siemens.com/press/en/feature/2012/industry/metals-technologies/2012–03-steel.php

16   Helm, D., *The Carbon Crunch*, p. 37.

17   Clark, D., '$CO_2(e)$ emissions from biomass and biofuels', Information paper – 4, Cundall Johnson & Partners LLP (29 July 2013), http://www.cundall.com/Cundall/fckeditor/editor/images/UserFilesUpload/file/WCIYB/IP-4%20-%20CO2e%20emissions%20from%20biomass%20and%20biofuels.pdf

18   Allen, M., 'Short-lived promise? The science and policy of cumulative and short-lived climate pollutants', Oxford University Martin School Policy Paper (February 2016), http://www.oxfordmartin.ox.ac.uk/downloads/briefings/Short_Lived_Promise.pdf

19   Σ means 'sum of', thus ΣE_i means sum of all the energy contributions, for all the fuel or energy types, i.e. the total energy used, **E**.

20   'NGV global news', Natural Gas Vehicle Industry (accessed 17 April 2016), http://www.ngvglobal.com

21   'New app tracks the crucial numbers in climate change', Sandbag (8 September 2015), https://sandbag.org.uk/blog/2015/sep/8/new-app-tracks-crucial-numbers-climate-change/

22   Adams, C., 'UK solar panel industry dismayed as subsidies face deep cuts', *Financial Times* (27 August 2015), http://www.ft.com/cms/s/0/33cc24d2-4cb2-11e5-b558-8a9722977189.html

23   Nicola, S., Roca, M., 'Germany tax on own use of renewables is first in Europe', Bloomberg (24 January 2014), http://www.bloomberg.com/news/articles/2014–01-24/germany-tax-on-own-use-of-renewables-is-first-in-europe

24   'March 2016 monthly energy review [spreadsheet]', US Energy Information Administration (accessed 17 April 2016), http://www.eia.gov/totalenergy/data/browser/xls.cfm?tbl=T07.02A&freq=m

25   'Table 4–5: Fuel consumption by mode of transportation in physical units', Bureau of Transportation, Statistics US Department of Transportation (accessed 17 April 2016), http://www.rita.dot.gov/bts/sites/rita.dot.gov.bts/files/publications/national_transportation_statistics/html/table_04_05.html

26   'Petroleum consumption by transport mode and fuel type: United Kingdom, 2000–2014', Department for Transport statistics UK Department of Energy and Environment (accessed 17 April 2016), https://www.gov.uk/government/uploads/system/uploads/attachment_data/file/384238/env0101.xls

27   McKibben, W., *Do the Math*, 350.org (November 2012), http://math.350.org

28   'Fossil fuel', Wikipedia (accessed 17 April 2016), https://en.wikipedia.org/wiki/Fossil_fuels

29   'Fossil fuel divestment', Wikipedia (accessed 17 April 2016), https://en.wikipedia.org/wiki/Fossil_fuel_divestment

30   'Oil boom possible but time is running out', News Durham University (14 October 2010), https://www.dur.ac.uk/news/newsitem/?itemno=10879

31   'About the White Rose CCS project', White Rose Carbon Capture & Storage Project (accessed 17 April 2016), http://www.whiteroseccs.co.uk/about-white-rose

32   Pidcock, R., 'Analysis: Is the UK relying on "negative emissions" to meet its climate targets?', *CarbonBrief* (15 April 2016), http://www.carbonbrief.org/analysis-how-much-is-the-uk-relying-on-negative-emissions-to-meet-its-climate-targets

33   Clark, P., 'UK energy policy under fire as Drax quits carbon-capture project', *Financial Times* (24 September 2015), http://www.ft.com/cms/s/0/0290c57e-62da-11e5-a28b-50226830d644.html

34   'Sea distance calculator', sea-distances.org (accessed 17 April 2016), http://www.sea-distances.org

35   Bates, J., Henry, S., 'Carbon factor for wood fuels for the supplier obligation: Final report', AEA report ED01858010, Issue 2, DEFRA (January 2009), https://www.gov.uk/government/uploads/system/uploads/attachment_data/file/48193/3153-final-report-carbon-factor.pdf

36   'Look at this – money in politics', National Institute on Money in State
      Politics (accessed 17 April 2016), http://www.followthemoney.org/look-
      at-this

37   Feynman, R.P., 'Appendix F – Personal observations on the reliability of the
      Shuttle', Rogers Commission NASA (June 1986), http://science.ksc.nasa.
      gov/shuttle/missions/51-l/docs/rogers-commission/Appendix-F.txt

CHAPTER ELEVEN

CARBON JUSTICE AND CLOSURE

There is a moral dimension

The extraordinary feature of climate change is that its effects are cumulative and largely distant from the source of emissions. How can the tools and strategies already described be used to ensure there is fairness – in other words carbon justice – for the vulnerable in both developed and developing countries and communities?

Righting a Wrong?

The evidence for climate change is hard to contradict. A primary cause is the cumulative build-up of carbon dioxide (CO_2) in the Earth's atmosphere. To avoid further adverse outcomes, possibly catastrophic outcomes, we must curtail our relationship with fossil fuels over the next few decades. Or, more specifically, decouple economic growth from the emissions of greenhouse gases, of which CO_2 is the worst offender in terms of sheer volume and impact. Dealing with CO_2 should be our highest priority.

One of the favoured strategies is to impose carbon pricing. This was discussed in Chapter Nine. The term 'carbon pricing' is the generic term for both emissions trading ('cap and trade') and carbon taxation. If some (but not all) major oil and gas companies are calling for carbon taxes,[1] it must be about time to do something about the impact of CO_2. Indeed, as we saw in Chapter Eight, we are acting on emissions as if it were still 1896.[2] But, in our collective enthusiasm to 'do something' after the Paris 2015 agreement, might we be about to do more harm than good? Is the policy thinking clear enough?[3]

In 1896, the scientist Svante Arrhenius set out the science of climate change (the greenhouse effect).[4] Had it been acted upon then, perhaps the emissions from coal, oil and gas could have been taxed or avoided from the outset. Of course, at the turn of the 20th century almost no one believed our emissions of CO_2 would persist in the atmosphere for as long as they do.[5] Consequently, the economic behaviour we have today – most of which involves consuming energy – may be painful to undo. Although there are energy taxes, and they vary widely, in most cases the revenue is returned to the general taxation pool and that usually begets more consumption[6] and administration.[7] The *status quo* rules.

The pain of 'righting the wrong' will not be distributed evenly across society. The 'do no harm' principle[8] advises that, in considering carbon pricing, the poorest in society should not be made poorer. And yet, in its simplest terms, putting a price on carbon means increasing the cost of energy and most goods, the majority of which are made using energy. The poorest households (particularly in developing countries) spend a disproportionate amount of their income on energy.[9] Can carbon pricing be implemented fairly?

Does the containment of environmental impact have more importance or legal authority than protecting an individual's right to ply their trade or protecting the poor? A 2016 legal decision by the European Court of Justice's Advocate General Paolo Mengozzi[10] indicates that the rules of the EU ETS (the CO_2 emissions trading scheme) override any hardship energy firms might experience because they cannot get all the emissions permits they would wish. This was determined under case law and the boundary is moving in the direction of environmental protection.

Separate Worlds, One World

The sources and impacts of climate change are often assumed to be in separate locations, that the emissions from developed countries impact on vulnerable nations. Here, too, the boundaries will become blurred if developing nations like Bangladesh install coal-fired power stations. Stories of climate hardship now come from all over the world: of farmers in Pakistan who find themselves at the complete mercy of adverse weather,[11] drought-driven poverty in Kenya,[12] typhoons in China,[13] and the coastal New Yorkers left destitute by Superstorm

Sandy.[14] Of course, it is hard to say to what extent climate was to blame for any one of these events. The science of event attribution is evolving[15] and Predict Ability Ltd has revealed that the average increase that climate change is now causing is 20% in the case of disasters and 15% overall. Both these percentages are rising with time.

Some claim that we now have 'climate refugees', from Syria and elsewhere, but we must be careful here as the reasons for enforced migration are multi-causal.[16] Mary Robinson, formerly President of Ireland and the United Nations High Commissioner for Human Rights (1997 to 2002), has devoted much of her energy to the question of climate justice. This means linking 'human rights and development to achieve a human-centred approach, safeguarding the rights of the most vulnerable people and sharing the burdens and benefits of climate change and its impacts equitably and fairly. Climate justice is informed by science, responds to science and acknowledges the need for equitable stewardship of the world's resources.'[17] Speaking to Anika Rahman[18] at the *Huffington Post*, Mary Robinson said:

> We now know that climate change is a driver of migration, and is expected to increase the displacement of populations.

Similarly, Oxfam claims that climate change threatens to undo decades of progress on hunger.[19] To compound the problem, the World Bank has revised dramatically upwards the number of poor people in the world by defining the poverty line as $1.90 a day.[20] But what is poverty?

Why Inequality Matters

Closely related to climate justice is inequality. It is harder to attain climate justice in a world of increasing inequality, but climate change alone is not the cause of inequality. For that we have to examine Parisian economist Thomas Piketty's work *Capital in the Twenty-First Century*,[21] the gist of which is: if $r > g$, if the return on capital (r) exceeds the rate of growth of the economy (g), then we have the basis for a society of rentiers – a state where an elite few own almost everything and the rest of us pay rent. What is the solution to this? Corrective taxation. Piketty admits that such remedies 'would require a very high and no doubt unrealistic level of international cooperation.'[22] Harvard economist Kenneth

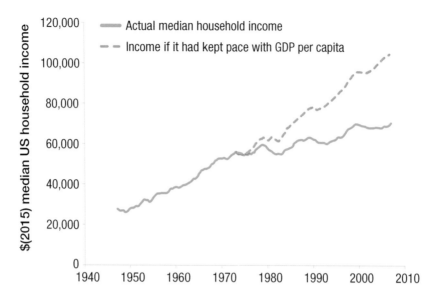

Figure 11.1. *Estimated US per household income from 1947 to 2008, showing median (middle) income and what it would have been if it had kept track with average GDP/household (updated 2007 data).*[23] *(© Predict Ability Ltd.)*

Rogoff[24] does not entirely agree with Piketty's conclusions. They may be true in developed, rich nations but the world as a whole has benefited massively from the growth of rich nations and that has led to major reductions in global poverty, creating millions of jobs through the globalisation of manufacturing, clothing and food production.

Another measure of inequality is median household income (by definition, the number of households with an income greater than the median equals the number of households with an income lower than the median). What Figure 11.1 shows is that from about 1973 onwards (perhaps the 1973 oil crisis[25] is significant here?) the median income failed to keep up with average income. In the United States the separation of the trends has worsened since 2008.

There seem to be three warnings here:

▸ A suddenly imposed energy tax or price increase significantly disrupts the economic progress of middle-income families (in the energy-intensive US, at least).

▸ No longer able to see a hopeful future, worker productivity stagnates or declines (although technology compensates and, overall, the profitability of companies increases).

▶ Additionally, the effects of climate change, although small initially, may be enough to drive the median income into a real-terms decline, creating economic and civil unrest.

The alternative view might be that the 1973 oil crisis is a coincidence and that what really changed was technology[26] (perhaps spurred on by the need to innovate to reduce energy costs) along with labour relations, monetary inflation and then, finally, globalisation.[27] In either scenario, the second and third points above persist.

Perhaps, post COP21 Paris,[28] the signs are already here.[29] If there is reduced social cohesion and if there is a sense of social injustice, there will be less consensus about climate change. In a crisis the near-term prevails and the social 'depreciation rate' increases. Nobel Prize winning economist and author of *The Price of Inequality*[30] Joseph Stiglitz explored the question of inequality and environmental policy in a 2012 seminar[31] organised by Resources for the Future (RFF), a Washington DC based economics, resources and environmental policy think-tank. The central question is intergenerational equity, which says humans 'hold the natural and cultural environment of the Earth in common both with other members of the present generation and with other generations, past and future.'[33] The Inca[34] people knew that the past, present and future were interconnected (Figure 11.2) and that particular insight served them well for centuries.[35]

As noted elsewhere, in the 1970s there was angst about whether natural resources (like helium) should be recovered or held back for future generations.[36] In the interim, market forces have overwhelmed that concern. And so it is with the burden that our CO_2 presents, there is angst amongst those who can afford angst but for most people the daily ordeals of their lives prevail. Stiglitz also makes the point that it is the median class, not the average class, which is significant here. GDP per capita is a meaningless quantity but, regrettably, ubiquitous. The so-called 'trickle-down effect' has not worked; the 'flooding-up effect' would be a better description. To compensate, Stiglitz says, the corporate world in the United States and elsewhere tries to persuade us that toxic things are good.

Figure 11.2. *Machu Picchu, Peru: the 15th-century Inca Temple of the Three Windows, believed to represent the transection of the past (Uku-Pacha, or underground), the present (Kay-Pacha) and the future (Hanan-Pacha, or heaven).*[32] *(© Shutterstock.)*

Fee and Dividend?

So, what is to be done? How can the great CO_2 imbalance be turned into a social good, to gain people's re-engagement with the environment? In September 2015, another event[37] at Resources for the Future (RFF) explored the issue of 'How pricing carbon impacts low-income households'. Perhaps carbon pricing is a way to stem the rise of inequality and redirect energy policy?

Two papers were presented at the RFF seminar. They examined the impacts of carbon pricing, using a notional price of $30/tonne CO_2, to gauge the significance of carbon revenue in general and, specifically, how it could be efficiently directed to low-income households. Roberton C. Williams III, a Senior Fellow at RFF, looked at the 'incidence' of carbon pricing, i.e. who pays when a tax is introduced? For the economy as a whole, directing the revenue towards capital investments is better value than giving lump-sum dividends to households. However, when applied to different income groups the picture reverses strongly, with dividends being the optimum strategy for low- and middle-income households (they are somewhat negative for high-income households). In the case of the middle-income households, the overall cost of the $30 carbon price was roughly $530 per year, but with a rebate of $809 that turned into a $279 gain.

So, if rebates are good, how can they be effectively directed? In the second RFF paper Chad Stone, Chief Economist at the US Center for Budget and Policy Priorities, explored the peculiarly labyrinthine bureaucracies needed to reach low-income households in the US, even though many federal and state structures for targeted income support already exist. He also pointed out that not all of the revenue would be so directed. Legislatures will inevitably seek to divert some of the funds towards deficit reduction, tax reform or public spending. What effect does all this have on emissions? Efficient and ethical revenue distribution is a formidable task.

Nevertheless, 'fee and dividend' schemes are still part of current thinking in Washington DC, where several bills lie before Congress.[38] The extraordinarily high carbon prices proposed have been reproduced graphically in Figure 11.3 using information provided by the Carbon Tax Center, New York. Note that Predict Ability Ltd's price, including the $25/tonne CO_2 figure needed to pay down past damages, lies well below those of the proposed taxes. This is because all the bills seek to decarbonise the economy as well as (in effect) paying for past damages. But has the impact of revenue been fully considered? The McDermott proposal would raise trillions of dollars annually. It is highly unlikely that any of these bills will ever become law.

A simple analysis confirms the relative inefficiency of pricing alone unless, as above, the carbon price is made artificially high. Table 11.1 illustrates that the impact of carbon pricing very much depends on what is done with the revenue. If it is not rebated, some low-income households could be nearly 10% worse off. If the revenue is mostly used for the AIM part of AIMS,[39] i.e. for adaptation projects, insurance and mitigation work, then a sizeable proportion of the mitigation budget will need to be set aside simply to protect low-income households. Energy-efficiency projects[40] will be needed to reduce the energy consumption of homes. Otherwise the 'do no harm' principle will be breached and low-income households could end up with doubled energy bills.[41]

At a national level it is clear: the imposition of carbon pricing demands that governments instigate major projects to improve the energy efficiency of homes. While some governments are enthused by the idea of smart metering,[42] they have become weary about energy efficiency. Just how effective are smart meters, though? It is hard and yet, without improved energy efficiency, there is

Case	Description	Energy-poor households (the 99%)	Highest-income households (the 1%)	Relative change in carbon emissions
	Table 11.1. Impact of carbon pricing on two household-income groups.			
1	Revenue-neutral, low carbon tax	1% better off	No change	Reduced by 4.5%
1a	As above with real-price elasticity	1% better off	0.5% worse off	Reduced by 2.3%
2	Revenue-neutral, high carbon tax	5.4% better off	0.2% better off	Reduced by 25%
2a	As above with real-price elasticity	7.7% better off	4.4% worse off	Reduced by 15%
3	As part of AIMS,[43] low carbon tax	0.9% worse off	No change	Reduced by 4.6%
3a	As above, with 10% improved energy efficiency	0.3% better off	No change	Reduced by 9.6%
4	As part of AIMS, high carbon tax	9.5% worse off	No change	Reduced by 25%
4a	As above, with 50% improved energy efficiency	1% better off	No change	Reduced by 50%

Assumptions: energy consumption proportional to income, with idealised and real-price elasticity[44] options; energy-poor households spend 10% of income on energy (assumed to be inelastic unless energy efficiency improves); a 'low' carbon tax increases energy costs 10% and a 'high' carbon tax doubles energy costs; in cases 3 and 4, 90% of revenue is used for AIM (adaptation, insurance, mitigation) but to protect low-income households much of the M part will be needed for energy-efficiency improvements; patterns of behaviour and fuel types do not change in the short term.

only so much the average household can, or would want to do to reduce energy demand. Never mind smart meters, there needs to be smart, energy-efficient housing (e.g. Figure 8.6). Unless it is of the 'fee and dividend' variety, carbon pricing will heavily burden low-income households.

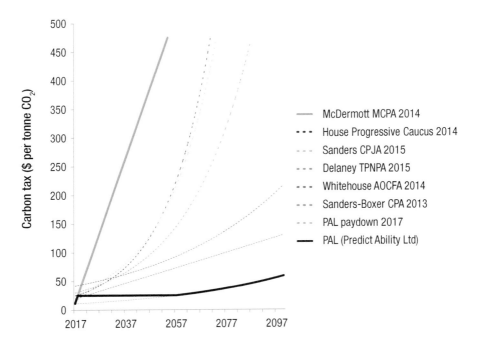

Figure 11.3. *Carbon tax bills presented in the 113th and 114th US Congress (2013–2016). (© Predict Ability Ltd.)*

An Insurance-Driven, Cell Phone-Led Alternative?

For carbon pricing to be effective it has to do more than raise revenue and distribute it straight back from whence it came, as most 'tax and dividend' schemes aim to do. Any benefits are in danger of being lost in the process of revenue distribution. The best outcome would be a tax coupled with a massive energy-efficiency drive. It would engage the public if there were a financial benefit and energy and emissions reductions. But would such a plan be possible? There is little evidence to show that governments have the level of commitment[45] necessary to achieve the energy-efficiency gains needed to avoid the backlash of penalising the energy-poor. Is there another way?

Dr Mo Ibrahim,[46] the telecoms engineer and billionaire businessman, recognised in the 1980s the tremendous potential for the growth of cell phones in Africa, where there is almost no reliable landline phone infrastructure. He sold Celtel, his African mobile-phone company, for $3.4bn in 2005. Now he leads the Mo Ibrahim Foundation,[47] which seeks to improve governance across Africa. 'Governance is everything. Without governance we have nothing', he says. It is not a leap of imagination to suggest that the now ubiquitous smartphone has the capacity to deliver not just communications, knowledge and trade but – increasingly – social justice, climate justice and carbon justice.

Whether it is to deliver micro-insurance to farmers, knowledge sharing, or health insurance, the cell phone is now a central pillar of millions if not billions of people's lives. And, with ever-advancing technological improvements, the security measures needed to ensure the correct person is claiming insurance or other services are now being put in place.

The time has come for the insurance industry to fully engage with this revolution. Instead of trying to painfully administer rebates to low-income households, why not use smartphones to deliver targeted insurance products that compensate for the price increases that carbon taxation causes? What is more valuable, a dollar-a-day of rebate or the peace of mind that access to basic health insurance, or crop insurance, or even education tokens bring? People's dreams of prosperity, good health and an education for their children are the silent casualties of disaster,[48] says Solomon M. Hsiang, Climate Risk Expert and Professor of Public Policy at UC Berkeley, in his talk 'Quantifying the economic cost of climate change'.

If, as shown in Chapter Eight, the insurance industry is due 30% of the revenue of global carbon pricing, then the World Bank, the UN and national governments should engage with the insurance industry in what should be a win-win arrangement. The expertise of the reinsurance giants is tapped to deliver, worldwide, the kind of insurance products that help offset the ongoing effects of climate change and the impact of carbon pricing. And, in the process, the insurance industry gains the data and finance it needs to grow into a truly global enterprise across all continents and cultures.

Do All Countries Need Carbon-Pricing Schemes?

Not all countries will have carbon-pricing schemes in the future. A global carbon-price strategy, such as that outlined in Chapter Nine, is widely supported,[49] but it may not be necessary for all countries to actively pursue carbon-pricing strategies in practice. In many places there are specific circumstances, such as conflicts, that make the administration of such schemes difficult. The impact of schemes will be low in countries with low emissions and there may be other priorities, such as the prevention of deforestation.

In each case an assessment would need to be made, using the criteria below and others, to see whether a carbon-pricing scheme is needed or is viable:

▶ What are the CO_2 and other GHG emissions, in total and per capita?
▶ What are the emissions embodied in imported and exported goods?
▶ How much funding support is there for mitigation (clean energy, etc)?
▶ How much funding support is there for adaptation (flood defences, etc)?
▶ If there is a carbon-pricing scheme in place, is it effective and sufficient?
▶ How much support is there for forest protection and how effective is it?
▶ How much overseas aid is given or received, and is it climate change related?

The balance of these terms would need to be considered and adjusted to take into account the relative level of development and capability of each country. In doing this it will become evident that carbon pricing is the key tool in a multi-factored approach that needs to include justice, humanitarian and social factors.

One of these criteria, overseas aid, can be an effective mechanism by which not only aid but a portion of the carbon-pricing requirements could be met. The UK, for example, meets the OECD 0.7% target[50] and has enshrined it into law. If all of the UK's aid were allocated to climate-change projects, this would equate to a carbon tax of around $18/tonne CO_2.[51]

Closure
Seeking Closure
In the notional '24 hour day' of life on Earth, mankind has appeared at the party at one minute before midnight[52] and now wants to change the rules of the game. The applicable laws of physics, however, remain firm. Today we have the capacity to clearly understand that the huge carbon debt (the CO_2 imbalance) we have created in the atmosphere is a dangerous threat. The lesson is that we must tread much more lightly with our environmental footprint. We need

to act now. Our future in our new climate is uncertain. This naturally makes people uncomfortable.

Faced with uncertainty, it is human nature to seek closure, to attain clarity of purpose and direction. One of the aims of this book is to help identify the priorities:

- It is the abnormal CO_2 concentration in the atmosphere that should be our greatest concern; it represents the carbon debt that we have accrued and it will not dissipate – it is like an albatross around our necks.
- The main consequence of the CO_2 imbalance is a changing climate that is already creating substantial loss and damage worldwide, and that affects vulnerable societies most of all.
- The proportion of the loss and damage that can be attributed to climate change (about 15% and rising) needs to be factored into the global economy in the form of carbon pricing.
- Anything that moves us in the right direction is useful – insure, mitigate, adapt.

Closure of the Feedback Loop

Carbon pricing helps create closure, a connection between the causes and consequences of CO_2 emissions. 'Record global temperatures are shocking – and yet we don't respond seriously', writes James Dyke,[53] lecturer in Complex Systems Simulation at the University of Southampton. Our detachment may be arrogance or disbelief (tipping points? surely not?), but it may also be about helplessness and despair.

Climate policy or, rather, climate strategy needs to connect with governments, with the economy and with the public. The feedback we need is within the capacity of people, provided they feel included and motivated. By using the power of the economy, carbon pricing can play a vital role in closing the climate feedback loop. This needs to be part of a suite of legal, economic and science-based strategies that must be clear, effective and equitable.

The carbon-pricing analyses presented in this book show that there is a slow-burning exponential equation at work. We have a short window of opportunity and we are acting as if it were still 1896. Globally, we are pricing CO_2 emissions at about \$1 per tonne CO_2. Our forbears did not know this, but we do. Soon, the carbon price will double the cost of burning a tonne of coal, as shown in Figure 11.4.

We need to react not just with renewable-energy projects (mitigation) but also through the subtle and challenging adaptations that are now needed to cope with today's climate and with what is predicted to come. The insurance industry is centrally placed to deal with this. It stands to benefit from carbon pricing, but, equally, it needs to lead on the social and adaptation work too.

Closure – Concluding Remarks

This book sets out a 'double helix' proposal for tackling climate change for current and future generations. It is scientifically and financially robust and it is socially just and sustainable. It achieves this by:

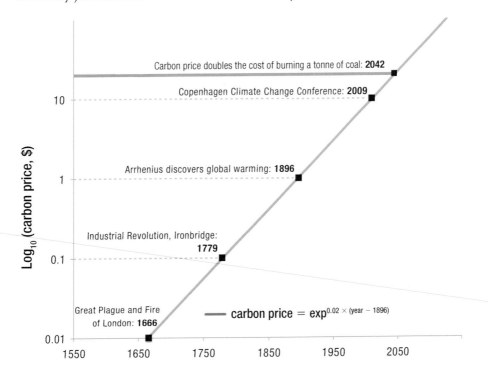

Figure 11.4. *Logarithmic-linear plot of the price of carbon in \$$_{2015}$ from 1665 to 2125, showing the historical mileposts on the road from 1¢ per tonne to \$100 per tonne CO_2. (© Predict Ability Ltd.)*

▸ quantifying the consequences of climate-change damage, both existing and future,

▸ recognising that the impacts and costs will be ongoing for centuries, and will grow with time,

▸ addressing adaptation, insurance and mitigation aspects, and

▸ incentivising behavioural change without penalising developing communities.

The philosophy of *Predicting the Price of Carbon* is to tax carbon impact across all energy types and use the revenue to fund AIMS:

Adaptation	improving the capacity of vulnerable communities to weather climate change
Insurance	enabling insurance companies to bear the costs of climate change and sustain their contractual commitments
Mitigation	incentivising the transition to low-carbon energy sources
Social dividend	'micro-insurance' schemes, administered by the insurance industry, the UN and the World Bank, to offset the impact of carbon pricing.

To deliver this philosophy, in practice, requires a credible carbon-pricing system. *Predicting the Price of Carbon* offers a solution for tackling climate change in financial terms that

▸ develops a scientifically robust method of pricing carbon that is fair, credible and future-proofed, and constantly evaluated and recalibrated as real-world data causes it to evolve,

▸ places a dollar loss on the damage caused by climate change,

▸ rationalises carbon pricing across all fuel and energy types, including renewables, to ensure that after the last giga-tonne of CO_2 is emitted the ongoing damage caused by our cumulative carbon emissions continues to be paid for,

▸ creates a market mechanism to correct for the hitherto widespread practice of emitting carbon pollution for free,

- ▶ scientifically determines the carbon price by analysing the damage attributable to man-made climate change,
- ▶ proposes a partnership of national carbon-pricing schemes underpinned by a credible carbon price floor, and
- ▶ underpins the evolving 'cap and trade' markets with a carbon price floor based on loss and damage that combines the efficiency of markets with carbon-price credibility.

In *Predicting the Price of Carbon* two simple models demonstrate

- ▶ why cumulative carbon emissions matter.
- ▶ why carbon revenue trumps the impact of carbon price itself, and
- ▶ why 30% of the revenue belongs to the insurance industry.

Notes to Chapter Eleven

1 Editorial Board, 'The case for a carbon tax', *The New York Times* (6 June 2015), http://www.nytimes.com/2015/06/07/opinion/the-case-for-a-carbon-tax.html

2 Hope, M., 'The state of carbon pricing: Around the world in 46 carbon markets', *CarbonBrief* (29 May 2014), http://www.carbonbrief.org/the-state-of-carbon-pricing-around-the-world-in-46-carbon-markets

3 Kopp, R.J., et al., 'How pricing carbon impacts low-income households', Resources for the Future (22 September 2015), http://www.rff.org/events/event/2015–09/how-pricing-carbon-impacts-low-income-households

4 Arrhenius, S., 'On the influence of carbonic acid in the air upon the temperature of the ground', *Philosophical Magazine and Journal of Science*, S.5, 41, pp. 237–276 (April 1896), http://www.rsc.org/images/Arrhenius1896_tcm18-173546.pdf

5 'The discovery of global warming: The carbon dioxide greenhouse effect', American Institute of Physics (accessed 17 April 2016), https://www.aip.org/history/climate/co2.htm

6 Garside, B., 'EU industry got €24bn windfall from the EU ETS – report', *Carbon Pulse* (15 March 2016), http://carbon-pulse.com/17016/

7 Garside, B., 'EU ETS administrative costs could soar after 2020 as regulators strive to curb windfalls – study', *Carbon Pulse* (15 March 2016), http://carbon-pulse.com/17021/

8 Stone, C., 'The design and implementation of policies to protect low-income households under a carbon tax', Issue Brief 15–02, Resources for the Future (September 2015), http://www.rff.org/files/document/file/RFF-IB-15-02.pdf

9 Robinson, M., 'Role of sustainable energy in ending poverty', International Energy Agency (accessed 17 April 2016), http://www.iea.org/topics/energypoverty/

10 Mengozzi, P., 'Advocate General's opinion DK, recycling und Roheisen v Commission Case C-540/14P', EUR-Lex (8 March 2016), http://curia.europa.eu/juris/celex.jsf?celex=62014CC0540&lang1=en&type=TXT&ancre=

11 Shaikh, S., Tunio, S., 'Pakistan farmers grapple with climate change', Al Jazeera (23 April 2013), http://www.aljazeera.com/indepth/features/2013/04/201342312421913125.html

12   Hatcher, J., 'Drought in northern Kenya: "Today you are rich, tomorrow you have nothing" ', *The Guardian* (30 July 2014), http://www.theguardian.com/global-development/2014/jul/30/kenya-drought-food-starvation

13   'Typhoon Fitow: China's Zhejiang on "red alert", huge waves batter coast', ABC News Australia (6 October 2013), http://www.abc.net.au/news/2013–10-07/an-china-storm/5001910

14   Kelly, C., Ross, T., 'One storm shy of despair: A climate-smart plan for the administration to help low-income communities', Center for American Progress (17 July 2014), https://www.americanprogress.org/issues/green/report/2014/07/17/93981/one-storm-shy-of-despair/

15   Pidcock, R., 'In-depth: The scientific challenge of extreme weather attribution', *CarbonBrief* (11 March 2016), http://www.carbonbrief.org/in-depth-the-scientific-challenge-of-extreme-weather-attribution/

16   Martin, M., 'Focus on migration: A closer look at "climate refugees" ', *SciDevNet* (23 October 2014), http://www.scidev.net/global/migration/analysis-blog/focus-on-migration-a-closer-look-at-climate-refugees.html

17   'Principles of climate justice', Mary Robinson Foundation (accessed 17 April 2016), http://www.mrfcj.org/principles-of-climate-justice/

18   Rahman, A., 'Climate-induced migration: A looming crisis', HuffPost Green (22 January 2015), http://www.huffingtonpost.com/anika-rahman/climateinduced-migration-_b_6497652.html

19   'Risk of reversal in progress on world hunger as climate change threatens food security', Oxfam Media Briefing Ref.07/2014 (31 March 2014), https://www.oxfam.org/sites/www.oxfam.org/files/mb-ipcc-oxfam-analysis-climate-change-food-security-310314-en.pdf

20   Donnan, S., 'Earth's poor set to swell as World Bank moves poverty line', *Financial Times* (23 September 2015), http://www.ft.com/cms/s/0/81b0ac66-61e5-11e5-9846-de406ccb37f2.html

21   Moore, H., 'Why is Thomas Piketty's 700-page book a bestseller?', *The Guardian* (21 September 2014), http://www.theguardian.com/money/2014/sep/21/-sp-thomas-piketty-bestseller-why

22   Shiller, R.J., 'Inequality disaster prevention', *Project Syndicate* (14 May 2014), https://www.project-syndicate.org/commentary/robert-j--shiller-praises-thomas-piketty-s-invaluable-contribution-to-a-debate-that-is-far-from-over

23   Kenworthy, L., 'GDP per capita versus median family income', Economist's View (4 September 2008), http://economistsview.typepad.com/economistsview/2008/09/gdp-per-capita.html

24 Rogoff, K., 'Where is the inequality problem?', *Project Syndicate* (8 May 2014), https://www.project-syndicate.org/commentary/kenneth-rogoff-says-that-thomas-piketty-is-right-about-rich-countries--but-wrong-about-the-world

25 Macallister, T., 'Background: What caused the 1970s oil price shock?', *The Guardian* (3 March 2011), http://www.theguardian.com/environment/2011/mar/03/1970s-oil-price-shock

26 'The Story of the Intel® 4004', Intel Corporation (accessed 17 April 2016), http://www.intel.co.uk/content/www/uk/en/history/museum-story-of-intel-4004.html

27 'Globalisation', BBC Bitesize (accessed 17 April 2016), http://www.bbc.co.uk/schools/gcsebitesize/geography/globalisation/globalisation_rev2.shtml

28 'Paris Agreement', European Commission Climate Action (accessed 17 April 2016), http://ec.europa.eu/clima/policies/international/negotiations/paris/index_en.htm

29 Darby, M., 'Is Brussels killing the Paris climate dream?', *Climate Change News* (9 March 2016), http://www.climatechangenews.com/2016/03/09/is-brussels-burying-the-paris-climate-dream/

30 Stiglitz, J.E., *The Price of Inequality: How Today's Divided Society Endangers Our Future*, W.W. Norton & Company (accessed 17 April 2016), http://books.wwnorton.com/books/The-Price-of-Inequality/

31 Stiglitz, J.E., 'Resources 2020 with Joseph E. Stiglitz', Resources for the Future (5 October 2012), http://www.rff.org/events/event/2012–10/resources-2020-joseph-e-stiglitz

32 http://www.shutterstock.com/pic-293960432/stock-photo-machu-picchu-temple-of-the-three-windows.html

33 Weiss, E.B., 'Intergenerational equity and rights of future generations', in: *The Modern World of Human Rights: Essays in Honour of Thomas Buergenthal* (ed. Trinidade, A.C.), Inter-American Institute for Human Rights, pp. 601–616 (1996), http://biblio.juridicas.unam.mx/libros/5/2043/32.pdf

34 Pfeifel, S., 'The Inca perception of time: Can we all be completely wrong?', Strangeness and Charm: the word according to Pfeifel (13 January 2015), https://shmuelpfeifel.wordpress.com/2015/01/13/the-inca-perception-of-time-can-we-all-be-completely-wrong/

35 Cooper, J., 'The Inca: Masters of the clouds', BBC 4 (27 February 2016), http://www.bbc.co.uk/programmes/b04xrsx6

36   Nuttall, W.J., Clarke, R.H., Glowacki, B.A. (eds.), *The Future of Helium as a Natural Resource*, Routledge (2012), https://www.routledge.com/products/9780415576970

37   Kopp, R.J., et al., 'How pricing carbon impacts low-income households', Resources for the Future (22 September 2015), http://www.rff.org/events/event/2015–09/how-pricing-carbon-impacts-low-income-households

38   'Bills – current proposals', Carbon Tax Center (accessed 17 April 2016), http://www.carbontax.org/bills/

39   As discussed in Chapter Eight, AIMS = Adaptation, Insurance, Mitigation and Social dividend.

40   'Forward-looking socio-economic research on energy efficiency in EU countries', EU Heron Project (accessed 17 April 2016), http://heron-project.eu

41   Evans, T., 'Why has the average energy bill doubled since 2004 and what next for prices?', This is Money (31 July 2011), http://www.thisismoney.co.uk/money/bills/article-2019735/Why-energy-bills-doubled-2004-gas-electricity-prices.html

42   'Smart meters: A guide', UK Government Climate Change and Energy Guidance (22 January 2013), https://www.gov.uk/guidance/smart-meters-how-they-work

43   As discussed in Chapter Eight, AIMS = Adaptation, Insurance, Mitigation and Social dividend.

44   'Price elasticity of demand', Economics Online (accessed 17 April 2016), http://www.economicsonline.co.uk/Competitive_markets/Price_elasticity_of_demand.html

45   Mathieusen, K., 'Watchdog urges reform of UK's "failed" energy efficiency drive', *The Guardian* (31 March 2015), http://www.theguardian.com/environment/2015/mar/31/watchdog-urges-reform-of-uks-failed-energy-efficiency-drive

46   Wallis, W., 'Lunch with the FT: Mo Ibrahim', *Financial Times* (15 February 2008), http://www.ft.com/cms/s/0/c6a7d87a-d93b-11dc-bd4d-0000779fd2ac.html

47   'Putting governance at the centre of African development', Mo Ibrahim Foundation (accessed 17 April 2016), http://www.moibrahimfoundation.org

48   Hsiang, S.M., 'Quantifying the economic cost of climate change', RMS Connection (30 April 2014), https://www.youtube.com/watch?v=yNYZJD_llno

49   'Frequently asked questions', carbon-price.com (accessed 17 April 2016), http://carbon-price.com/faq

50   Booth, L., 'The 0.7% aid target', House of Commons Library Economic Policy & Statistics Standard Note SN/EP/3714 (28 July 2014), http://www.parliament.uk/briefing-papers/SN03714.pdf

51   = 0.7% × \$2.7trillion (GDP)/1 billion tonnes CO_2 (emissions including imported goods).

52   Yau, N., 'History of Earth in 24-hour clock', https://flowingdata.com/2012/10/09/history-of-earth-in-24-hour-clock/

53   Dyke, J., 'Record global temperatures are shocking – and yet we don't respond seriously', *The Guardian* (15 March 2016), http://www.theguardian.com/environment/2016/mar/15/record-global-temperatures-are-shocking-and-yet-we-dont-respond-seriously/

NOTATION

C	carbon dioxide (CO_2) emissions (giga-tonnes per year)
D	cumulative total of CO_2 emissions (giga-tonnes since 1945)
d_i	disaster losses (insured) (\$)
d_o	disaster overall losses (insured and non-insured) (\$)
e	carbon intensity of energy source or fuel (tonnes CO_2 per GWh)
E	useful energy input from a given fuel or energy source (GWh)
f	weighting factor ($1/f$ = average carbon intensity)
g	rate of economic growth (Piketty's equation)
k_a	coefficient in PALca
k_b	coefficient in PALca
k_t	coefficient linking T_a and CO_2 concentration
k'	cumulative emissions loss coefficient (\$ / tonne CO_2)
k''	attribution rate (0.0125% per giga-tonne)
k_1	ratio of d_o/d_i ~ 2.67
k_2	disaster loss offset (~\$40 billion)
k_3	overall loss / disaster loss ratio (~26.7)
k^o	linearity correction (used with k'') (~0.01)
L	losses (total, disaster or catastrophe)
N	proportion of energy or fuel type supplied by a given company
P_1	disaster event probability (counter-factual or 'no CO_2 emissions' case)
P_2	disaster event probability (current conditions 'with CO_2 emissions' case)
R	revenue from carbon pricing
r	rate of return on capital (Piketty's equation)
t	time (year)
T	temperature (°C)
T_a	temperature anomaly
x	proportion of a disaster (loss) attributable to climate change*
y	carbon price (\$ / tonne CO_2)
y'	carbon price adjusted to maintain revenue R, p. 211
z	revenue weighting factor (see Appendix 10.1)

---

* the symbol $\times$ means multiply, as in $L \times x$

GLOSSARY

AIMS	Adaptation, Insurance, Mitigation and Social fund
AMO	Atlantic Multidecadal Oscillation (ocean current)
Anthropocene	Current geological age (human-dominated)
arXiv	Electronic repository of scientific paper pre-prints
BBC	British Broadcasting Corporation, London
BC	years before Christ
Billion	one thousand million (10^9)
BMGF	Bill & Melinda Gates Foundation, Seattle WA, USA
BOC	British Oxygen Company, now part of Linde (industrial gases)
BTU	British Thermal Unit (1055 Joules)
$CaCO_3$	Calcium carbonate (chalk, limestone, etc)
CAPE	Convective Available Potential Energy (see Figure 7.4)
CC	Climate change
CCEI	Center for Clean Energy Innovation, Washington DC
CCFE	Culham Centre for Fusion Energy, Oxfordshire, UK
CCS	Carbon capture and storage
CDM	Clean Development Mechanism (Kyoto Protocol)
CEO	Chief Executive Officer
CIW	Carbon intensity weighting (see Chapter Ten)
CO_2	Carbon dioxide gas (GHG)
COP	Conference of Parties (e.g. COP21) of the UNFCCC
CP	Carbon price (see tables in Chapter Six)
CRED	Centre for Research on the Epidemiology of Disasters, Belgium
CSR	Corporate social responsibility
CTC	Center for Carbon Taxation, New York
CUP	Cambridge University Press
CWE	Carcass Weight Equivalent
DARA	Independent organisation aiming to improve the effectiveness of humanitarian aid, Madrid, Spain
DC	Direct current (electricity)
DECC	Department of Energy and Climate Change, London
EIA	Energy Information Administration, Washington DC
EM-DAT	Database of Emergency Events (CRED)
ENSO	El Niño-Southern Oscillation (ocean current)
Enthalpy	Thermodynamic term; internal energy of a system
Eocene	Geological epoch, 56–33.9 million years ago
EOR	Enhanced Oil Recovery
ETS	Emissions Trading Scheme (e.g. EU ETS)

FiT	Feed-in Tariff (renewable energy subsidy)
GDP	Gross Domestic Product, a measure of economic growth
GHG	Greenhouse gases (e.g. CO_2, methane)
GM	Genetically modified (foodstuffs)
GTL	Gas to Liquids (e.g. methane to liquid petroleum products)
GW	Global warming (climate change)
GWh	Gigawatt hours (amount of electricity)
H_2	Hydrogen gas
HFC	Hydrofluorocarbon (ozone-friendlier refrigerant)
HIPPO	Habitat destruction, Invasive species, Population, Pollution, Overharvesting
HSB	Hartford Steam Boiler (insurance company), Hartford CT, USA
IET	International Emissions Trading (under Kyoto Protocol)
IETA	International Emissions Trading Association, London
IMF	International Monetary Fund, Washington DC
IPCC	Intergovernmental Panel on Climate Change, Geneva
JET	Joint European Torus, experimental fusion reactor at CCFE
JET-A	Jet engine fuel used in the United States
JI	Joint Implementation (Kyoto Protocol)
Joule	SI (International System) unit of work or energy
Kyoto Protocol	Treaty based on 1992 UNFCCC; GHG emissions reduction
LBNL	Lawrence Berkeley National Laboratory, Berkeley CA, USA
LFTR	Liquid Fluoride Thorium Reactor (nuclear reactor)
Li	Lithium (used in batteries)
LiN	Liquid Nitrogen (sometimes called LN_2)
LSE	London School of Economics
MD	Managing Director
Met Office	Meteorological Office
MIT	Massachusetts Institute of Technology, Cambridge MA, USA
MP	Member of Parliament (law maker)
MSR	Market Stability Reserve (floor pricing for EU ETS)
NASA	National Aeronautics and Space Administration, Washington DC
Nathan	Munich RE's disaster and catastrophe loss database
NDC	Normalised disaster and catastrophe ratio (see Chapter Seven)
NEI	Nuclear Energy Institute, Washington DC
NFIP	National Flood Insurance Program, Washington DC
NOAA	National Oceanic and Atmospheric Administration, Silver Spring MD, USA
NPV	Net Present Value (accounting term)
NSTA	National Science Teachers Association, Arlington VA, US
OCO-2	Orbiting Carbon Observatory (NASA)
OECD	Organisation for Economic Co-Operation and Development, Paris
p-value	Statistical significance test (the Null Hypothesis)

PAL	Predict Ability Ltd, Farnborough, UK
PALca	PAL's algorithm for estimating global attribution
PALca$_{body}$	Global attribution value – all losses
PALca$_{tail}$	Global attribution value – disaster and catastrophe losses
PALcarbon	PAL's carbon-pricing product
PALgamma	PAL's disaster-frequency, location and loss-prediction tool
PBMR	Pebble-bed modular reactor (small-scale nuclear plant)
PBS	Public Broadcasting Service, Arlington VA, USA
PC	Personal computer
PDO	Pacific Decadal Oscillation (ocean current)
PDSI	Palmer Drought Severity Index (soil moisture calculation)
PEA	Probabilistic Event Attribution (see Chapter Seven)
PIK	Potsdam Institute for Climate Impact Research, Potsdam, Germany
PV	Photovoltaic (solar panel)
R^2	Coefficient of determination (statistical goodness of fit)
RD&D	Research, Development and Demonstration
RE	Reinsurance (companies that insure insurance companies)
REACT	Reinsurance Event Attributed Carbon Tax (see Chapter Seven)
REDD+	Reducing Emissions from Deforestation and Forest Degradation (UN programme), Geneva, Switzerland
REE	Rare earth element
REI	Renewable Energy Investment (see Chapter Five)
RFF	Resources for the Future (think tank), Washington DC
RGGI	Regional Greenhouse Gas Initiative Inc, New York
Rio+20	UN Conference on Sustainable Development, Rio de Janeiro, Brazil
RITA	Research and Innovative Technology Administration, Washington DC
RoI	Return on Investment
S&P	Standard & Poor's (market index), New York
SD	Standard Deviation (statistics, the amount of variation in a dataset)
SD	System Dynamics (a tool for analysing complex systems)
SLR	Sea-level rise
TITAN	Cray supercomputer at Oak Ridge National Laboratory, Oak Ridge TN, USA
Trillion	Million million (10^{12})
UK	United Kingdom
UKERC	UK Energy Research Centre, London
UN	United Nations, New York
UNFCCC	UN Framework Convention on Climate Change, New York
UNISDR	UN Office for Disaster Risk Reduction, Geneva, Switzerland
US	United States of America

US$	US currency (assume US dollars unless stated otherwise)
VAT	Value Added Tax
VEI	Volcanic Explosivity Index (logarithmic, relative measure of a volcano's explosiveness)
WALL-E	Waste Allocation Load Lifter – Earth Class (Pixar / Disney Pictures)
WEC	World Energy Council, London
WEF	World Economic Forum, Cologny, Switzerland
WRI	World Resources Institute, Washington DC
WW2	Second World War

BIBLIOGRAPHY

Benson, J., *Environmental Ethics: An Introduction with Readings*, Routledge (2000).

Berners-Lee, M., Clark, D., *The Burning Question*, Profile Books (2013).

Bostrom, N., Ćirković, M. M., *Global Catastrophic Risks*, Oxford (2008–2012).

Capilla, A.V., Delgado, A.V., *Thanatia: The Destiny of the Earth's Mineral Resources: A Thermodynamic Cradle-To-Cradle Assessment*, World Scientific Publishing (2014).

Cook, E., *Man, Energy, Society*, W.H. Freeman & Company (1976).

Dawson, B., Spannagle, M., *The Complete Guide to Climate Change*, Routledge (2009).

Diamond, J., *Collapse: How Societies Choose to Fail or Survive*, Penguin (2005–2011).

Diamond, J., *The World Until Yesterday*, Allen Lane (2012).

Flannery, T., *Atmosphere of Hope*, Penguin Books (2015).

Funk, M., *Windfall: The Booming Business of Global Warming*, The Penguin Press (2014).

Giddens, A., *The Politics of Climate Change*, Polity Press (2011, 2012).

Goodall, C., *How to Live a Low-Carbon Life*, Earthscan (2007).

Gore, A., *An Inconvenient Truth: The Crisis of Global Warming*, Bloomsbury, (2006).

Grubb, M., *Planetary Economics: Energy, Climate Change and the Three Domains of Sustainable Development*, Routledge (2014).

Hansen, J., *Storms of My Grandchildren*, Bloomsbury, (2009).

Helm, D., *The Carbon Crunch*, Yale University Press (2012).

Hewitt, W.F., *A Newer World: Politics, Money, Technology, and What's Really Being Done to Solve the Climate Crisis*, University of New Hampshire Press (2013).

Hone, D., *Why Carbon Pricing Matters*, Whitefox (2015).

Hulme, M., *Why We Disagree About Climate Change*, Cambridge University Press (2009).

Kieffer, S.W., *The Dynamics of Disaster*, W.H. Norton & Company (2013).

Kolbert, E., *Field Notes from a Catastrophe*, Bloomsbury (2006, 2007).

Lawson, N., *An Appeal to Reason: A Cool Look at Global Warming*, Duckworth Overlook (2008–2012).

Lenton, T., *Earth System Science: A Very Short Introduction*, OUP (2016).

Lovelock, J., *A Rough Ride to the Future*, Allen Lane (2014).

Maslin, M.A., *Climate Change: A Very Short Introduction*, OUP (2014).

Nordhaus, W., *A Question of Balance: Weighing the Options on Global Warming Policies*, Yale University Press (2008).

Nordhaus, W., *The Climate Casino: Risk, Uncertainty and Economics for a Warming World*, Yale University Press (2013).

Mackay, D.J.C., *Sustainable Energy: Without the Hot Air*, UIT Cambridge (2009).

Parry, I., Morris, A., Williams, R.C. III, *Implementing a US Carbon Tax*, Routledge (2015).

Pielke Jr, R., *The Climate Fix*, Basic Books (2010).

Pielke Jr, R., *The Rightful Place of Science: Disasters and Climate Change*, Consortium for Science, Policy and Outcomes, Arizona State University (2014).

Pittock, A.B., *Climate Change: The Science, Impacts and Solutions* (2nd Edition), CSIRO (2009).

Sachs, J.D., *The Age of Sustainable Development*, Columbia University Press (2015).

Schumacher, D., *Energy: Crisis or Opportunity? An Introduction to Energy Studies*, Macmillan (1985).

Silver, N., *The Signal and the Noise: The Art and Science of Prediction*, Penguin (2012).

Wagner, G., Weitzman, M., *Climate Shock: The Economic Consequences of a Hotter Planet*, Princeton University Press (2015).

INDEX

Please note that Mc is treated the same as Mac.
Page numbers in italics indicate an illustration or caption.

Lightning Source UK Ltd.
Milton Keynes UK
UKRC01n2129030816
279891UK00003B/11